Current Topics in Bioenergetics

Volume 5

Advisory Board

Contributors to This Volume

Edwin W. Abrahamson

R. Brian Beechey

Kenneth J. Cattell

Britton Chance

P. Leslie Dutton

Maria Erecińska

Roger S. Fager

Darrell E. Fleischman

Joseph J. Katz

Berger C. Mayne

James R. Norris, Jr.

Anthony San Pietro

James Siedow

Edwin W. Taylor

Michal Wagner

David F. Wilson

C. R. Worthington

Charles F. Yocum

Current Topics in Bioenergetics

Edited by
D. RAO SANADI
Boston Biomedical Research Institute
Boston, Massachusetts

and
LESTER PACKER
Department of Physiology
University of California at Berkeley
Berkeley, California

VOLUME 5

1973

ACADEMIC PRESS   NEW YORK AND LONDON

ACADEMIC PRESS, INC.
111 Fifth Avenue, New York, New York 10003

United Kingdom Edition published by
ACADEMIC PRESS, INC. (LONDON) LTD.
24/28 Oval Road, London NW1

LIBRARY OF CONGRESS CATALOG CARD NUMBER: 66-28678

PRINTED IN THE UNITED STATES OF AMERICA

Contents

X-Ray Diffraction Studies on Biological Membranes

C. R. WORTHINGTON

Chlorophyll and Light Energy Transduction in Photosynthesis

JOSEPH J. KATZ AND JAMES R. NORRIS, JR.

Chemically and Physically Induced Luminescence as a Probe of Photosynthetic Mechanisms

DARRELL E. FLEISCHMAN AND BERGER C. MAYNE

The Reducing Side of Photosystem I

JAMES SIEDOW, CHARLES F. YOCUM, AND ANTHONY SAN PIETRO

The Chemistry of Vertebrate and Invertebrate Visual Photoreceptors

EDWIN W. ABRAHAMSON AND ROGER S. FAGER

Mechanism of Actomyosin ATPase and the Problem of Muscle Contraction

EDWIN W. TAYLOR

Energy-Transducing Components in Mitochondrial Respiration

DAVID F. WILSON, P. LESLIE DUTTON, AND MICHAL WAGNER

Kinetics of Cytochromes b

MARIA ERECIŃSKA, MICHAL WAGNER, AND BRITTON CHANCE

Mitochondrial Coupling Factors

R. BRIAN BEECHEY AND KENNETH J. CATTELL

List of Contributors

Numbers in parentheses indicate the pages on which the authors' contributions begin.

EDWIN W. ABRAHAMSON (125), *Department of Chemistry, Case Western Reserve University, Cleveland, Ohio*

R. BRIAN BEECHEY (305), *Shell Research Limited, Woodstock Agricultural Research Centre, Sittingbourne, Kent, and Chelsea College, Manresa Road, London, England*

KENNETH J. CATTELL[1] (305), *Shell Research Limited, Woodstock Agricultural Research Centre, Sittingbourne, Kent, England*

BRITTON CHANCE (267), *Department of Biophysics and Physical Biochemistry, Johnson Research Foundation, University of Pennsylvania Medical School, Philadelphia, Pennsylvania*

P. LESLIE DUTTON (233), *Department of Biophysics and Physical Biochemistry, Johnson Research Foundation, University of Pennsylvania Medical School, Philadelphia, Pennsylvania*

MARIA ERECIŃSKA (267), *Department of Biophysics and Physical Biochemistry, Johnson Research Foundation, University of Pennsylvania Medical School, Philadelphia, Pennsylvania*

ROGER S. FAGER (125), *Department of Chemistry, Case Western Reserve University, Cleveland, Ohio*

DARRELL E. FLEISCHMAN (77), *C. F. Kettering Research Laboratory, Yellow Springs, Ohio*

JOSEPH J. KATZ (41), *Chemistry Division, Argonne National Laboratory, Argonne, Illinois*

---

[1]*Present address:* Department of Biological Sciences, The Polytechnic, Wolverhampton, England.

BERGER C. MAYNE (77), *C. F. Kettering Research Laboratory, Yellow Springs, Ohio*

JAMES R. NORRIS, JR. (41), *Chemistry Division, Argonne National Laboratory, Argonne, Illinois*

ANTHONY SAN PIETRO (107), *Department of Plant Sciences, Indiana University, Bloomington, Indiana*

JAMES SIEDOW[2] (107), *Department of Plant Sciences, Indiana University, Bloomington, Indiana*

EDWIN W. TAYLOR (201), *MRC Muscle Biophysics Unit, Kings College, London, England*

MICHAL WAGNER (233, 267), *Department of Biophysics and Physical Biochemistry, Johnson Research Foundation, University of Pennsylvania Medical School, Philadelphia, Pennsylvania*

DAVID F. WILSON (233), *Department of Biophysics and Physical Biochemistry, Johnson Research Foundation, University of Pennsylvania Medical School, Philadelphia, Pennsylvania*

C. R. WORTHINGTON (1), *Department of Biological Sciences and Physics, Carnegie-Mellon University, Pittsburgh, Pennsylvania*

CHARLES F. YOCUM[3] (107), *Department of Plant Sciences, Indiana University, Bloomington, Indiana*

[2]*Present address:* Department of Biophysics, University of Michigan, Ann Arbor, Michigan.
[3]*Present address:* Department of Biochemistry and Molecular Biology, Cornell University, Ithaca, New York.

Preface

Since the beginning of this serial publication, the specialized field of bioenergetics has grown, as anticipated, and several new journals devoted to it have been started. Although the essence of the energy transduction problem still remains unsolved, a basis for optimism is emerging, particularly in the research on oxidative phosphorylation. Instead of dealing with vague nomenclatures and generalities, research is now addressed to molecular properties of purified enzymes and defined reactions.

Recent contributions to the knowledge of membrane structure based on X-ray diffraction analysis is discussed for the first time in these volumes. The reactions of chlorophyll in model systems and the luminescence associated with light absorptions relate to the early events in photosynthesis. The diversity of newly described electron carriers in the region of the primary acceptor in photosystem I forms a timely topic. The kinetic properties of actomyosin are related critically to the contractile cycle. The attempts to relate spectroscopic and EPR measurements to redox changes associated with energy coupling in the mitochondrial electron carriers are clearly provocative. The role of soluble proteins in the energy transfer process of oxidative phosphorylation has been examined. Finally, the structural and chemical properties of the photoreceptors in the visual process have been extensively documented.

Again, we have attempted to bring together articles at the cutting edge of science in the wide and complex field of bioenergetics.

D. RAO SANADI
LESTER PACKER

February, 1973

Contents of Previous Volumes

Volume 3

Volume 4

X-Ray Diffraction Studies on Biological Membranes[1]

C. R. WORTHINGTON

*Department of Biological Sciences and Physics,
Carnegie-Mellon University,
Pittsburgh, Pennsylvania*

I. Introduction

Cell membranes are directly involved in many life processes, and a concentrated effort using a variety of physical and chemical techniques is under way in an attempt to elucidate the molecular structure of biological membranes. This review is concerned with the results of recent X-ray diffraction studies on membranes. Membrane ultrastructure is more often studied by electron microscopy, but the X-ray

[1]Original work by the author and associates discussed in this review was supported by U.S. Public Health Service Grant NS 09329.

1

diffraction method has an important advantage in that membranes can be maintained in a living condition during the X-ray experiment. Prior to 1960, many attempts were made to study membranes by X-ray diffraction, but these earlier studies failed to provide an electron density description of membrane structure. There were two reasons for this failure; only a few X-ray reflections were recorded and valid procedures for structure analysis did not exist. This situation is no longer true, and, during the last few years, there has been a revival of interest in this endeavor.

On the experimental side, the development of an optically focusing X-ray camera (Elliott and Worthington, 1963) in conjunction with a microfocus X-ray source has enabled improved X-ray diffraction patterns to be recorded from many biological systems and, in partic-ular, from membranes; for a discussion of these technical advances, see Worthington (1971a). Specimen preparation is also an important factor; a suitable specimen for X-ray diffraction should be about 1 mm thick, if copper $K\alpha$ radiation is used. Suitable X-ray specimens are those which occur naturally in a multilayered form, for example, nerve myelin, retinal photoreceptors, chloroplasts, and mitochondria. On the other hand, membranes which do not occur naturally in a multi-layered form can, sometimes, be assembled in this form by sediment-ing in the ultracentrifuge. X-Ray studies have been made on these artificially ordered membrane preparations derived from, for example, red blood cells, cell walls of bacteria, sarcoplasmic reticulum, and mitochondria. More recently, X-ray patterns have also been obtained from membrane dispersions consisting of a suspension of the intact cells or isolated envelopes. Thus, there is a choice of X-ray studies to present. However, no attempt has been made to present a balanced review, and prominence is given to the work carried out by the author and associates.

X-Ray studies on membranes have their own rules and do not follow the step-by-step procedures used in the study of crystals. It is widely recognized that structural interpretations of X-ray diffraction data from biological systems are especially difficult. The main reason for this difficulty is that a continuous electron density distribution is sought. Before a correct electron density description can be obtained, a solution to the phase problem is required. Although as a rule, the phase problem cannot be directly solved, by making a few plausible assumptions, often a possible solution can be found. This kind of situation is not ideal as it would be desirable to have an exact answer. Surprisingly, under certain conditions, this is possible in the structure analysis of membranes. It is evident that the structure analysis is an important consideration, and a brief account of the basic theory and some recent developments is given in Section II.

II. Structure Analysis

A. BASIC THEORY

In order to explain the basic steps involved, consider the lamellar structure of a single unit cell which consists of one or more planar membranes. Let $t(x)$ represent the electron density of the single unit cell at right angles to the plane of the membrane, and let $T(X)$ represent its Fourier transform, where x, X are real and reciprocal space coordinates. Because the membrane specimen has limited order, the experimentally observed intensity $I(X)$ has to be corrected before an estimate of the Fourier transform can be obtained, and this requires a separate study (Blaurock and Worthington, 1966). If a suitable correction can be found, then a corrected intensity curve is obtained.

Consider a multilayered assembly of membranes consisting of N unit cells with a repeat distance d. If N is not small, then discrete diffraction is recorded at $X = h/d$, where h is the order of diffraction. It is also convenient to assume that each unit cell of thickness d is centrosymmetrical, and the Fourier transform values $T(h)$ are now given by $T(h) = \{\pm\}|T(h)|$. The phase information in the centrosymmetrical case reduces to a set of signs $\{\pm\}$. The integrated intensity $I(h)$ is measured, and hence a set of corrected intensities is obtained. The usual formulas for the Fourier synthesis and the Patterson function now apply.

The structure analysis proper concerns a search for the phases so that a Fourier synthesis can be derived. This Fourier is often called the observed Fourier, as it is computed using the observed X-ray data. In a crystal structure analysis, a Fourier synthesis (which is three-dimensional) represents the end result, for it usually gives the spatial atomic configuration of the crystal. However, in the study of biological systems, the observed Fourier synthesis is seldom the end result for two reasons. The first reason is that it does not provide the true structure; the electron density profile has a ripple contour superimposed on the true structure due to the limited resolution Δx, where $\Delta x = d[2h]^{-1}$. The second reason is that even if a correct electron density description is available, there is always the problem of how the various molecular components are assembled in the membranes. In order to study the molecular distribution, it is convenient to interpret the observed Fourier in terms of some electron density model. The Fourier series representation of this electron density model should be very similar to the Fourier computed using the observed X-ray data. Thus, knowledge of observed Fourier is only academic, as this electron density profile is more usefully expressed in terms of a set of electron density model parameters.

An electron density model can be directly derived from the observed X-ray data; the independent model parameters cannot exceed the number of diffraction orders h. In the model approach, a model is derived from the intensity data, whereas in the Fourier approach, a model is deduced from the Fourier synthesis. Both methods are dependent on obtaining the correct set of phases. The model approach is a convenient one, and strip models which have uniform electron densities confined to layers parallel to the membrane surface are often used. The use of electron density strip models in the interpretation of X-ray data from membranes has been described (Worthington, 1969a).

If a possible solution to the phase problem has been obtained using either the model approach or the Fourier approach, then this phase solution is based on certain assumptions. In the model approach, these assumptions relate to the particular restraints imposed on the model, for example, a symmetrical bilayer model or a strip model with a finite number of parameters, whereas, in the Fourier approach, these assumptions relate to the criteria used to choose the particular Fourier. No matter how plausible these assumptions may appear (to the investigator) nevertheless some proof of correctness is still required before the model can be accepted as being correct. Fortunately, in the study of membranes, it is sometimes possible to obtain a proof of correctness or, in other words, to directly solve the phase problem.

B. DIRECT METHODS

Membranes either occur naturally or can be artificially prepared in certain well-defined configurations. The application of direct methods of structure analysis to the X-ray data recorded from certain configurations provides a solution to the phase problem. This is an important new development in membrane research. The three methods described here, sampling theorem, autocorrelation function and X-ray holograms, are effective for symmetrical structures. Two of the methods, sampling theorem and X-ray holograms, can also be used to study asymmetrical structures.

1. Sampling Theorem

Membranes have an important property in that they swell or shrink as a result of changes in the immersion medium. On occasions, the separation distances between individual membranes can be varied without any change in internal structure. The X-ray data from two or more such membrane assemblies provide measurements on the same Fourier transform but at different values of X. One set of X-ray data gives values of $|T(X)|$ at $X = h/d$, whereas the other set gives values of $|T(X)|$ at $X = n/g$, where n is the order of diffraction and g is the new repeat distance. A solution to the phase problem is directly obtained using the sampling theorem (King and Worthington, 1971; Worthington, 1972). If the two sets of X-ray data are confined to within the region X_0, then the phases of $T(h)$ within this region and the value of $T(O)$ are obtained. The experimental basis for the method is that both sets of X-ray data provide values of the same Fourier transform, but at different sample points. An important extension of this method is possible. If the phases of these two sets of data are known within the region X_0, and if one set of data shows higher orders of diffraction, that is, $X > X_0$, then the sampling theorem can be used as a method of extrapolation. The method is essentially an analytic continuation of the Fourier transform (King and Worthington, 1971). The success of the method depends on recording higher order diffraction which has sufficient intensity to significantly influence the Fourier transform values with the region X_0.

2. Autocorrelation Function

The phase problem can be solved if the autocorrelation function $A(x)$ of a single centrosymmetrical membrane unit cell can be found. The original theory was developed by Hosemann and Bagchi (1962). It is convenient to note that the autocorrelation function $A(x)$ has a one-to-one correspondence with a centrosymmetrical n-strip electron density model. There are essentially two ways to interpret $A(x)$: by building a model to match the shape of $A(x)$ or by deconvolution of $A(x)$. The deconvolution is straightforward if the recursion method can be used; in the recursion method, the boundary values of $A(x)$ are first used to obtain the boundary values of the model and a similar procedure is repeated until all values are obtained. The autocorrelation function of the repeating unit can be obtained in two different membrane configurations. The first configuration is when there are only a few unit cells in the diffracting assembly (Hosemann and Bagchi, 1962; Lesslauer and Blasie, 1972) and the other configuration is when the membranes are in a swollen state (Worthington, 1969a; Worthington and Gras, 1972).

In the first configuration, the diffracting membrane assembly contains only a few unit cells, N is small, and the X-ray reflections now have a broadened line shape. The X-ray data refer to a corrected intensity curve. The Patterson function of this intensity curve is also the autocorrelation function of the N unit cells and has width $2Nd$ such that $A(x)$ can be found from the boundary values of the Patterson function. An n-strip centrosymmetrical model is then derived from $A(x)$ using the recursion method. This method is ideal for a study of model membrane systems that can be prepared by forming a small number of oriented lipid bilayers. Multilayers of Ba stearate were first studied in this manner (Lesslauer and Blasie, 1972).

In the other configuration, the diffracting membrane assembly contains many unit cells, N is comparatively large, but the membrane units are in the swollen state. Let the unit cell of electron density $t(x)$ contain a membrane structure of width v with a fluid layer between the adjacent membrane structures. The fluid layer has electron density F and has width $d-v$. The swollen state is defined by the condition that $d \geqslant 2v$, that is, when the width of the fluid layer is equal to or greater than the width of the membrane structure. Let $A(x)$ also denote the autocorrelation of a single unit cell $t(x)$ (minus the fluid F), and $A(x)$ has width $2v$. In the swollen state, $A(x)$ can be directly obtained from the Patterson function. This property was first recognized a few years ago, and it has been used in model-building considerations (Worthington, 1969a). But $A(x)$ can be directly interpreted in terms of an n-strip centrosymmetrical electron density model, and this model refers to the membrane structure $t(x)$. This direct method of structure analysis is ideal for a study of multilayered assemblies of biological membranes which either occur naturally in the swollen state or else can be transformed to this state by changing the immersion medium. Nerve myelin and retinal photoreceptors were first studied in this manner (Worthington and Gras, 1972; King and Worthington, 1972).

3. X-Ray Fourier Transform Holograms

The successful design of an X-ray microscope with atomic resolution would solve all structural problems in biology. The use of holography as a method of microscopy has been considered (see Leith et al., 1965). In an attempt to define a holographic microscope, the Fourier transform hologram was discovered by Winthrop and Worthington (1965) and two methods of recording X-ray Fourier transform holograms were described. In one of these methods, the pinhole method, the specimen contained a known structure, $p(x)$, and an unknown structure, $t(x)$, but separated by a distance a. Let $p(x)$ and $t(x)$ have Fourier transforms $P(X)$ and $T(X)$ and phases $\alpha(X)$ and $\beta(X)$, respectively. The diffraction pattern then contains an interference term, $|P(X)||T(X)|$ cos $[2\pi aX + \beta(X) - \alpha(X)]$, where $\beta(X)$ are the unknown phases. It follows that the unknown structure $t(x)$ is reconstructed by a Fourier transformation of this hologram; this has been shown in an optical analog experiment by Winthrop and Worthington (1966).

Although X-ray holographic microscopes remain to be developed, nevertheless, an X-ray Fourier transform hologram of a membrane specimen has been recorded by Lesslauer and Blasie (1971). The membrane specimen contained layers of known and unknown membranes; the membranes were either single or multilayered so that the separation distance a was known. The interference term was recorded and the unknown phases $\beta(X)$ were readily obtained. So far only symmetrical model system membrane structures have been examined, but this holographic method is general and can be used to study other kinds of structures including asymmetric membranes.

III. Surface Structure of Membranes

The central theme underlying the molecular structure of membranes has been, and still is, the idea that lipid bilayers occur in membranes. This idea is supported by electron microscopy in that the familiar triple-layered membrane unit is well documented. Although other kinds of studies also provide support for lipid bilayers, nevertheless direct evidence for the lipid bilayer configuration has been difficult to obtain. In the early 1960's there was a new development in that the previous triple-layered unit occasionally showed a globular subunit structure in some electron micrographs. The evidence for subunit structure in membranes was first obtained by Fernández-Morán (1962) and Sjöstrand (1963). The occurrence of lipid bilayers in membranes was now seriously questioned, and various other possibilities such as lipid micelles or lipoprotein building blocks were considered. However, no evidence for the presence of lipid micelles or discrete lipoprotein building blocks has ever been obtained. It is now realized that subunit structure in membranes refers to the surface structure of membranes.

A membrane is a three-dimensional structure, and a drawing of a single membrane is shown in Fig. 1. Let $t(r)$ represent the electron density of the single three-dimensional membrane and $t(r) = t(x)m(y,z)$, where $t(x)$ is the lamellar structure and $m(y,z)$ is the electron density in the surface of the membrane. The diffraction arising from $t(x)$ and $m(y,z)$ can be distinguished. An X-ray beam (slit collimation) parallel to the surface of the membrane gives rise to lamellar diffraction, whereas an X-ray beam (slit collimation) at right angles to the surface of the membrane produces the surface structure diffraction.

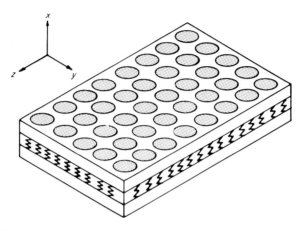

FIG. 1. A three-dimensional drawing of a triple-layered planar membrane. The one-dimensional lamellar structure refers to the electron density distribution along x. Possible subunit structure is shown in the top layer of the planar membrane.

Evidence for subunit structure was obtained in a study of retinal photoreceptor disc membranes of the frog by electron microscopy and X-ray diffraction (Blasie et al., 1965). There was excellent correlation between the X-ray diffraction of air-dried disc membranes, and the electron microscopy for both studies indicated that the subunits occurred in a square array of about 70 Å. These subunits have been identified with the photopigment molecules (Blasie et al., 1969), and their arrangement in the fully hydrated disc membranes has been described (Blasie and Worthington, 1969). These studies have been recently reviewed (Dewey and Barr, 1970; Worthington, 1971c) so that only a brief account is given here.

It was deduced from the X-ray studies that the photopigment molecule (rhodopsin) was a sphere of uniform electron density with a diameter of 42 Å. In the air-dried state, the rhodopsins occurred in a square array, whereas, in the wet state, they had a more random packing. The arrangement of the rhodopsin molecules was temperature dependent; at low temperatures the rhodopsins tended to pack in a square array, but at higher temperatures, they had a considerable degree of freedom. It was suggested that the rhodopsin molecules in the disc membranes behave like a planar liquid. The question whether the rhodopsins were on one side of the disc membrane or on both sides was not directly answered by these studies. However, an answer can be given by using the value of 2.5 mM for the concentration of rhodopsin inside the retinal rod obtained from dichroism measurements (Liebman, 1962). The X-ray studies give a value of 4900 Å^2 for the planar area per rhodopsin molecule, and hence there are only enough rhodopsin molecules to cover one side of the disc membrane. Thus, it is argued that there is only one layer of photopigment molecules per disc membrane.

It is likely that other membranes might also have surface structure, and this is supported by electron microscopy, for nowadays it is common to see subunit structure in electron micrographs of membranes. But, so far X-ray evidence of subunit structure has been obtained only from two other membranes, the membranes from chloroplasts and the purple membrane of *Halobacterium halobium*. In the case of chloroplasts the situation is uncertain in that the X-ray patterns recorded from intact fully hydrated chloroplasts provide little information on surface structure. The only X-ray evidence for surface structure in chloroplasts is indirect; it comes from air-dried protein preparations extracted from chloroplasts (Kreutz, 1965). However, there is convincing evidence in the case of the purple membrane of *H. halobium* (Blaurock and Stoeckenius, 1971). The X-ray and electron microscope studies both indicate that the subunits in the purple membrane are in a planar hexagonal array of about 63 Å; the subunit is thought to be a retinal protein complex similar to rhodopsin (Oesterhelt and Stoeckenius, 1971). The X-ray measurements indicate a planar area of 3400 Å^2 per subunit. The subunits in the purple membrane, unlike the rhodopsins in the disc membrane, do not depend on hydration and remain in a hexagonal lattice even in the wet state (Blaurock and Stoeckenius, 1971). There is 75% protein in the purple membrane and the subunit is the only protein present in the membrane (Oesterhelt and Stoeckenius, 1971). There is evidence from electron microscopy that the purple membrane is asymmetrical (Stoeckenius, 1972) and hence the subunits may occur on only one side of the membrane, but further work is necessary before the location of the protein molecules can be established.

X-Ray evidence of subunit structure has recently been reported in mouse hepatocyte gap junctions (Goodenough and Stockenius, 1972) and in sarcoplasmic reticulum membranes (Liu and Worthington, 1973). These studies reflect the progress made in obtaining new preparations of isolated cell membranes. The gap junction, or nexus, is a specialized area where two cell membranes become closely apposed. Note that the description of subunit structure given here refers primarily to single cell membranes and does not necessarily apply to gap junctions. A hexagonal array of subunits is visible in electron micrographs of mouse hepatocyte gap junctions and the X-ray studies are in support of this observation (Goodenough and Stockenius, 1972). However the X-ray evidence for subunit structure in the gap junction membranes is not particularly strong as the X-ray studies were made on wet unoriented preparations. Surprisingly, the dimensions of the hexagonal array appear to be the same in air-dried and wet preparations. Thus, the subunits in the gap junction, like the subunits in the purple membrane, do not depend on hydration. The X-ray evidence for subunit structure in sarcoplasmic reticulum membranes (Liu and Worthington, 1973) is decisive as the X-ray patterns were obtained from preparations of wet oriented membranes. The membranes are assembled in a multilayered form, and with the X-ray beam parallel to the membrane surface X-ray patterns are recorded using pinhole collimation. The X-ray diffraction from the subunit structure and from the lamellar repeat has been identified. Subunits of 40 Å diameter have been seen on the outer surfaces of sarcoplasmic reticulum membranes in electron micrographs (Martonosi, 1968) but no particular array was recognized. The subunit diffraction is diffuse and the principal reflection occurs at a Bragg spacing of 67 Å. Thus it can be argued that the protein molecules in the sarcoplasmic reticulum membrane have a liquidlike arrangement similar to the rhodopsin molecules in the disc membrane.

IV. Lamellar Structure of Nerve Myelin

A. Low Resolution Studies

Nerve myelin, a naturally occurring biological membrane structure, has been extensively studied by X-ray diffraction and electron microscopy. An account of the early history of structural studies on nerve and some of the results in the period 1960–1970 can be found in recent reviews (Finean, 1969; Worthington, 1971b). Since 1966 a renewed research effort has been in progress in an attempt to obtain an electron density description of nerve myelin. Advances have been made in theory and experiment. So far, the correct electron density description of nerve myelin at low resolution, $\Delta x \approx 14$ Å, has been obtained. This result is of some importance because, although lipid bilayers were anticipated as early as 1925 (Gorter and Grendel, 1925), one can now say with authority that the nerve myelin membranes actually contain a lipid bilayer construction. In addition, considerable progress has been made toward obtaining a correct electron density description at moderate resolution, $\Delta x \approx 5$–7 Å. Before describing the moderate resolution studies, a concise account of the low resolution studies is presented.

Prior to 1966 the X-ray pattern of peripheral nerve myelin showed $h = 1$–5 orders of a radial repeat distance $d \approx 170$–185 Å (Schmitt *et al.*, 1941). In 1966 new X-ray data consisting of $h \approx 12$ orders were recorded (Blaurock and Worthington, 1969) and, later in 1968, $h \approx 18$ orders were recorded (Worthington, 1971b). A theoretical study (Blaurock and Worthington, 1966; Worthington, 1971b) provided the correction factor so that a set of corrected intensities was available. A structure analysis of the live nerve data was the next logical step. However, it was evident that, even after assuming a center of symmetry, the structure analysis of a single set of data from live nerve was not likely to succeed. On the other hand, a structural analysis of swollen nerve was an obvious way to proceed.

Nerve myelin was known to swell in hypotonic solutions (Finean and Millington, 1957; Robertson, 1958), but the pioneering X-ray analyses of these swollen patterns by Finean and Burge (1963) and by Moody (1963) were not complete. In 1966 improved X-ray patterns of peripheral nerve myelin (frog sciatic nerve) swollen in distilled water and in sucrose solutions were recorded (Worthington and Blaurock, 1969a). The structure analysis of the swollen nerve data followed from a theoretical study utilizing strip models; the Fourier transform of a symmetrical triple-layered membrane was derived (Worthington, 1969a). An important property of this Fourier transform was that it had zeros[2] in the ratio $1:3:5$ and it was noted that the swollen nerve data also showed zeroes in the same ratio. Thus, a symmetrical bilayer model was examined as a possible model for swollen nerve and it gave excellent agreement with the X-ray data.

It is convenient to discuss these results in terms of a seven-parameter electron density strip model which is referred to as the basic model (Worthington, 1969b, 1972). This model is shown in Fig. 2. The following properties are noted. The repeat period d contains two membranes of width m. The two membranes are separated by a cytoplasmic fluid layer of width c and form the membrane pair of width v, where $v = 2\,m + c$. The origin of the unit cell is at the center of the

---

[2]The zeros of the Fourier transform $|T(X)|$ are defined as the particular values of X which satisfy the equation $|T(X)| = 0$. In X-ray studies of membranes the identification and the location of the zeros of the Fourier transform are an important help in interpreting the diffraction pattern.

membrane pair. There is an extracellular fluid layer of width d-v between adjacent membrane pairs. Each single membrane has a low electron density region of width l in the central part of the membrane. The membrane profile is asymmetrical, and the asymmetry σ is given by $\sigma = q - p$, where q is the width of the high density layer on the extracellular side and p is the width of the high density layer on the cytoplasmic side. P refers to the electron density of the high density regions and L refers to the electron density of the low density region.

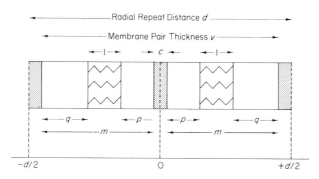

FIG. 2. Basic model for nerve myelin is centrosymmetrical and has repeat distance d and membrane pair thickness v. The membrane pair contains two asymmetric membranes of width m with a fluid layer of width c separating the membranes. The clear regions refer to electron density P, the zigzag lines refer to electron density L, and the dotted regions refer to the fluid electron density F. From Worthington, *Ann. N.Y. Acad. Sci.* **195**, 293 (1972).

The swollen nerve model had two symmetric bilayers end to end ($c = 0$, $\sigma = 0$) but with a large extracellular fluid space. The resolution of the swollen nerve data was $\Delta x \approx 15$ Å and this compared to the live nerve data, $h = 5$, with $\Delta x \approx 17$ Å. A symmetrical bilayer model ($c = 0$, $\sigma = 0$) was also examined as a possible model for live nerve. An important property of this model was the presence of an extracellular fluid layer of about 10–20 Å (Worthington and Blaurock, 1968, 1969b). However, this model gave only fair agreement with the live nerve data. Better agreement was soon obtained, for it was later realized that the membrane pair of live nerve contained a cytoplasmic fluid layer (Worthington, 1969b). When nerve myelin swells in distilled water there is a large increase in the width of the extracellular fluid layer between membrane pairs and, at the same time, there is a decrease in the width of the cytoplasmic fluid layer. In a reinvestigation of X-ray patterns from nerve swollen in distilled water we now find there is, more often than not, only a slight decrease in the width of c (McIntosh and Worthington, 1973). In our original experiments (Worthington and Blaurock, 1969a), there was a marked decrease in the width of c, and this explains why a model with $c = 0$ gave such good agreement. So far it would appear the molecular structure of the nerve myelin membrane remains unchanged during swelling (Worthington, 1972). This conclusion is supported by the experimental observation that the transformation of live nerve to swollen nerve is reversible (Worthington and Blaurock, 1969a).

It was originally argued from model-building considerations that a solution to the phase problem of swollen and live nerve had been obtained at low resolution (Worthington and Blaurock, 1969b). The original arguments are perfectly valid, and nowadays this is even more evident when the arguments are restated in terms of direct methods. Note that at low resolution, $\Delta x \approx 14$–17 Å, the phases of swollen and live nerve are the same; at moderate resolution, differences in phases will appear because of the different c values. The choice of phases for swollen nerve have now been verified in two other ways. One way was by examination of two sets of swollen nerve data; each set has a different value of d, using the sampling theorem; this provides a direct solution to the phase problem (King and Worthington, 1972). The other way is to first obtain $A(x)$, the autocorrelation function of a single membrane pair minus the fluid, and then to derive an n-strip electron density model by deconvolution methods (King and Worthington, 1972). Now at low resolution the phases of live nerve follow directly from the swollen nerve analysis. Thus the correct sign combination for live nerve is $(-,+,+,-,-)$ for the first five orders of diffraction. It should be mentioned that another choice of signs, $(+,+,+,+,+)$, was put forward by Akers and Parsons (1970) to account for the X-ray intensities recorded from chemically treated nerve. But this phase assignment was shown to be incorrect (Worthington, 1970), and, moreover, it was shown that the results obtained by Akers and Parsons (1970) did not conflict with the earlier choice. An independent analysis of the Akers and Parsons (1970) data by Harker (1972) also supports the earlier choice of phases. The phases for live nerve have now been verified. Two sets of X-ray data with different lattice sampling points have been obtained (Worthington, 1972; King and Worthington, 1972). A study of these two sets of data using the sampling theorem has given the following sign combination, $(-,+,+,-,-,+)$, for $h = 1$–6 orders of live nerve. Thus a correct electron density description of nerve at a resolution of $\Delta x \approx 14$ Å has now been obtained.

A Fourier synthesis for live nerve (frog sciatic nerve) using $h = 1$–6 orders and the above signs is shown in Fig. 3. At this resolution the observed Fourier shows a fairly smooth bilayer profile. It would be useful to interpret this electron density profile in terms of structural parameters. For illustration purposes, the basic model with parameters obtained in an earlier study (Worthington, 1969b) is superimposed on the observed Fourier. This model together with an electron density scale in electrons/Å³ (Worthington and Blaurock, 1969b) is also shown in Fig. 3. The Fourier computed from this model is not shown, but it is closely similar to the observed Fourier. Some model parameters for frog sciatic nerve are noted. There are two well-defined fluid layers per radial repeat and each membrane is about 75 Å wide.

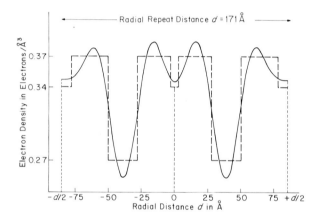

FIG. 3. The basic model for frog sciatic nerve is superimposed on the observed Fourier synthesis. The Fourier synthesis for frog sciatic nerve was computed using the first six reflections. The electron density scale in electrons/Å³ refers to the electron density strip model, whereas the scale of the Fourier has been chosen to give a reasonable match with the model solely for illustration purposes.

The width of the low density region is unexpectedly narrow (about 20 Å). This central region is identifiable with the hydrocarbon chains of the lipid molecules as $L \approx 0.27$ electron/Å³. Although an absolute electron density scale is available, nevertheless, it is not profitable to consider the molecular distribution at this resolution because there are too few model parameters.

B. Moderate Resolution Studies

A structure analysis using the higher orders of diffraction can give an electron density description of nerve myelin at moderate resolution. A variety of methods of analysis have been tried. It will be recalled that a symmetrical bilayer model was first used to obtain the correct phases for swollen and live nerve at low resolution. However, although fair agreement was obtained with this model, nevertheless the presence of a symmetric membrane within nerve myelin was not established. It can be seen from the Fourier synthesis in Fig. 3 that the nerve membrane appears slightly asymmetrical, and this is also shown by the superimposed model. Therefore, even at low resolution, the nerve membrane is not symmetrical but shows a finite asymmetry. This is an important consideration because one could easily have made the mistake of assuming a symmetrical membrane profile in order to interpret the higher orders of diffraction. Notwithstanding, if one does persist with a symmetric membrane, the resulting Fourier at higher resolution is more or less symmetrical. This has been shown using the early symmetrical model (Worthington, 1972). Caspar and Kirschner (1971) describe such a Fourier synthesis for nerve myelin. They make two assumptions; the membrane is symmetric, and the membrane profiles of sciatic and optic nerves are the same. The first assumption is untenable. The second assumption may be approximately correct, but this is of little consequence. Even at low resolution the membranes of sciatic and optic nerves show small differences. These differences will be discussed in Section IV, D.

The basic model was first tried with the moderate resolution data, but additional model parameters were clearly needed. In later work, a model with a total of 12 parameters was developed (Worthington, 1971b; Worthington and King, 1971). The 12-parameter model is shown in Fig. 4. The electron densities have the following variation: J is high, I is moderately high, S is moderate, and L is low. The twelve

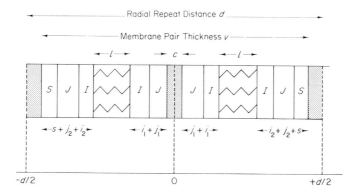

FIG. 4. The 12-parameter electron density model is centrosymmetrical and contains two asymmetric membranes per radial repeat. The clear regions refer to electron densities I, J, and S, the zigzag lines refer to electron density L, and the dotted regions refer to the fluid electron density F. Each asymmetric membrane has width m, where $m = j_1 + i_1 + l + i_2 + j_2 + s$. From Worthington, Ann. N.Y. Acad. Sci. **195**, 293 (1972).

parameters consist of five electron densities (F, J, I, L, S) and seven widths ($c, i_1, i_2, j_1, j_2, l, s$). Model parameters have been assigned to sciatic nerves of frog and rat and to frog optic nerve. The values obtained for the various strip widths in the three cases are listed in Table I. The 12-parameter model is in very good agreement with the X-ray data from these three nerves.

TABLE I
WIDTHS IN ANGSTROMS OF THE ELECTRON DENSITY REGIONS IN THE
12-PARAMETER MODEL FOR THREE NERVES

	d	m	c	j_1	i_1	l	i_2	j_2	s	d-v
Frog sciatic nerve	171	75	11	13	10	21	9	12	10	10
Rat sciatic nerve	176	75	13	13	10	21	9	12	10	13
Frog optic nerve	154	70	10	11	10	21	9	13	6	4

Thus an interpretation of the higher orders of diffraction from live nerve has been obtained. The phases are conveniently divided into three sets; $h = 1$–6, $h = 7$–12, and $h = 13$–18. The phases $h = 1$–6 are known. So far little can be said about the correctness of the phases $h = 13$–18, but the correctness of the phases $h = 7$–12 given by the model has been studied. Two sets of X-ray data but with different sampling points have been found; one set of data is from live nerve, $h = 1$–12, and the other set is from shrunken nerve, $h = 1$–6. The sampling theorem can be used as a method of analytic continuation (King and Worthington, 1971), and the phases $h = 8, 10, 11,$ and 12 obtained using this direct method were the same as given by the 12-parameter model (Worthington, 1972; Worthington and King, 1971). There is, therefore, independent evidence which is in support of the phases given by the 12-parameter model.

A Fourier synthesis for live nerve (frog sciatic nerve) using $h \approx 12$ reflections and the model phases is shown in Fig. 5. The continuous curve refers to the observed Fourier computed using the X-ray data whereas the dotted curve refers to the calculated Fourier computed using the theoretical amplitudes derived from the model. Both Fouriers have resolution $\Delta x = 7$ Å. In Fig. 5 it is evident that the calculated or model Fourier is closely similar to the observed Fourier. Thus at this moderate resolution the 12-parameter electron density model is a valid representation for live nerve. Fourier syntheses at a higher resolution $\Delta x = 4.8$ Å using $h \approx 18$ orders have also been derived (Worthington, 1971b; Worthington and King, 1971), but they are not shown here as the correctness of phases $h = 13$–18 has not been studied apart from model-building considerations.

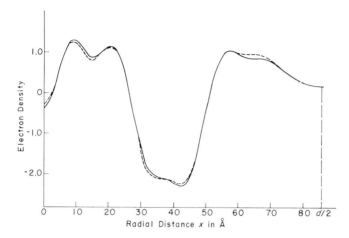

FIG. 5. Fourier series representations for the myelin layers of frog sciatic nerve computed using the first twelve reflections. The continuous curve refers to the observed Fourier, and the discontinuous curve refers to the calculated Fourier. The resolution of each synthesis is 7 Å. From Worthington, *Ann. N.Y. Acad. Sci.* **195**, 293 (1972).

The electron densities of the model shown in Fig. 4 can be expressed in terms of electrons/Å³ as an absolute scale has been established (Worthington and Blaurock, 1969b; Worthington and King, 1971). The following values for frog sciatic nerve were obtained: $J = 0.37$ electron/Å³, $I = 0.36$ electron/Å³, $S = 0.35$ electron/Å³, and $L = 0.27$ electron/Å³. It can be seen from Table I that the widths of the electron density layers I and J have the property that $i_1 \approx i_2$ and $j_1 \approx j_2$. Therefore the five layers (j_1, i_1, l, i_2, j_2) have an approximate center of symmetry. This suggests that the nerve membrane contains a symmetrical lipid bilayer. The first possibility is that the protein component may be entirely located within the outer strip s, but the possibility that some of the protein component may be contained within strips j_1 and j_2 as well as outer strip s merits further consideration. In any case the asymmetry arises mainly from the presence of the layer of moderate electron density S which has width s and faces the extracellular fluid space.

A recent X-ray study on frog sciatic nerve has been reported. This study was completed in the latter part of 1972 (after this chapter was submitted for publication). The important result is that the phases

$h=12$ for frog sciatic nerve have been uniquely determined using direct methods of structure analysis (Worthington and McIntosh, 1973; McIntosh and Worthington, 1973). This was accomplished by recording improved X-ray patterns of frog sciatic nerve swollen in glycerol solutions; unlike previous swollen nerve patterns (Worthington and Blaurock, 1969a) the diffraction extended out to a resolution Δx of 7 Å. Phases for swollen nerve were obtained by deconvolution methods described in Section II, B,2. Moreover, the molecular structure of the membrane pair of swollen nerve did not change during the process of swelling. Thus the results of the structure analysis of swollen nerve apply to live nerve. The phases $h=12$ for live nerve are therefore uniquely determined. The correct phases prove to be the same as given by the 12-parameter model except for $h=7$. The $h=7$ reflection has weak intensity and only weakly influences the shape of the Fourier synthesis. The correct Fourier synthesis for live nerve (frog sciatic nerve) using $h=12$ reflections is therefore closely similar to the Fourier synthesis shown in Fig. 5. It also follows that the considerations on the molecular distribution which were deduced from the X-ray studies prior to 1972 still apply.

C. MOLECULAR DISTRIBUTION

The molecular distribution for nerve myelin has been studied. The derived parameters of the present model are sufficient in number to limit the kinds of possible molecular distributions which can be proposed. A molecular model for the symmetrical lipid bilayer construction in nerve myelin has been proposed (Worthington, 1971b; King and Worthington, 1972). The molecular model is shown in Fig. 6. The earlier molar ratio of 2:2:1 for phospholipid, cholesterol, and cerebroside was used. Ten lipid molecules consisting of 2 lecithins, 2 sphingomyelins, 2 cerebrosides, and 4 cholesterols were constructed using CPK atomic models. The cholesterols are equally distributed in the high density regions on either side of the low density region. In the model shown in Fig. 6, it is assumed that the protein component is on only one side of the membrane and is confined to the 10 Å layer facing the extracellular fluid layer. The hydrocarbon chains are interdigitated in the low density region which has a narrow width of 21 Å.

The molecular model was assembled to agree with the derived electron density contour and it serves only to illustrate the kind of packing between cholesterol and the other lipid molecules. It is recognized that the earlier molar ratio is only approximate. With the data of O'Brien (1967) a molar ratio of 8:7:5 for cholesterol, glycerolipids, and sphingolipids is more correct. According to this later molar

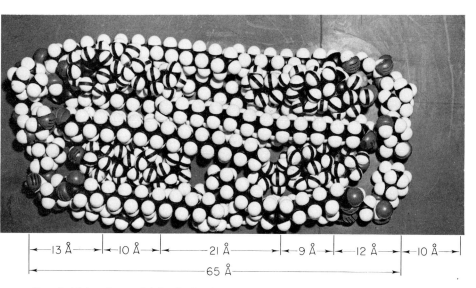

FIG. 6. Molecular model for the lipid bilayer construction within frog sciatic nerve. The width of the symmetrical lipid bilayer is 65 Å. The widths of the six strips within the bilayer model are shown. The hydrogen atoms of the cholesterol molecules have a black line on a white background. From C. R. Worthington, *In* "Biophysics and Physiology of Excitable Membranes" (W. J. Adelman, ed.) © 1971 by Litton Educational Publishing, Inc. Reprinted by permission of Van Nostrand-Reinhold Company.

ratio the molecular model contains too many sphingolipids. However, even allowing for variations in the lipid molecules, different chain lengths and differences in the degree of saturation of the chains, the principal features of the molecular model remain unchanged. This is because myelin has a large number of cholesterol molecules and a high proportion of lipids which contain saturated and long fatty acid chains. The cholesterol molecules will tend to form a complex with adjacent lipid molecules and they are equally distributed in the intermediate regions (i_1 and i_2) with the tail portions located in the central low density region. There is supporting evidence in favor of this kind of model. Various arguments for the presence of a cholesterol:lipid complex in myelin have been given by Vanderheuvel (1963), Eng and Smith (1966), and O'Brien (1967).

D. Sciatic and Optic Nerves

Differences in the molecular organization of the myelin sheaths of peripheral and central nervous system nerves are apparent at the electron microscope level (see, for example, Peters, 1968). Although the two kinds of nerve myelins have the same mode of formation, they are derived from different cells, namely, the Schwann cell and the neuroglial cell. Differences in the low-angle X-ray diffraction patterns recorded from the two kinds of nerve are also evident. Peripheral nerves have been frequently studied and the structure analysis is more advanced, whereas only a few X-ray studies have been made on central nervous system nerves. Until 1966, only two orders had been recorded (Finean, 1960) but additional orders $h \approx 12$ have now been recorded from central nervous system nerves by Blaurock and Worthington (1969). However, many of these orders are weak and the intensities have not been measured as accurately as the X-ray intensities from peripheral nerves.

The radial repeat distances of peripheral nerves are 170–185 Å compared to 150–160 Å for central nervous system nerves. The intensity variation for peripheral nerves is $I(2) > I(4) > I(3) > I(5) > I(1)$, whereas the intensity variation for central nervous system nerves is $I(2) > I(4) > I(1) \approx I(3) \approx I(5)$. The so called "difference factor" refers to the occurrence of the odd orders of diffraction. The "difference factor" is larger in peripheral nerves, whereas it is smaller in central nervous system nerves. The first explanation of the "difference factor" utilized the different widths of the fluid layers; an unequal and larger separation between membranes in peripheral nerves was described (Worthington, 1969b). This description was valid at low resolution, but a detailed explanation of the "difference factor" concerns both the asymmetry of the membranes and the actual widths of the fluid layers. As a result of the moderate resolution studies, a better estimate of structural parameters are available. From Table I the two sciatic nerves and the one optic nerve show differences in model parameters. The "difference factor" for the sciatic nerves arises from the asymmetry of the membranes for the fluid layers are equal in width. The "difference factor" for the one optic nerve is relatively small for $c \approx d\text{-}v + \sigma$ and thus it arises from differences in electron densities S and F.

The swelling behavior of sciatic and optic nerves is also different; sciatic nerve swells in hypotonic solutions, whereas optic nerve does not swell. When sciatic nerve swells the extracellular fluid layer $d\text{-}v$ increases. The width $d\text{-}v$ for live frog sciatic nerve is 10 Å whereas the same width for live frog optic nerve is 4 Å. This small width for optic nerve increases the possibility of "bridges" between membranes which would tend to prevent swelling.

The two kinds of nerve have about the same relative amounts of cholesterol, glycolipids, and sphingolipids (O'Brien, 1967), but the total lipid content is slightly greater in central nervous system nerves. Thus, it can be argued that the lipid bilayer part is very similar for both kinds of nerve, but the membrane profiles are slightly different because of the lipid:protein ratios. From Table I the model parameters for two sciatic nerves and one optic nerve have these properties. The lipid bilayer parameters are very similar. Differences in membrane thickness are noted: 75 Å for sciatic nerve and 70 Å for optic nerve. The widths of the outer strip of moderate electron density are 10 Å and 6 Å, respectively; this is in the right direction as sciatic nerves contain slightly more protein by dry weight.

V. Lamellar Structure of Retinal Photoreceptors

A. Low Resolution Studies

Retinal photoreceptors are an intriguing system for study by X-ray diffraction for they have an elegant multilayered membrane structure. The lamellar repeat is the disc-to-disc distance inside the photo-receptor. However, the X-ray experiment is not easy as a portion of the retina containing well-oriented rod outer segments has to be positioned in the X-ray beam; the retina is immersed in buffered saline solution at a controlled temperature. Improved X-ray diffraction patterns from retina were first reported in 1969. X-Ray patterns showing $h \approx 11$ orders of a disc-to-disc repeat of $d \approx 300$ Å were obtained by Gras and Worthington (1969) from five types of intact retinas. These retinas refer to frogs (*Rana pipiens* and *Rana catesbeiana*), rat, cattle, monkey. Similar X-ray patterns have also been obtained from another frog (*Rana temporaria*) by Blaurock and Wilkins (1969).

Before a structure analysis can be considered, a set of corrected intensities is needed. In the case of X-ray data recorded using slit collimation, no correction factor was used by Gras and Worthington (1969), whereas Blaurock and Wilkins (1969) corrected the observed data by a factor h. Unfortunately, the correction factor is not easily derived. The appropriate diffraction theory has been developed, but so far it has only been published in a doctoral thesis (Worthington, 1955). Our X-ray patterns of retina using pinhole collimation and those of Blaurock and Wilkins (1969) indicate a small disorientation of the rods about the average rod axis. Calculations show that this disorientation is relatively unimportant so that only a small correction is necessary, and, hence, at low resolution it is approximately correct to simply use the observed X-ray data.

The basic model shown in Fig. 3 was tried with the X-ray data from frog retina. The disc in the retina corresponds to the membrane pair in nerve myelin. The fluid layers are renamed; c now refers to the width of the intradisc space and d-v refers to the width of the interdisc space. Note that the interdisc space refers to the cytoplasm of the outer segments. In the original analysis only $h = 1$–8 orders from a disc-to-disc repeat of $d = 314$ Å were used (Gras and Worthington, 1969). The model which gave excellent agreement with the X-ray data had the following parameter values: $m = 74.5$ Å, $c = 5$ Å, $p = 40$ Å, $l = 16$ Å, and $q = 18.5$ Å with d-$v = 160$ Å. The width of the disc membrane is almost identical to nerve myelin and the low density region is even narrower than in the case of nerve. The disc membrane is markedly asymmetrical with $p = 40$ Å compared to $q = 18.5$ Å. From X-ray studies the diameter of the rhodopsin molecule was found to be 42 Å (Blasie and Worthington, 1969) and, because $p = 40$ Å, it is reasonable to assign the rhodopsin molecules to the layer facing the intradisc space (Gras and Worthington, 1969). This assignment is supported by considerations on the actual number of rhodopsin molecules present in the disc membrane (Worthington, 1971c).

Like the case of nerve myelin, an absolute electron density scale has been obtained (Gras and Worthington, 1970; Worthington, 1971c). The average electron density of the disc membrane was found to be 0.36 electron/Å^3. This result is consistent with the composition (dry weight) of the disc membranes, for they contain about 50% protein (Nielsen et al., 1970). The high density regions in the model contain 0.39 electron/Å^3, whereas the low electron density region contains 0.29 electron/Å^3. This low electron density is identifiable with the hydrocarbon chains of the lipid molecules.

The phases $h = 1$–8 given by the disc membrane model have now been verified (Worthington and Gras, 1972). It was recognized that retinal rods are in a swollen state with $d \approx 300$ Å and $v \approx 150$ Å. $A(x)$, the autocorrelation function of a single disc, is obtained from the Patterson function, and a deconvolution of $A(x)$ using the recursion method provides an n-strip electron density model. The phases $h = 1$–8 derived by this direct method are the same as given by the proposed model. Thus, a correct electron density description for the lamellar structure of retinal photoreceptors is known at a resolution of $\Delta x \approx 19$ Å.

It is important to point out that the shape of the electron density profile depends on the correction factor, whereas the phases do not depend on the correction factor. In the model analysis, no correction factor was used and an asymmetrical disc membrane was obtained. On the other hand, if the observed data are corrected by the factor h, then the asymmetry is considerably reduced, but the disc membrane still remains asymmetrical with $\sigma < 0$ as before. If, for argument sake, a symmetrical disc membrane ($\sigma = 0$) is considered, then the zeroes of the theoretical diffraction would occur in the ratio 1:3:5, but the observed X-ray data from retina does not have this property (Worthington, 1972). Hence, the disc membrane is asymmetrical, but the actual value of the asymmetry σ depends on the processing of the X-ray data.

B. MODERATE RESOLUTION STUDIES

The problem of obtaining an electron density description of photoreceptors at moderate resolution has been considered. Higher orders of diffraction $h \approx 15$ (Worthington, 1971c) and $h \approx 20$ (Gras and Worthington, 1971) have been recorded from frog retina. Although many of these higher orders have been known since 1969, it has taken a long time to obtain a reliable set of observed intensities. The main reason for this delay is that small structural changes frequently occur during long X-ray exposures. These structural changes probably arise from small variations in the widths of the intra- and interdisc spaces. Thus, the observed X-ray diffraction pattern recorded after a long exposure is a composite of many slightly different diffraction patterns. Improved and reproducible X-ray patterns have now been obtained using shorter exposure times of only a few hours duration (Gras and Worthington, 1971). At the present time, the X-ray intensities $h = 1–11$ have been accurately measured, the corresponding resolution is $\Delta x \approx 14$ Å. The phases $h = 1–8$ are known and the phases $h = 9–11$ have also been derived from a deconvolution of the autocorrelation function of a single disc.

A Fourier synthesis for frog retina using $h = 11$ reflections and the above phases is shown in Fig. 7. The observed Fourier shows a smooth asymmetrical bilayer profile at a resolution of $\Delta x \approx 14$ Å. This Fourier has not yet been expressed in terms of structural parameters. Now the calculated Fourier of the 1969 disc model computed at a slightly lower resolution has a similar profile to the observed Fourier in Fig. 7, and therefore the same kind of asymmetrical bilayer is implied. Because more accurate intensities and more orders of diffraction are included in the analysis, small changes in model parameters are to be expected. However, even though an absolute electron density scale is available, it is not profitable to study the molecular distribution at this resolution because there are too few structural parameters. Molecular model-building will be difficult for disc membranes contain about 50% protein. By analogy to the case of nerve myelin it is anticipated that the disc membranelike nerve myelin has a lipid bilayer construction with the hydrocarbon chains interdigitated.

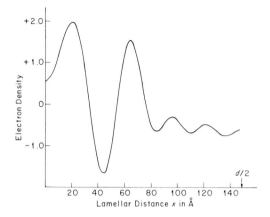

FIG. 7. Fourier series representation for the disc membranes in frog retina. The Fourier synthesis was computed using the first 11 reflections and the resolution of the synthesis is 14 Å. The origin of the Fourier is at the center of the intradisc space between the two disc membranes which form the disc. The disc-to-disc repeat distance is 296 Å.

C. BLEACHED AND UNBLEACHED RETINAS

X-Ray experiments have been carried out on bleached and unbleached retinas. Rhodopsin molecules undergo a molecular rearrangement on bleaching and it would be important if this molecular event could be detected by X-ray diffraction. In the original studies (Gras and Worthington, 1969; Blaurock and Wilkins, 1969) no significant differences in X-ray patterns from bleached and unbleached retinas were reported. However, since 1969, it has been recognized (Gras and Worthington, 1971) that the diffraction patterns of bleached and unbleached retinas do show some differences. The difficulty is in obtaining reliable sets of X-ray data which show significant differences. X-Ray diffraction intensities $h = 1$–11 from intact bleached and unbleached frog retinas have been accurately measured; the repeat period $d = 296$ Å is the same, before and after bleaching. The Patterson functions of bleached and unbleached frog retinas computed using $h \approx 11$ orders are shown in Fig. 8. The Patterson functions have been matched by setting the origin values equal.

$A(x)$, the autocorrelation function for a single disc, has the same profile as the Patterson function. The three main peaks of $A(x)$ have been interpreted in terms of the 1969 disc model (Gras and Worthington, 1969). The first peak (nearest to the origin) refers primarily to the correlation between the hydrocarbon region and the intradisc space, the second peak refers to the correlation between single disc membranes, and the third peak (nearest to $d/2$) refers to the correlation between the high density layers facing the cytoplasm or the interdisc space.

The Patterson functions in Fig. 8 are similar in that the three peaks occur in the same positions. However, the shape of the three peaks are different; the peaks are sharpened in the unbleached retina. This can be traced, in part, to the fact that the intensity of the $h = 7$ reflection is stronger in the unbleached retina. Note that differences in the shape of the peaks are not due to general disorder in the bleached retina for the X-ray intensities from the bleached retina do not show this behavior.

Corless (1972) in a Fourier analysis of the X-ray data from frog has claimed to see some differences between bleached and unbleached retinas. These differences referred to alterations of the membrane surface facing the cytoplasm between discs, thus suggesting the location of rhodopsins. If this were the case, then only the third peak would be sensitive to the bleaching process. But, from Fig. 8, the

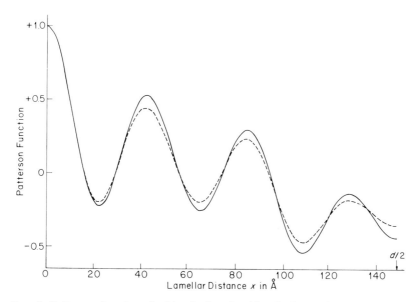

FIG. 8. Patterson functions for bleached and unbleached retinal photoreceptors of frog. The Patterson functions were computed using the first 11 corrected intensities in each case. The continuous line refers to unbleached retina, whereas the dotted line refers to bleached retina. The disc-to-disc repeat distance is 296 Å in each case.

third peak is the least affected on bleaching. Thus, the Patterson functions of bleached and unbleached retinas do not provide evidence for this conclusion.

The bleached and unbleached disc membranes are asymmetrical and the rhodopsin molecules are in a layer facing the intradisc space. The action of light induces small changes in the molecular structure of disc membranes; this is shown by the differences in the Patterson functions. Work is currently in progress to rigorously interpret in molecular terms the differences between the diffraction patterns of bleached and unbleached retinas. Although it it too early at this time to give an explanation of these changes, nevertheless, some tentative observations can be made. If some rearrangement of material in the high density layer occurred on bleaching, then this would tend to account for the reduced height of the first two peaks. Moreover, it appears as if the electron density of the intradisc space increases on bleaching. Also, if some small rearrangement of material in the high density layer facing the cytoplasm occurred on bleaching, this would account for the reduced height of the third peak. These observations give support to the presence of rhodopsin molecules in the layer facing the intradisc space; but, on the other hand, the molecular rearrangement on the side facing the cytoplasm is somewhat puzzling.

VI. Oriented Membrane Preparations

An important development in membrane research is that substantial X-ray diffraction data have been obtained from a variety of isolated cell membranes. Membranes which do not occur naturally in a multilayered form can often be oriented into a multilayered specimen by sedimenting in the centrifuge. Fully hydrated ordered preparations seldom give a well-defined lamellar repeat, the notable exception is a preparation of disc membranes isolated from frog retina (Blasie et al., 1965). If the wet oriented specimen is now partially air-dried, but maintained at a certain level of hydration, the isolated membranes may condense together to form a multilayered specimen. In this way, lamellar diffraction has been observed from rat erythrocyte ghosts (Finean et al., 1966), rat liver mitochondria (Thompson et al., 1968), and brush border membranes of the guinea pig intestinal epithelial cell (Limbrick and Finean, 1970). A symmetrical bilayer model suffices to give fair agreement with the first few orders of diffraction from these condensed membrane preparations (Finean, 1969). Moreover, Finean (1969) suggests that the dominant features of this bilayer profile are common to many if not all membranes. However, the structural analysis of these X-ray patterns which only shows a few orders of a lamellar repeat is far from complete. Nevertheless, this is a promising line of research and there are good prospects for studying many other membranes in this way.

Sometimes, it is necessary to air-dry the oriented specimen in order that the isolated membranes may condense together to form a multi-layered specimen. In this way lamellar diffraction has been observed from cilia membranes (Silvester, 1964) and membranes from the bacterium *Proteus vulgaris* (Burge and Draper, 1967). Again, the structure analysis of these patterns, even at low resolution, is incomplete. Nevertheless, a correct interpretation would contain important structural information. In some cases, for example, in mitochondria (Worthington, 1960), only diffraction from air-dried specimens have been recorded. If an interpretation were forthcoming it would be important to know to what extent this air dried membrane structure is maintained in the natural state. Although it can be argued that air-dried membranes still retain a bilayer profile, nevertheless, molecular changes do occur during the process of air-drying. In the case of nerve myelin, the air-dried nerve membrane has a bilayer profile, but the width of the low density layer is about 40 Å compared to 20 Å for the corresponding layer in live nerve. These structural changes on air-drying merit further study.

It has been mentioned that ordered wet preparations seldom give a well-defined lamellar repeat. It may happen that the separation distances between the oriented membranes vary sufficiently so that continuous diffraction is recorded. This intensity curve is related to the Fourier transform of the individual membrane. X-Ray data have been recorded from wet oriented specimens of *Mycoplasma laidlawii* membranes (Engelman, 1971) and purple membranes from *H. halobium* (Blaurock and Stoeckenius, 1971). Structural interpretations have been suggested in terms of a symmetrical bilayer profile. The same kind of interpretation has also been suggested in order to account for the X-ray data obtained from random dispersions of membranes.

A recent X-ray study on a preparation of wet isolated cell membranes has been reported; this study was made in the latter part of 1972 (after this chapter was submitted for publication). Lamellar diffraction has been recorded from a preparation of wet oriented sarcoplasmic reticulum membranes (Liu and Worthington, 1973). The membranes in excess fluid are assembled into a multilayered array by sedimenting in the centrifuge. Discrete reflections from a lamellar repeat of 220 Å to 260 Å have been recorded. This repeat unit contains a membrane pair with a well-defined fluid layer between adjacent membrane pairs. Electron density profiles at a resolution Δx of 19 Å have been derived (Liu and Worthington, 1973). The sarcoplasmic reticulum membranes are about 75 Å wide and they have a lipid bilayer construction with a markedly asymmetrical profile.

VII. Membrane Dispersions

The first X-ray studies on dispersions consisting of an aqueous suspension of small vesicles were carried out on model systems. Model systems mainly refer to lipid systems of known chemical composition which, under certain conditions, can be assembled as bilayers. Continuous X-ray diffraction has been recorded from lecithin dispersions by Wilkins *et al* (1971) and from lecithin–cardiolipin dispersions by Lesslauer *et al.* (1971). Dispersions may be regarded with good approximation as a random array of single planar membranes. Accordingly, the observed diffraction from model system dispersions has been interpreted as arising from a symmetrical bilayer structure. It is pertinent to consider the theoretical diffraction from a single symmetrical bilayer model; the Fourier transform of this model has been derived (Worthington, 1969a). Let the symmetric model chosen resemble the lipid bilayer part of nerve myelin with $m = 2p + l = 65$ Å, $l = 21$ Å, $P = 0.38$ electron/Å^3, $L = 0.28$ electron/Å^3 and the bilayer is immersed in a fluid of 0.34 electron/Å^3. The theoretical intensity of diffraction from this symmetrical bilayer model is shown in Fig. 9. Note, oriented membrane arrays immersed in the same fluid medium have the same intensity profile as shown by dispersions but only values at $X = h/d$ are recorded. The intensity profile shown in Fig. 9 has a number of zeros, but these do not usually occur in a

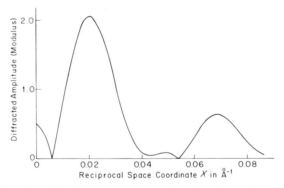

FIG. 9. Diffracted amplitude or Fourier transform (modulus) of a symmetrical lipid bilayer. The lipid bilayer parameters are similar to those derived for the lipid bilayer part of the nerve membrane in the myelin sheath. The modulus of the Fourier transform is plotted so that this theoretical curve can be conveniently compared to the square root of the corrected intensity curve.

simple ratio. Also, the assignment of phases is not necessarily straightforward, for the occurrence of a zero does not always imply a phase
change. Phases for lecithin have been assigned assuming that a phase
change does occur, although the actual choice was also supported by
other considerations (Levine and Wilkins, 1971). However, the phases
of model systems can be directly obtained as demonstrated by Lesslauer *et al.* (1971). The Fourier transform of the intensity data from
membrane dispersions is the autocorrelation function $A(x)$ of the
single membrane. A deconvolution of $A(x)$ using the recursion method
then gives a symmetrical n-strip model. This model for lecithin–
cardiolipin shows a bilayer profile (Lesslauer *et al.*, 1971).

Continuous diffraction has been recorded from membrane dispersions derived from *M. laidlawii* membranes, nerve terminal membranes, and rat erythrocyte ghosts (Wilkins *et al.*, 1971) and the purple
membrane fraction of *H. halobium* (Blaurock and Stoeckenius, 1971).
These experimental curves are certainly more complex than the
corresponding curves for model systems. Although no quantitative
analysis was presented, Wilkins *et al.* (1971) interpreted this diffraction as arising from a bilayer configuration. All the various membranes
show a broad peak between $d = 30$ Å to $d = 60$ Å; the maximum value
of this peak for *M. laidlawii*, nerve terminal and rat erythrocyte membranes occurs at about 45 Å and at about 43 Å for the purple membranes. In Fig. 9 the maximum of the first peak for the symmetrical
lipid bilayer model occurs at about 42 Å. Thus, there is evidence that
the various membranes have a bilayer construction.

Although one can draw on analogies to model systems, nevertheless a rigorous interpretation of the X-ray data from biological membrane dispersions has not been obtained, and at this time, it is unlikely that it can be done. It is pointed out that the experimental
curves do not show zeros in the range of diffraction recorded, even
after applying a small correction for possible diffraction arising from
surface structure. If it is assumed that these experimental curves
actually refer to the Fourier transform (intensity) of a single membrane, then the membrane is asymmetrical. The Fourier transform
$T(X)$ of an asymmetric membrane is given by $T(X) = a(X) + ib(X)$
where $a(X)$ and $b(X)$ are the symmetric and nonsymmetric parts.
Now, both $a^2(X)$ and $b^2(X)$ show zeros, but $|T(X)|^2 = a^2(X) + b^2(X)$
is unlikely to show zeros. Hence the four membranes so far examined
as dispersions are likely to be asymmetrical. The interpretation of X-
ray data from a single asymmetric membrane is not promising. Phases
are not easily assigned and the deconvolution procedures for symmetrical structures cannot be used. Therefore, structure analysis

based upon a symmetical bilayer is a mistake for the X-ray evidence from real membranes indicates that the bilayer profile is asymmetrical. In conclusion, it has been amply demonstrated that substantial X-ray diffraction can be recorded from membrane dispersions, but it remains to be demonstrated whether or not precise details can be extracted from the X-ray curves.

VIII.   The Arrangement of the Lipid Hydrocarbon Chains

It is now known that the hydrocarbon chains of *M. laidlawii* membranes (Engelman, 1971) and *Escherichia coli* membranes (Esfahani *et al.*, 1971) can be in either of two arrangements; the actual arrangement depends on whether the temperature is above or below the transition temperature. The X-ray data consists of a single X-ray reflection which arises because the hydrocarbon chains have an average separation distance. The 4.2 Å reflection refers to a hexagonal crystallike packing whereas the 4.7 Å reflection is usually interpreted as arising from a liquidlike packing or, at least, a more fluid state. Whether other membranes will also show this kind of phase transition is not known, but all biological membranes in the natural state show the 4.7 Å reflection. The description of the low temperature packing is straightforward, but there is disagreement on the description of the packing of the hydrocarbon chains in the high temperature form.

The 4.2 Å reflection is readily interpreted as arising from a hexagonal packing of hydrocarbon chains similar to the packing shown by lipid crystals in the solid state. This 4.2 Å reflection is also observed from a variety of air-dried membranes. In a study of lecithin multilayers (Levine *et al.*, 1968) the orientation of the 4.2 Å reflection indicated that the lecithin chains were at right angles to the surface of the multilayers. Also, the packing of the lecithin chains did not change with hydration.

The 4.7 Å reflection is not so easily interpreted. Note that the peak value of this reflection varies from 4.5 Å to 4.8 Å with different membranes. This reflection is often correlated with a similar reflection shown by liquid hydrocarbons. There has been a tendency for some workers to consider that the hydrocarbon phase in the central part of the membrane is, in fact, liquidlike with the hydrocarbons in disorder (see, for example, Finean, 1969). However, there are a number of arguments against this point of view. In the literature there are numerous birefringence studies on membranes which tend to indicate that the hydrocarbon chains are aligned at right angles to the membrane surface. Molecular model-building considerations also indicate that the hydrocarbon chains in the central region of the bi-

layer are unlikely to be disordered. If a lipid bilayer model is constructed with the lipid heads confined to the surface of the bilayer
then the chains tend to be ordered. This ordering is more noticeable
if it is assumed that the central region of the model has a uniform
electron density.

Considerations on the thickness of egg lecithin bilayers which show
the 4.7 Å reflection and the surface area of the lecithin molecule indicate that the lecithin hydrocarbon chains are almost fully extended
(Levine and Wilkins, 1971). The relevant X-ray reflection, $d = 4.6$
Å, from the egg lecithin multilayers shows a definite arcing and hence
the chains have an average orientation at right angles to the membrane
surface. The corresponding X-ray reflection from egg lecithin–
cholesterol multilayers occurs at $d = 4.8$ Å and the shape of this reflection indicates that the chains are even better oriented than in the
case of lecithin alone. Similar results for biological membranes are
not available. However, the case of nerve myelin is considered. The
wide-angle X-ray pattern of nerve myelin shows a meridionally
accentuated reflection at 4.7 Å. A quantitative interpretation of the
shape of the 4.7 Å reflection has not been given. However, it has been
known for some time (see, for example, Worthington, 1971b) that a
model with chains perfectly aligned at right angles to the surface gives
a reflection which is more sharply accentuated on the meridian than is
actually observed. Thus, it can be argued that the lipid chains in nerve
myelin have a certain degree of disorder. On the other hand, a model
with the hydrocarbon chains in disorder gives a reflection which is a
ring, and there is no extra intensity on the meridian. Hence this model
with a liquidlike arrangement of lipid chains is inappropriate for
nerve myelin. Preliminary calculations indicate that if the chains are
allowed to tilt away from an average direction at right angles to the
surface, according to a Gaussian distribution, then only a small half-
cone angle of tilt is needed to give the 4.7 Å reflection with the observed arcing on the meridian. Therefore, the hydrocarbon chains
of nerve myelin are more ordered than disordered. Although the
chains do not have perfect order, the degree of disorder is small.

IX. The Localization of the Terminal Methyl Groups

A prominent feature of the bilayer profile in some model systems
is the presence of a sharply defined low density region thought to be
due to the localization of the terminal methyl groups of the lipid
hydrocarbon chains at the center of the bilayer. This feature is shown
by multilayers of lecithin (Levine and Wilkins, 1971), barium stearate
(Lesslauer and Blasie, 1972), magnesium stearate, and lecithin–

cardiolipin (Lesslauer *et al.*, 1971). This localization of methyl groups is readily accounted for if the chains have uniform length and are oriented at right angles to the surface. The X-ray evidence indicates that the chains are aligned in these model systems. Wilkins *et al.* (1971) argue that the localization of methyl groups also applies to biological membranes including nerve myelin. The argument is by analogy to model systems, and it is based upon a study of the continuous diffraction shown by membrane and model system dispersions. It was pointed out that this localization in the case of nerve myelin tends to account for the observed peak near $d = 15$ Å. However, although this effect may be in the right direction, a symmetrical bilayer already has this property. The calculated intensity profile from a lipid bilayer model shown in Fig. 9 has a pronounced peak at $d \approx 15$ Å. The symmetrical lipid bilayer model has a central uniform low density region $l = 21$ Å, and hence there is no evidence for the localization of methyl groups in nerve myelin.

It has been deduced in Section VIII that the lipid chains in biological membranes are approximately aligned at right angles to the membrane surface. Now, because of the actual number of carbon atoms in the fatty acid chains, the lipid molecules have a range of different lengths. If there was no interdigitation of chains then a shallow minimum of electron density would be present in the central part of the bilayer. But, in the case of nerve myelin, a central uniform electron density region has been found. This result is readily accounted for if the hydrocarbon chains interdigitate in the central part of the bilayer. It is of interest to inquire whether other membranes besides nerve myelin have this property. It is likely that the bilayer profile in retinal photoreceptors also has a central uniform low density region.

X.   Summary and Conclusions

The most significant result of the recent X-ray studies is that the existence of a lipid bilayer configuration in membranes has been established. The X-ray analysis leading to this conclusion is definite and, furthermore, a proof of correctness has been obtained from recent theoretical work on direct methods of structure determination. Two naturally occurring membranes, nerve myelin and retinal photoreceptors, have been shown to have a bilayer profile and a variety of model membrane systems have also been shown to have, as anticipated, a lipid bilayer arrangement.

The importance of the structure analysis in the study of membranes has been emphasized. The first part of the structure analysis concerns the derivation of the correct electron density distribution while the second part concerns the determination of the molecular distribution. The problem of the molecular distribution can only be considered when the chemical composition is known and when the correct Fourier synthesis is known at moderate resolution together with an absolute electron density scale. It is puzzling why so many X-ray analyses on model systems have stopped at the completion of the first part; no attempt was made to interpret the derived Fourier synthesis. The view point expressed here is that the information contained within the Fourier synthesis is conveniently extracted by a study of the differences between the observed Fourier and the Fourier calculated from some electron density model. So far this kind of analysis has been used in the study of nerve myelin and photoreceptors.

A feature of the X-ray analyses on membranes has been the assumption of a symmetrical membrane profile. The low resolution analysis of swollen and live nerve myelin and the analysis of partially dried oriented membrane preparations were based on this idea. However, careful analysis applied to nerve myelin and retinal photoreceptors shows that these membranes have an asymmetrical profile. Also, the X-ray studies on membrane dispersions tend to indicate that the observed diffraction arises from asymmetric membranes. Hence, only limited progress, if any, can be made if the assumption of a symmetric membrane is retained in the case of biological membranes.

The advantages of studying naturally occurring multilayer assemblies now become even more apparent. Because of the mode of formation of these membrane assemblies, the repeating unit contains two membranes which merge together to form the membrane pair. Although the individual membrane units within the membrane pair may by asymmetrical, nevertheless, the repeating unit is centrosymmetrical. Thus, the asymmetrical membrane profile is conveniently studied. On the other hand, the interpretation of the diffraction recorded from various arrangements of single asymmetric membranes is not conveniently studied at the present time.

Some attempts have been made to determine the molecular arrangements of the lipid bilayer construction in membranes. The molecular model for nerve myelin has the property that the hydrocarbon chains are interdigitated. For the sake of argument, the cholesterol molecules are considered to be separate from the lipid molecules. Because of the interdigitation of chains, the lipid molecules occupy only half of the surface area of the lipid bilayer; actually the lipid molecules will occupy more than half the surface area as the lipid molecules with the shorter chains are unlikely to be interdigitated. Thus there are "holes" in the lipid bilayer. In the molecular model for nerve myelin, the cholesterol molecules occupy the "holes" and make a compact structure. Other membranes generally have less cholesterol and a higher proportion of protein than nerve myelin. Therefore, if interdigitation occurs, it is likely that both cholesterol and protein could occupy the "holes" in other membranes. It is understood that in order to accommodate the larger protein molecules in the membrane more than one lipid molecule has to be replaced and thus, to be rigorous, interdigitation applies only to a continuous lipid bilayer.

One of the consequences of finding the correct electron density distribution for a membrane is that the earlier membrane models can now be critically examined. In the past, all kinds of membrane models have been proposed to account for one or more experimental facts. In order to determine whether these membrane models have any relevance for nerve myelin or photoreceptors, the electron density contours of these models should be computed. If the observed and calculated electron density contours are not similar, then the earlier membrane models can be rejected. It can also be argued that no new model should be considered unless a description in terms of electrons/$Å^3$ is given so that the electron density contour of the proposed model can be readily examined.

It has been demonstrated that X-ray studies on membranes can nowadays yield reliable structural parameters. This step forward is now recognized and current activity is reflected in that nearly all the X-ray studies described here were made during the last few years. Looking toward the future, it is anticipated that X-ray studies will continue to provide significant information on membrane structure and, furthermore, these studies will be extended to many different membranes. Progress in this field depends on obtaining even better X-ray patterns than presently available and applying very careful attention to structure analysis. However, meteoric progress is not expected, for both these steps tend to be time-consuming.

XI. General Perspective

The X-ray results reviewed here refer mainly to two particular membranes, the nerve myelin membrane and the photoreceptor disc membrane. These membranes are appropriate choices for study by X-ray diffraction and, at present, more is known about the molecular structure of these two membranes than of any other biological membrane. On the other hand, in recent years, many different cell membranes have been studied by a variety of physical techniques such as nuclear magnetic resonance and infrared spectroscopy, circular dichroism measurements, thermal analysis, spin-label studies, electron microscopy and freeze-fracture experiments [Chapman, 1968; for recent reviews, see a series of papers in *Annals of New York Academy of Sciences*, Vol. **195** (1972)]. The reader might well ask what is the relevance of the present X-ray results to the structure of other biological membranes and are the X-ray results in accord with the many results obtained using other techniques. Although decisive answers cannot be given and one must be careful in generalizing the present X-ray results to other kinds of specialized membranes, nevertheless, it is possible to make reasonable guesses at some of the design principles of membrane architecture.

The Danielli–Davson (1935) and the Robertson (1959) unit-membrane model contains a continuous bimolecular leaflet of lipids with a layer of protein on both sides of the leaflet. The usual arguments against this kind of model refer to the diversity of membranes; that is, biological membranes differ in thickness, chemical composition, and biological function. Strong objections to the unit-membrane model were raised following the electron microscope observation of globular subunit structure in several membranes by Fernández-Morán (1962) and Sjöstrand (1963). Many different membranes show a subunit structure which is usually in an organized array. These include membranes from mitochondria and chloroplasts, the purple membrane of *H. halobium* (Blaurock and Stoeckenius, 1971), rat liver plasma membranes (Benedetti and Emmelot, 1968), mouse bladder luminal membranes (Vergara *et al.*, 1969), and sarcoplasmic reticulum membranes (Martonosi, 1968). A critical survey of the electron microscopy data from membranes has been made by Dewey and Barr (1970) and by Staehelin and Probine (1970). It was originally argued that the observation of globular subunit arrays in electron micrographs suggests that membranes may be composed of either lipid micelles or lipoprotein building blocks. The X-ray results on isolated photoreceptor disc membranes are usually quoted as strong evidence for the subunit theory of membranes. But this is not correct, for the X-ray results do not support the subunit model. On the other hand, the X-ray data on retina can be interpreted in terms of the model shown in Fig. 1. This model (Worthington, 1971c) has much in common with the iceberg model of Dewey and Barr (1970) and the fluid mosaic model of Singer and Nicolson (1972).

The subunit arrays seen in electron micrographs refer to the surface structure of the membrane. The electron micrographs and also the drawing in Fig. 1 suggest that the subunits are arranged in some definite lattice. However, real membranes are dynamic structures and, moreover, the X-ray results indicate that the photopigment molecules of the disc membrane have a planar liquidlike arrangement. Thus the photopigment molecules in the intact disc membrane have a freedom of movement. The square array of particles seen in the electron micrographs occurs only after dehydration or after cooling. By analogy it can be argued that the subunits in other membranes are also protein molecules, and they are in a liquidlike arrangement as they also have a freedom of movement in the surface of the membrane.

It is clear that the X-ray results do not support the subunit theory of membranes, but one might ask to what extent is the unit membrane model correct. The lipid bilayer concept is first considered. The historic question is whether membranes actually contain lipid bilayers. The answer is yes, but a proviso must be added for it is unlikely that the lipid bilayer is continuous in all membranes. Support for the presence of a hydrocarbon phase also comes from electron microscopy, thermal analysis, spin-label experiments, and X-ray results on dispersions (Wilkins *et al.*, 1971). The lipid bilayer construction, however, differs from the classical extended end-to-end bilayer thought to be present in the unit membrane model in that the low density hydrocarbon chain region is only 20 Å thick. The X-ray results verify that nerve myelin has a lipid bilayer construction which is essentially continuous. In the molecular model shown in Fig. 6 the lipid hydrocarbon chains interdigitate in the central low density region. The cholesterol molecules then occupy the "holes" in the lipid bilayer.

The unit membrane model has protein on both sides of a continuous lipid bilayer. The X-ray results indicate that cell membranes are asymmetrical with the major part of the protein component confined to only one side of the membrane. This asymmetry is probably necessary for biological function. In the past little attention has been directed toward the asymmetry of membranes, but there is an increasing amount of evidence in favor of the asymmetry of membranes (Singer and Nicolson, 1972). The lipid-labeling experiments by Dratz *et al.* (1972) on bovine rod outer segments also provide support for the asymmetry of photoreceptor membranes. The location of the protein molecules in the membrane is an important consideration. Membrane thickness in electron micrographs are usually quoted as 70–95 Å. This width is unlikely to be sufficient to accommodate a comparatively large protein molecule on the outside of even one side of a continuous lipid bilayer. The X-ray results on retina suggest that the photopigment molecule "replaces" a number of lipid molecules in a hypothetical continuous lipid bilayer but on only one side, the side facing the intradisc space. The nonpolar part of rhodopsin is located in the vicinity of the low density hydrocarbon region whereas the polar part of rhodopsin may project a small distance from the surface of the membrane. It is tempting to speculate that protein molecules of other membranes have an arrangement similar to the disc membrane. It should be emphasized, however, that the above description of the way the protein molecules are packed in the membrane is no more than a reasonable guess at this stage because the precise molecular details of this kind of model are unknown. Nevertheless, it is anticipated that a variety of experimental results on the location of protein molecules in the membrane will soon be forthcoming.

It is of interest to examine the lipid area: cell membrane area ratio for the kind of model described here. The Gorter and Grendel (1925) proposal that lipid bilayers are present in cell membranes was based on obtaining a ratio of 2.0 for red blood cells. Later work in the 1960's indicated that the correct value of this ratio for red blood cells was between 1.0 and 2.0. The sarcoplasmic reticulum membranes also have a value between 1.0 and 2.0 (Inesi, 1972). The area per lipid hydrocarbon chain can be readily calculated (Worthington, 1971b) using the average separation of hydrocarbon chains as measured by wide-angle X-ray diffraction and from a knowledge of the electron density of the hydrocarbon phase. Two observations can be made. Interdigitation of the hydrocarbon chains in the lipid bilayer decreases the value of this ratio. If the protein molecules "replace" some of the lipids from a hypothetical continuous lipid bilayer, then this ratio will be further decreased. Thus the membrane model described here will have a lipid area: cell membrane area ratio close to the observed ratios.

In summary the membrane model which is in agreement with the results obtained using many different techniques has the following properties. It is asymmetrical. The protein molecules are predominantly on one side of the membrane, and they have a freedom of movement in the surface of the membrane. The protein molecules "replace" lipid molecules in a hypothetical lipid bilayer and thus lipid bilayers in biological membranes are not continuous. Nerve myelin may be a special case in that the nerve myelin membrane apparently has a continuous lipid bilayer.

REFERENCES

Akers, C. K., and Parsons, D. F. (1970). *Biophys. J.* **10**, 116.
Benedetti, E. L., and Emmelot, P. (1968). *In* "The Membranes" (A. Dalton and F. Haguenau, eds.), pp. 33–114. Academic Press, New York.

Blasie, J. K., and Worthington, C. R. (1969). *J. Mol. Biol.* **39**, 417.
Blasie, J. K., Dewey, M. M., Blaurock, A. E., and Worthington, C. R. (1965). *J. Mol. Biol.* **14**, 143.
Blasie, J. K., Worthington, C. R., and Dewey, M. M. (1969). *J. Mol. Biol.* **39**, 407.
Blaurock, A. E., and Stoeckenius, W. (1971). *Nature (London)* **233**, 152.
Blaurock, A. E., and Wilkins, M. H. F. (1969). *Nature (London)* **223**, 906.
Blaurock, A. E., and Worthington, C. R. (1966). *Biophys. J.* **6**, 305.
Blaurock, A. E., and Worthington, C. R. (1969). *Biochim. Biophys. Acta* **173**, 419.
Burge, R. E., and Draper, J. C. (1967). *J. Mol. Biol.* **28**, 189.
Caspar, D. L. D., and Kirschner, D. A. (1971). *Nature (London)* **231**, 46.
Chapman, D. (1968). *In* "Biological Membranes" (D. Chapman, ed.), pp. 125–199. Academic Press, New York.
Corless, J. M. (1972). *Nature (London)* **237**, 229.
Danielli, J. F., and Davson, J. (1935). *J. Cell. Comp. Physiol.* **5**, 495.
Dewey, M. M., and Barr, L. (1970). *In* "Current Topics in Membranes and Transport" (F. Bronner and A. Kleinzeller, eds.), Vol. 1, pp. 1–33. Academic Press, New York.
Dratz, E. A., Gaw, J. E., Schwartz, S., and Ching, W. (1972). *Nature (London)* **237**, 99.
Elliott, G. F., and Worthington, C. R. (1963). *J. Ultrastruct. Res.* **9**, 166.
Eng, L. F., and Smith, M. E. (1966). *Lipids* **1**, 296.
Engelman, D. M. (1971). *J. Mol. Biol.* **58**, 153.
Esfahani, M., Limbrick, A. R., Knutton, S., Oka, T., and Wakil, S. J. (1971). *Proc. Nat. Acad. Sci. U.S.* **68**, 3180.
Fernández-Morán, H. (1962). *Circulation* **26**, 1039.
Finean, J. B. (1960). *In* "Modern Scientific Aspects of Neurology" (J. N. Cumings, ed.), pp. 232–254. Arnold, London.
Finean, J. B. (1969). *Quart. Rev. Biophys.* **2**, 1.
Finean, J. B., and Burge, R. E. (1963). *J. Mol. Biol.* **7**, 672.
Finean, J. B., and Millington, P. F. (1957). *J. Biophys. Biochem. Cytol.* **3**, 89.
Finean, J. B., Coleman, R., Green, W. G., and Limbrick, A. R. (1966). *J. Cell Sci.* **1**, 287.
Goodenough, D. A., and Stoeckenius, W. (1972). *J. Cell Biol.* **54**, 646.
Gorter, E., and Grendel, F. (1925). *J. Exp. Med.* **41**, 439.
Gras, W. J., and Worthington, C. R. (1969). *Proc. Nat. Acad. Sci. U.S.* **63**, 233.
Gras, W. J., and Worthington, C. R. (1970). *Abstr. Biophys. Soc., 14th Annu. Meet.* p. 52a.
Gras, W. J., and Worthington, C. R. (1971). Unpublished data.
Harker, D. (1972). *Biophys. J.* **12**, 1285.
Hosemann, R., and Bagchi, S. N. (1962). "Direct Analysis of Diffraction by Matter." North-Holland Publ., Amsterdam.
Inesi, G. (1972). *Annu. Rev. Biophys. Bioeng.* **1**, 191.
King, G. I., and Worthington, C. R. (1971). *Phys. Lett. A* **35**, 259.
King, G. I., and Worthington, C. R. (1972). *Abstr. Biophys. Soc. 16th Annu. Meet.* p. 253a.
Kreutz, W. (1965). *Nature (London)* **206**, 1358.
Leith, E. N., Upatnieks, J., and Haines, K. A. (1965). *J. Opt. Soc. Amer.* **55**, 981.
Lesslauer, W., and Blasie, J. K. (1971). *Acta Crystallogr., Sect. A* **27**, 456.
Lesslauer, W., and Blasie, J. K. (1972). *Biophys. J.* **12**, 175.
Lesslauer, W., Cain, J., and Blasie, J. K. (1971). *Biochim. Biophys. Acta* **241**, 547.
Levine, Y. K., and Wilkins, M. H. F. (1971). *Nature (London)* **230**, 69.
Levine, Y. K., Bailey, A. I., and Wilkins, M. H. F. (1968). *Nature (London)* **220**, 577.

Liebman, P. A. (1962). *Biophys. J.* **2**, 161.

Limbrick, A. R., and Finean, J. B. (1970). *J. Cell Sci.* **7**, 373.

Liu, S. C., and Worthington, C. R. (1973). *Abstr. Biophys. Soc. 17th Annu. Meet.* p. 91a.

McIntosh, T., and Worthington, C. R. (1973). *Abstr. Biophys. Soc. 17th Annu. Meet.* p. 91a.

Martonosi, A. (1968). *Biochim. Biophys. Acta* **150**, 694.

Moody, M. F. (1963). *Science* **142**, 1173.

Nielsen, N. C., Fleischer, S., and McConnell, D. G. (1970). *Biochim. Biophys. Acta* **211**, 10.

O'Brien, J. S. (1967). *J. Theor. Biol.* **15**, 307.

Oesterhelt, D., and Stoeckenius, W. (1971). *Nature (London)* **233**, 149.

Peters, A. (1968). *In* "The Structure and Function of Nervous Tissue" (G. H. Bourne, ed.), Vol. 1, pp. 142–183. Academic Press, New York.

Robertson, J. D. (1958). *J. Biophys. Biochem. Cytol.* **3**, 1043.

Robertson, J. D. (1959). *Biochem. Soc. Symp.* **16**, 3.

Schmitt, F. O., Bear, R. S., and Palmer, K. S. (1941). *J. Cell. Comp. Physiol.* **18**, 31.

Silvester, N. R. (1964). *J. Mol. Biol.* **8**, 11.

Singer, S. J., and Nicolson, G. L. (1972). *Science* **175**, 720.

Sjöstrand, F. S. (1963). *J. Ultrastruct. Res.* **9**, 340.

Staehelin, L. A., and Probine, M. C. (1970). *Advan. Bot. Res.* **3**, 1–47.

Stoeckenius, W. (1972). Unpublished data.

Thompson, J. E., Coleman, R., and Finean, J. B. (1968). *Biochim. Biophys. Acta* **150**, 405.

Vanderheuvel, F. A. (1963). *J. Amer. Oil Chem. Soc.* **40**, 455.

Vergara, J., Longley, W., and Robertson, J. D. (1969). *J. Mol. Biol.* **46**, 593.

Wilkins, M. H. F., Blaurock, A. E., and Engelman, D. M. (1971). *Nature (London)* **230**, 72.

Winthrop, J. T., and Worthington, C. R. (1965). *Phys. Lett.* **15**, 124.

Winthrop, J. T., and Worthington, C. R. (1966). *Phys. Lett.* **21**, 413.

Worthington, C. R. (1955). Ph.D. Thesis, Adelaide University, Adelaide, Australia.

Worthington, C. R. (1960). *J. Mol. Biol.* **2**, 327.

Worthington, C. R. (1969a). *Biophys. J.* **9**, 222.

Worthington, C. R. (1969b). *Proc. Nat. Acad. Sci. U.S.* **63**, 604.

Worthington, C. R. (1970). *Biophys. J.* **10**, 675.

Worthington, C. R. (1971a). *In* "Probes of Structure and Function of Macromolecules and Membranes" (B. Chance, C. P. Lee, and J. K. Blasie, eds.), Vol. 1, pp. 179–187. Academic Press, New York.

Worthington, C. R. (1971b). *In* "Biophysics and Physiology of Excitable Membranes" (W. J. Adelman, ed.), pp. 1–46. Von Nostrand-Reinhold, Princeton, New Jersey.

Worthington, C. R. (1971c). *Fed Proc., Fed. Amer. Soc. Exp. Biol.* **30**, 57.

Worthington, C. R. (1972). *Ann. N.Y. Acad. Sci.* **195**, 293.

Worthington, C. R., and Blaurock, A. E. (1968). *Nature (London)* **218**, 87.

Worthington, C. R., and Blaurock, A. E. (1969a). *Biochim. Biophys. Acta* **173**, 427.

Worthington, C. R., and Blaurock, A. E. (1969b). *Biophys. J.* **9**, 970.

Worthington, C. R., and Gras, W. J. (1972). *Abstr. Biophys. Soc., 16th Annu. Meet.* p. 255a.

Worthington, C. R., and King, G. I. (1971). *Nature (London)* **234**, 143.

Worthington, C. R., and McIntosh, T. (1973). In preparation.

Chlorophyll and Light Energy Transduction in Photosynthesis[1]

JOSEPH J. KATZ and JAMES R. NORRIS, JR.
Chemistry Division,
Argonne National Laboratory,
Argonne, Illinois

I. Introduction

All life as we know it depends on energy derived from visible light. Photosynthetic organisms use the energy of light quanta to convert the inorganic compounds carbon dioxide and water to the organic compounds required for survival by all other living organisms. The transformation of the energy of light quanta into oxidants and reductants useful for chemical synthesis thus assumes central importance in biology. In the sequence of events that begins with the absorption of light and culminates in the vast array of organic compounds characteristic of living organisms, chlorophyll plays a crucial role.

[1] Work performed under the auspices of the U.S. Atomic Energy Commission.

A. Chlorophyll Structure

The chlorophylls constitute a small family of closely related pigments long recognized as the primary photoacceptors of photosynthetic organisms (Kamen, 1963; Clayton, 1965). The principal chlorophylls are chlorophylls a and b (Chl a and Chl b, green plants, algae), bacteriochlorophyll (BChl, purple photosynthetic bacteria), chlorobium chlorophyll (green photosynthetic bacteria). Chlorophylls c_1 and c_2 (Dougherty et al., 1970; Strain et al., 1971) (diatoms, marine brown algae) and chlorophyll d (marine red algae) are minor, auxiliary chlorophylls. Chlorophyll a is without exception present in all organisms that carry out photosynthesis with the evolution of molecular oxygen. The discussion here will largely deal with chlorophyll a, the most widely distributed and most intensively studied of the chlorophylls. The chlorophylls are all cyclic tetrapyrroles (Fig. 1) and

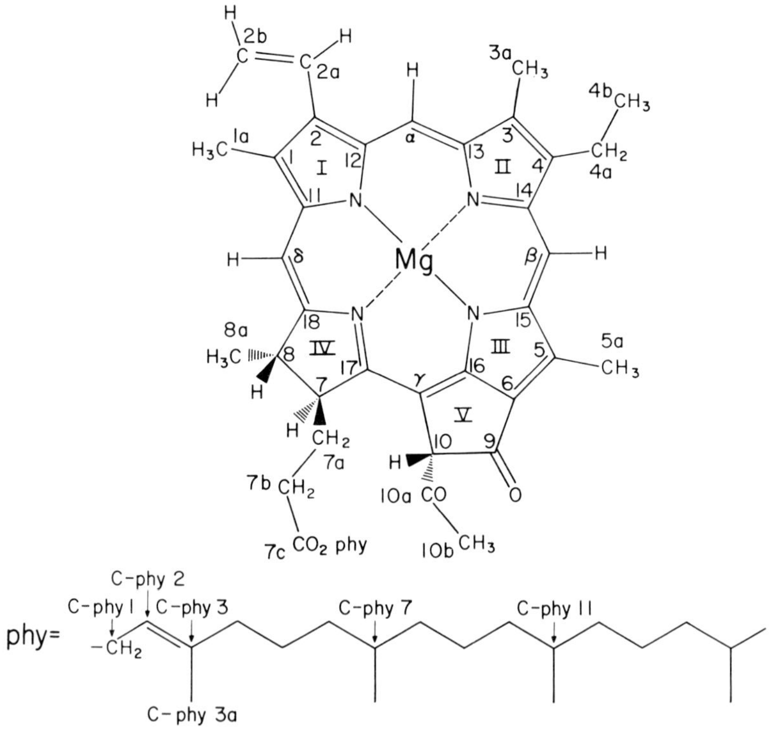

FIG. 1. Structure and numbering system for chlorophyll a. Chlorophyll b has a —CHO group in place of the CH_3— group at 3a. Bacteriochlorophyll has CH_3CO— at position 2 in place of vinyl, and 2H at positions 3 and 4 in ring II. The esterifying alcohol may be phytyl or a related unsaturated aliphatic alcohol. Pheophytin a is chlorophyll a with 2H in place of Mg.

as such are members of the porphyrin family, which has important functions in living organisms in respiratory pigments, electron transport agents, and oxidative enzymes. Certain structural features, however, sharply differentiate the chlorophylls from the porphyrins. The side chains present in the chlorophylls are largely the methyl, ethyl, vinyl, and propionic acid groups present in the porphyrins, an identity that has been taken to indicate a common biosynthetic pathway for chlorophylls and porphyrins. The major chlorophylls, however, are in lower oxidation states than the porphyrins, chlorophylls a and b containing two additional hydrogen atoms in ring IV, and bacteriochlorophyll still an additional 2H in ring II. The lower oxidation state of the chlorophylls has important consequences for the π-systems of the macrocycles, and hence for their electronic transition spectra. An even more striking structural difference between chlorophylls and porphyrins is the alicyclic ring V present in all chlorophylls. This 5-membered ring containing a keto $C=O$ function is found only in the plant and bacterial chlorophylls. Indeed the presence of this ring is sufficient in itself to characterize a substance as a chlorophyll, even if the oxidation state is that of a porphyrin, which is the case for chlorophylls c_1 and c_2, and protochlorophyll. The H atom at position 10 of ring IV and the δ methine H atom of chlorophylls a and b, and the α, β, and δ methine hydrogens of bacteriochlorophyll are all readily exchangeable (Dougherty et al., 1965), but this property does not appear to have functional importance in photosynthesis (Katz et al., 1964). In chlorophylls a and b, the propionic acid side chain at position 7 is esterified with phytol, $C_{20}H_{39}OH$, a long-chain aliphatic alcohol. Phytol is also the esterifying alcohol for bacteriochlorophyll extracted from some species of photosynthetic purple bacteria, but in bacteriochlorophyll from *Rhodospirillum rubrum*, an organism widely used for photosynthetic studies, the esterifying alcohol has been shown to be all-*trans* geranylgeraniol (Katz et al., 1972a). The esterifying alcohol divides the chlorophyll molecule into a polar and a nonpolar, lipophilic portion. The chlorophyll macrocycle is essentially insoluble in water but is a polar entity, and the presence of regions of quite different polarity in the chlorophyll molecule has important consequences for the behavior of chlorophyll in organic solvents. The final structural feature of chlorophyll, and one whose importance can scarcely be exaggerated, is the central magnesium atom. All chlorophylls are chelate compounds of magnesium. Because Mg^{2+} is the ion of a regular element it has been of less interest to the chemist than are the transition metal ions usually found in porphyrins in nature. Nevertheless, we shall see that the coordination properties of the central Mg atom are at the crux of chlorophyll function in photosynthesis (Katz, 1968).

B. Chlorophyll in Vivo

It is generally considered that chlorophyll in the plant is organized into photosynthetic units, variously estimated to consist of between 2500 and 300 chlorophyll molecules (Rabinowitch and Govindjee, 1969), the smaller number being favored in recent times. The bulk of the chlorophyll in the unit appears to be photochemically inert, and, because it appears to function primarily to gather light, it is often referred to as antenna chlorophyll. The incident light energy collected by the antenna chlorophyll is then conducted to a small number of special chlorophyll molecules where energy conversion occurs. These special chlorophylls constitute the photoreaction centers where energy transduction actually occurs.

Most of what is known or inferred about the function of chlorophyll in the plant is based on absorption and fluorescence spectroscopy in the visible. Consequently, an appreciation of the nuances of chlorophyll electronic transition spectra both in vitro and in vivo is essential. In all photosynthetic organisms, the main long wavelength absorption band in the red is due to chlorophyll. Light absorption by other cellular components in this region of the spectrum is minimal, hence the red absorption band of chlorophyll has been the principal focus of attention for both in vitro and in vivo investigations. The numerous in vitro studies (Rabinowitch, 1945a; Seely and Jensen, 1965; Seely, 1965; Sauer et al., 1966; Amster and Porter, 1966; Amster, 1969) establish that chlorophyll a in polar, electron donor solvents such as methanol, acetone, tetrahydrofuran, pyridine, or other Lewis bases (nucleophiles) shows a single major red maximum lying between 661 and 670 nm, the exact position and band half-width being dependent on solvent dielectric constant and refractive index (Seely, 1965). In very dry nonpolar solvents (carbon tetrachloride, benzene), the chlorophyll a red band develops a distinct shoulder near 680 nm on its long wavelength side (Livingston, 1960; Livingston et al., 1949; Freed, 1957; Fernandez and Becker, 1959). The intensity of absorption at the red shoulder is concentration dependent (Sauer et al., 1966), particularly in hydrocarbon solvents (Lavorel, 1957). The conventional interpretation of the red shoulder attributes it to dimer formation by the equilibrium $2\ Chl \rightleftarrows Chl_2$, with the intensity of absorption at the red shoulder a measure of dimer concentration. However, there is now good reason to suppose that, in nonpolar solvents free of adventitious nucleophiles, this equilibrium is always strongly displaced to the right, with an equilibrium constant probably greater than 10^6, so that the concentration of monomeric chlorophyll in these nonpolar solvent systems must be vanishingly small. The general similarity in the visible absorption spectra of chlorophyll dissolved in dry CCl_4 or benzene solution and chlorophyll in the plant has long been recognized (Brody, 1968).

The red maximum of chlorophyll in the plant is shifted to longer wavelengths relative to chlorophyll *a* solutions in polar solvents, and its band shape *in vivo* is strongly broadened (Fig. 2). French

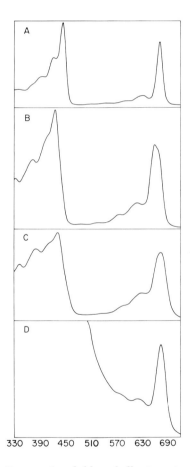

330 390 450 510 570 630 690

FIG. 2. Visible absorption spectra of chlorophyll *a* in various environments: (A) in a polar solvent, tetrahydrofuran; (B) a dilute solution ($5 \times 10^{-4} M$) in CCl_4; (C) a concentrated solution ($0.1 M$) in hexane; (D) a dispersion of the green alga *Tribonema aequale*. Concentration of chlorophyll varies, and therefore the relative spectral intensities cannot be deduced from the spectra. Spectrum D runs off scale at higher frequencies because absorption in the red is relatively weak, and a concentrated suspension is used to record the spectrum.

(1971), French *et al.*, (1971, 1972), French and Praeger (1969), Brown (1963, 1972), Michel-Wolwertz *et al.* (1969), and Wiesner and French (1970) have recorded the visible absorption spectra of numerous plants and chloroplast preparations and have subjected the spectra to computer deconvolution. They conclude that there are four universal forms of chlorophyll present in plants, because all the envelopes can be deconvoluted into Gaussian components located at 661.6, 669.6, 677.1, and 683.7 nm. There are some serious problems with this interpretation. The spectra were recorded at liquid nitrogen temperature, $-196°C$. At room temperature, the absorption curves are not nearly so well defined, and mathematically unique deconvolutions cannot be obtained. However, Freed and Sancier (1951) showed that marked changes occur in the spectra of chlorophyll solutions in nonpolar solvents when the temperature is lowered, changes that are best interpreted as changes in the chlorophyll species present. The relationship between plant spectra at room temperature and those recorded at $-196°C$ is thus not at all clear. Even more troublesome, the spectrum of chlorophyll *a* in CCl_4 (Fig. 2B) belongs to a single chlorophyll species, the dimer, Chl_2. This envelope can also be deconvoluted into a number of Gaussian components (see below), but in fact only one chlorophyll species as determined by several independent criteria is actually present in this system. The Gaussian component into which the envelope can be deconvoluted may well have physical significance, but identification of deconvolution components with separate chlorophyll species seems difficult to justify. The whole envelope may be the property of a single species with a multiplicity of electronic transitions. The work of French *et al.* (1972) and the similar studies by Gulyayev and Litvin (1970) thus do not establish the existence of a multiplicity of chlorophyll forms in the plant.

If the chlorophyll spectrum is observed in the plant during photosynthesis, absorption at 700 nm is found to diminish reversibly. Absorption at 700 nm in plants is also removed by oxidizing agents, such as ferricyanide, and restored by reducing agents. Concomitant with the bleaching at 700 nm is the appearance of an electron spin resonance (ESR) signal, first described by Commoner *et al.* (1956). It is generally agreed that the entity absorbing near 700 nm, which is intimately involved in light conversions [designated P700 by its discoverer Kok (1959)], is chlorophyll whose absorption spectrum is somehow modified and red shifted by its environment. These P700 reaction center chlorophylls, which constitute perhaps 1% of the chlorophyll present in the plant, are presumed to give rise to free radical species during transient oxidation of the pigments; the photobleaching is the optical consequence of the photooxidation.

The nature of antenna chlorophyll and of reaction center (P700) chlorophyll are the central problems in energy transduction in photosynthesis. Most of the research directed to these problems has taken an analytical approach. That is, the photochemical apparatus of the plant is subjected to treatment meant to simplify the system. Chloroplasts are isolated from plants, fragmented, the antenna chlorophyll is removed by selective solvents, the residue further separated by gradient ultracentrifugation, all with the object of so simplifying the system while it still retains biological activity that chemical identification of the active entities can then be made. This is obviously a valid approach, even if it largely begs the question of artifact production during the treatment of the photosynthetic material. The other approach is synthetic and is the one adopted here. Start with pure chlorophyll, thoroughly characterize the chlorophyll in simple laboratory systems, compare these systems with the chlorophyll in the living plant, and increase the complexity of the system by the incorporation of other chloroplast components until the properties of the laboratory and the *in vivo* systems begin to coincide. We will show here that the optical and ESR properties of both antenna and reaction center chlorophyll can be simulated very closely or interpreted in terms of remarkably simple laboratory systems.

II. Chlorophyll as Electron Donor–Acceptor

Many features of chlorophyll behavior can best be interpreted in terms of electron donor–acceptor properties. We use this term in the sense of Mulliken and Person (1969) and Briegleb (1961) for charge transfer interactions of the sort that generate molecular complexes. Not included in this term are conventional oxidation-reduction reactions, i.e., allomerization (Seely, 1966), or the Krasnovsky reaction (Rabinowitch, 1956) where electrons are transferred between chlorophyll and the oxidant or reductant. The structural formula of chlorophyll as usually written (Fig. 1) assigns the central Mg atom a coordination number of 4. Spectroscopic investigations, including absorption spectroscopy in the visible (Cotton *et al.*, 1972a) and infrared (Katz *et al.*, 1963; Anderson and Calvin, 1964; Boucher and Katz, 1967a,b; Henry and Leicknam, 1970), ^1H (Closs *et al.*, 1963; Katz *et al.*, 1966, 1968a), and ^{13}C (Katz *et al.*, 1972b; Katz and Janson, 1972) magnetic resonance, and molecular weight determinations by vapor phase osmometry (Ballschmiter *et al.*, 1969b) and ultracentrifugation (Svec *et al.*, 1972) all support the thesis that the central Mg atom with coordination number 4 is coordinatively unsaturated and acts as an electron acceptor, and that the keto $C=O$ function of ring V has electron donor properties. Thus, the chlorophyll molecule has a quite unusual combination of electron donor and acceptor properties. Although compounds possessing both donor and acceptor properties have been the subject of speculation (Mulliken and Person, 1969), chlorophyll appears to be the first such substance to be characterized. More specifically, the central Mg atom is in the terminology of Mulliken and Person (1969) an increvalent v electron acceptor, and the keto $C=O$ is an increvalent n donor. It is the operation of these electron donor–acceptor forces between chlorophyll and electron donor molecules or between chlorophyll molecules that largely determine the state of chlorophyll.

Chlorophyll donor–acceptor interactions can be conveniently divided into *endogamous* interactions, where one chlorophyll serves as donor to another chlorophyll as acceptor, and *exogamous*, where chlorophyll acts as acceptor to an extraneous nucleophile donor (Katz, 1972). Endogamous interactions will generate chlorophyll dimers and oligomers held together by keto $C=O$ --- Mg interactions. Exogamous interactions of chlorophyll with nucleophiles will form two series of chlorophyll–nucleophile adducts, depending upon the number of electron donor centers in the nucleophile. Monofunctional donors such as tetrahydrofuran, acetone or pyridine form the monomeric chlorophyll species $Chl \cdot L_1$ and $Chl \cdot L_2$ in which the ligand occupies one, or, under forcing conditions, both of the Mg axial positions. Bifunctional ligands, such as dioxane, pyrazine or particularly water, can cross-link chlorophyll molecules to produce large organized entities of colloidal dimensions. Establishing the structure of these chlorophyll species is obviously essential if the optical and ESR spectra of chlorophyll in the plant are to be used as a basis for conclusions about structure.

III. Endogamous Chlorophyll Dimers and Oligomers

A. FROM INFRARED SPECTRA

Infrared (IR) and nuclear magnetic resonance (NMR) spectroscopy provide an excellent insight into the nature of the chlorophyll species present in various solvent systems. The solvent dependence of the spectra provides the essential clues for interpretation. In polar solvents such as tetrahydrofuran (THF), chlorophyll *a* shows a three-banded spectrum (Fig. 3A) in the 1800–1600 cm^{-1} region assignable in terms of the structural formula of Fig. 1. The absorption peak at 1737 cm^{-1} can be assigned to the two ester $C=O$ groups, the peak at 1695 cm^{-1} to the keto $C=O$ function in ring V, and the peak at 1595 cm^{-1} to skeletal ($C=C$, $C=N$) vibrations in the macrocycle. In CCl_4 or benzene, however, chlorophyll *a* shows a four-banded spectrum

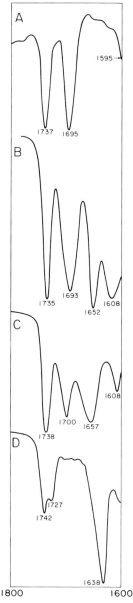

FIG. 3. Solvent dependence of infrared spectra of chlorophyll a (A) in a polar solvent, tetrahydrofuran; (B) in a good nonpolar solvent, CCl_4; (C) in a poor nonpolar solvent, n-butylcyclohexane; (D) chlorophyll–water adduct, $(Chl \cdot H_2O)_n$, in hexadecane.

(Fig. 3B) which cannot be assigned simply in terms of the structure of monomeric chlorophyll. Addition of base to the CCl_4 or benzene solution causes the peak at 1652 cm^{-1} to decrease in size and ultimately vanish, while the peak at 1695 cm^{-1} increases in intensity. The peak at 1652 cm^{-1} is observed only in chlorophyll a solutions rigorously free of nucleophiles, and thus is best interpreted as arising from a keto C=O---Mg endogamous interaction between chlorophyll molecules (Katz et $al.$, 1963). In a dimer, on the average, half of the keto C=O groups are free, the other half are coordinated to Mg, and consequently absorption peaks characteristic of both free and coordinated keto C=O are present in a dimer spectrum. The 1652 cm^{-1} absorption peak is therefore termed an aggregation peak and is diagnostic of aggregation interactions between chlorophyll molecules.

B. FROM ^{1}H AND ^{13}CMR

Proton magnetic resonance (^{1}HMR) spectra show exactly the same kind of solvent dependence and can be interpreted in precisely the same way, with the additional advantage that ^{1}HMR provides structural information about the chlorophyll aggregates present in CCl$_4$ or benzene solution. In polar solvents, the chlorophyll a ^{1}HMR spectrum can be completely assigned (Fig. 4A). All the proton resonances in the macrocycle can be identified with particular protons or groups of protons shown in the structural formula. The methine protons are found at unusually low field because of the deshielding effect of the macrocycle ring current. The vinyl protons at positions 2a and 2b form an easily recognizable pattern, and the single resonance near 5.5 ppm can be assigned to the proton at C-10. The methyl groups directly on the conjugated system at positions 1a, 3a, 5a, and 10b constitute a set of four peaks in resonance at a lower field than usual for methyl groups in organic compounds, while the "aliphatic" protons of the propionic acid side chain and the methyl groups at 8a and 4b are as expected observed in the high field portion of the spectrum. For a detailed exposition of the rationale of the assignment, see Katz et $al.$ (1966).

In nonpolar solvents, however, the ^{1}HMR spectra are considerably less well defined, and the resonance peaks are fewer than expected (Fig. 4B). The resonance of the C-10 proton, clearly visible near 6 ppm in Fig. 4A, is not evident at all in Fig. 4B, and at least two of the low field methyl resonances can be seen in Fig. 4B as compared to the four of Fig. 4A. In fact, if the ^{1}HMR spectrum of chlorophyll a in CCl$_4$ solution were the only spectrum available, it would be concluded that the conventional structural formula must be in serious error. If a Lewis base is now added to a solution of chlorophyll a in

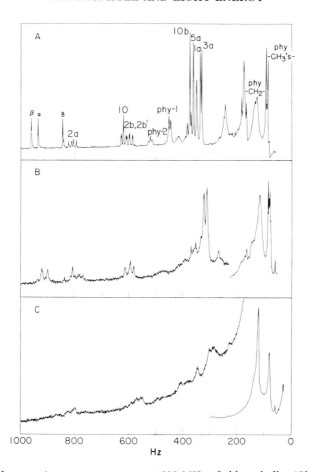

FIG. 4. ¹H magnetic resonance spectra at 100 MHz of chlorophyll *a* (Chl *a*) in solvents of various polarities: (A) 0.13 *M* Chl *a* in tetrahydrofuran-d_8, a polar solvent, showing a very well defined spectrum; (B) 0.06 *M* Chl *a* in CCl₄, a nonpolar solvent; note the absence of the C-10 resonance, near 6 ppm, and the anomalous low-field methyl region; (C) 0.04 *M* Chl *a* in *n*-octane-d_8, an aliphatic hydrocarbon solvent. Line broadening indicates a much larger aggregate than in B. A partial assignment of the ¹HMR resonances is shown in (A).

CCl₄, the ¹HMR spectrum is observed to change, and when a 10-fold molar excess of base has been added, the ¹HMR spectrum in CCl₄ becomes identical with one observed in THF. The addition of base can be carried out as a titration, and the chemical shift changes in the ¹HMR spectrum recorded as shown in Fig. 5.

The key to the interpretation of the ¹HMR titration experiments on chlorophyll *a* in nonpolar solvents lies in the ring current effects on

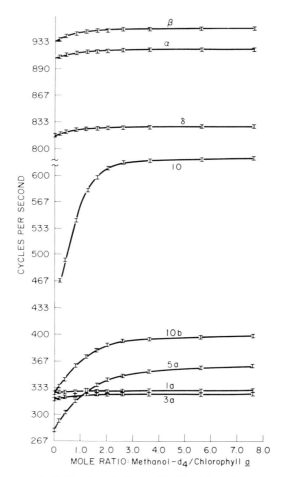

FIG. 5. Titration of 0.15 M chlorophyll a in $CDCl_3$ with the base methanol. Chemical shift changes are given in Hz at 100 MHz and are downfield from tetramethylsilane.

the proton resonances. The macrocycle ring of the chlorophyll molecule has associated with it a π-system of 18 electrons delocalized over the entire macrocycle. Insertion into a strong magnetic field causes these electrons to precess and thus to generate a local magnetic field that can strongly affect the resonance positions of the protons. Protons sited above or below the plane of the macrocycle have their resonances shifted to much higher fields by the local ring current (Katz et al., 1968a). It can be seen in Fig. 5 that the protons of chlorophyll a are divided into two categories by the addition of base. The first consists of the α, β, and δ methine protons, and the CH_3 groups at positions 1a and 3a, for which the chemical shifts are essentially independent of the presence or absence of base. The second category, consisting of the protons at positions 5a, 10, and 10b, are strongly deshielded and moved to lower field by the addition of base. These data strongly suggest that those chlorophyll *a* protons that appear at abnormally high field in CCl_4 or benzene solution are subject to an upfield ring current effect, resulting from dimer formation in the nonpolar solvent. That all the protons are not equally affected by the ring current means that the dimer is asymmetric and that only a part of the ring of one chlorophyll molecule is eclipsed by the other. The titration results can be displayed in the form of an "aggregation map" (Fig. 6). Here, the maximum chemical shift differences observed in the titration experiment are shown for the individual protons whose resonances can be followed in the titration.

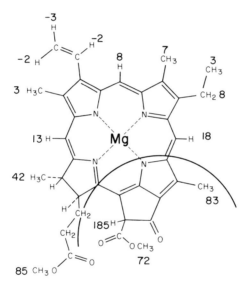

FIG. 6. Aggregation map of chlorophyll *a* from the data in Fig. 5. The boldface numbers indicate the change in Hz in the indicated resonance between dimer (aggregated) and monomer (fully disaggregated) chlorophyll. The semicircle indicates the area of overlap in the dimer.

The larger the chemical shift difference, the greater the extent to which the proton has been subject to an upfield ring current. The region of ring overlap is clearly defined to occur near ring V. A chlorophyll *a* dimer (Fig. 7A) overlapped in just this way is produced by coordination of the keto $C=O$ function in the ring V of one chlorophyll molecule with the central Mg atom of the other. For chlorophyll *b*, and bacteriochlorophyll, each of which contain two donor $C=O$

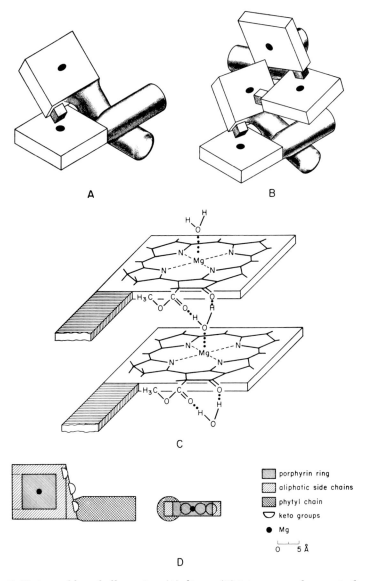

FIG. 7. Various chlorophyll species. (A) dimer; (B) tetramer, or fragment of an oligomer; (C) the chlorophyll–water adduct, showing one unit of the $(\mathrm{Chl} \cdot H_2O)_n$ micelle; (D) dimensions of the chlorophyll molecule taken from a Courtauld space-filling model (Ballschmiter and Katz, 1969).

groups, the ^{1}HMR results clearly indicate two regions of overlap in the aggregates. These observations are consistent with molecular weight measurements that show chlorophyll *a* to be largely a dimer in CCl_4 solution, whereas chlorophyll b and bacteriochlorophyll are trimers (Ballschmiter et al., 1969b). Thus, the [1]HMR and IR results are entirely compatible with dimer (and trimer) formation in CCl_4 or benzene solution. Recent [13]CMR titration experiments (Katz and Janson, 1972) provide additional support for this view.

Inspection of the spectra of chlorophyll a in hydrocarbon solvents (Figs. 3C and 4C) strongly suggests that the state of chlorophyll in hydrocarbon solvents is distinctly different from that in CCl_4 or benzene. Saturated hydrocarbon solvents are essentially nonpolarizable, they are unable to solvate the macrocycle portion of chlorophyll, whereas CCl_4 or benzene are polarizable and are thus better solvents for this purpose. Therefore, in aliphatic hydrocarbon solvents, the equilibrium $n(Chl_2) \rightleftarrows (Chl_2)_n$ is displaced to the right to an extent determined by chlorophyll concentration, temperature, and solvent. In concentrated aliphatic hydrocarbon solvents, additional keto $C{=}O{-}{-}{-}Mg$ interactions occur between chlorophyll dimers and trimers, with the formation of oligomers of sizeable proportions. The [1]HMR spectra clearly indicate that the entity present in n-octane solution is larger than that present in CCl_4, and the IR spectra show much diminished free keto $C{=}O$ absorption near 1700 cm^{-1} in aliphatic hydrocarbon solvents. Molecular weight determinations by vapor phase osmometry (Ballschmiter et al., 1969b) and ultracentrifugation show that in a 0.1 M solution of chlorophyll a in n-hexane, chlorophyll oligomers with a molecular weight greater than 20,000 $[(Chl_2)_n, n > 10]$ exist. Figure 7B shows a representation of a portion of such an oligomer.

IV. Visible Absorption Spectra of Chlorophyll Oligomers and the Nature of Antenna Chlorophyll

That it is possible to produce long wavelength forms of chlorophyll in the laboratory has been known for a long time (see, for example, Goedheer, 1966; Gurinovich et al., 1968; Krasnovsky, 1969). However, because the range of chlorophyll species that can be present in nonpolar solvents was not fully appreciated, consistent correlations between in vivo and in vitro chlorophyll spectra could not be made. An additional complication in the past in comparisons between in vivo and in vitro visible absorption spectra results from the way in which the in vivo data are collected. The chlorophyll in chloroplasts is estimated to be more concentrated than 0.1 M (Rabinowitch, 1945b). Chlorophyll is, of course, an intense absorber of light, so that spectra collected in conventional spectroscopic cells are almost always recorded at concentrations below 10^{-4} M. Because the equilibrium

$n(\text{CHl}_2) \rightleftarrows (\text{Chl}_2)_n$ is displaced to the left at low chlorophyll concentrations, dilute chlorophyll solutions will have smaller aggregates than those present in concentrated solutions. Optical equipment with precisely known light paths has therefore been devised to permit the direct observation of electron transition spectra of 0.1 M chlorophyll *a* solutions (Uphaus and Katz, 1970). *In vitro* spectra of highly concentrated chlorophyll *a* solutions in hydrocarbon solvents do, in fact, resemble much more closely *in vivo* spectra. To make the comparison less subjective, recourse has been had to computer deconvolution methods. While such techniques have been applied to *in vivo* spectra (cf. Cederstrand *et al.*, 1966; French *et al.*, 1972; Gulyayev and Litvin, 1967, 1970), they do not appear to have been used for *in vitro* spectra previously.

For curve resolution, a program written by the Applied Mathematics Division at Argonne was used (Chamot, 1967). The program uses a variable metric minimization procedure (Davidon, 1966) and resolves the envelope into components peaks by a least squares fit to the equation:

$$y = \sum_{j=1}^{M} a_j e^{-\frac{1}{2}\left(\frac{x-b_j}{c_j}\right)^2} \tag{1}$$

where a_j = peak height, b_j = peak location (in nm), and c_j = the standard deviation, i.e., the band half-width, δ. As input, the number of desired peaks (M) and initial estimates for the parameters a_j, b_j, and c_j are specified. Successive iterations by the computer supply a best fit. The computer program allows the choice from a large range of line shapes, but we have chosen to use Gaussian line shapes because monomer chlorophyll *a* solutions (in polar solvents) have a red envelope very nearly truly Gaussian.

The spectra of chlorophyll *a* in dilute CCl_4 solution show a distinct red shoulder (Fig. 2B), but concentrated solutions have a smooth and quite structureless appearance (Fig. 2C). As a result, there is little difficulty in securing unique deconvolutions for the spectra of dilute solutions, but for spectra taken on concentrated solutions the computer can supply many different but equally good fits. Consequently, the assumption is made that changes in the structure of the chlorophyll species that occur in going from the most dilute to the most concentrated solutions are gradual and progressive, and that the spectrum of the most concentrated solution is related to that of the most dilute by a series of small changes. This in effect requires the deconvolution to be self-consistent over the entire concentration range. A deconvolution experiment based on these premises on a series of chlorophyll *a* solutions ranging from 10^{-6} to 10^{-1} *M* in hexane is shown in Fig. 8.

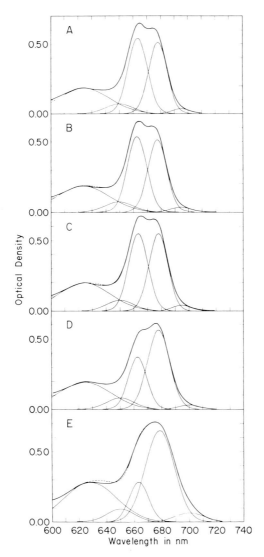

FIG. 8. Computer deconvolution of chlorophyll *a* electronic transition spectra in hexane over the concentration range 1.3×10^{-6} *M* to 1.2×10^{-1} *M*. See text for deconvolution details. Over the entire range, deconvolution with the same parameters provides an excellent fit, but the relative areas of the two principal red components change with concentration. (A) 1.3×10^{-6} *M*; (B) 1.3×10^{-5} *M*; (C) 1.3×10^{-4} *M*; (D) 2×10^{-3} *M*; (E) 1.2×10^{-1} *M*.

All the spectra in Fig. 8 can be deconvoluted into Gaussian components located at 624, 650, 663, 678, and 695 nm. What is remarkable is that the locations of the components do not move appreciably with increasing concentration, but the relative areas of the main components at 663 and 678 nm change with increasing concentration, the 678 nm component increasing in area at the expense of the 663 nm component. In the very dilute solution, the areas of the 663 and 678 nm components are almost equal, but in the most concentrated solution, the area of the 678 nm component is 3.3 times larger than the 663 nm component. In even more concentrated solutions, the 663 nm component becomes almost vestigial. We consider the 678 nm component to be structural in origin and to reflect macrocycle overlap in the chlorophyll *a* dimer or oligomer. If the relative positions of the macrocycles in the oligomer were rigidly fixed, the relative areas of the 663 and 678 nm components might be an accurate indicator of the size of the oligomer. However, as the oligomer increases in size, it is likely that the relative positions of at least some of the chlorophyll molecules in the oligomer change, and thus the relative areas of the two major components is only a rough measure of oligomer size. The minor component at 694–705 nm that must be included for spectra recorded on solutions more concentrated than 10^{-5} M can also be taken to indicate structural differences between small and large oligomers. Whether this long wavelength component has any relationship to P700 or whether it has biological significance remains in doubt.

Contrary to naive expectations, increase in size of the chlorophyll *a* oligomers does not lead to a red shift in the absorption maxima of the envelope. The reason for this is evident from Fig. 7B. In the chlorophyll *a* dimer, the planes of the chlorophyll macrocycles are neither parallel nor perpendicular, but are at a small angle, say between 20° (Closs *et al.*, 1963) and 45° (Houssier and Sauer, 1970) to each other. The amount of ring overlap is thus limited. Linking dimers together into oligomers does not radically increase the extent of overlap, so that really large red shifts are not realized even when the maximum number of keto $C = O$---Mg interactions occur. Thus, the chlorophyll oligomers are red-shifted, but only modestly so, and large shifts are found only in chlorophyll species of quite different structure.

In Fig. 9 deconvoluted visible absorption spectra for photosynthetic organisms and preparations are compared to those of a concentrated solution of chlorophyll *a* in hexane. Included in the comparison is a sonicated suspension of the alga *Tribonema aequale*. This organism contains only chlorophyll *a* and no other chlorophyll or phycobilin photosynthetic pigments. The visible absorption spec-

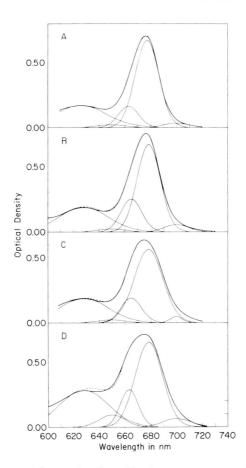

FIG. 9. Comparison of deconvoluted visible absorption spectra of algae and active center preparations with a concentrated solution of chlorophyll *a* in hexane. (A) Sonicate of *Tribonema aequale;* (B) active center preparation from *Synechococcus lividus,* HP700; (C) active center preparation from *Anabaena variabilis,* HP700; (C) 1.2×10^{-1} *M* chlorophyll *a* in very dry hexane.

tra of this organism in the red is thus less ambiguous than for organisms that contain chlorophyll *b*. The spectra of active center preparations prepared by the procedure of Ogawa and Vernon (1970) and Ogawa *et al.* (1969), in which much, but not all, of the antenna chlorophyll has been removed, are likewise shown. The smaller size of the active center particles is advantageous for comparison purposes because light scattering is minimized when the spectra are recorded. All three photosynthetic preparations have very similar spectra, and all can be deconvoluted with the same parameters used for the deconvolution of the concentrated chlorophyll *a* solution in hexane. The resemblance between the spectra of the photosynthetically active preparations and a concentrated solution of chlorophyll *a* in hexane in terms of band position, band half-widths, and relative areas, is striking. Based on the relative areas of the Gaussian components, chlorophyll in the chloroplasts or in active center preparations appears to be even more concentrated, or, more precisely, is likely to be a larger oligomer than those present in the 0.1 *M* hexane solution. We consider these data to provide good experimental support for the view that bulk or antenna chlorophyll in the plant is very similar to, if not actually identical with, the chlorophyll oligomers, $(Chl_2)_n$, that are present in concentrated chlorophyll *a* solutions in aliphatic hydrocarbons.

V. Exogamous Chlorophyll–Nucleophile Adducts

Electron donors (ligands, nucleophiles) can compete for coordination sites at Mg in chlorophyll dimers or oligomers. Monofunctional ligands react according to the equilibrium $(Chl_2)_n + nL \rightleftarrows n\ Chl \cdot L_1$. The species $Chl \cdot L_2$ appear to be important only under strongly forcing conditions, as in a neat solvent (Katz *et al.*, 1968a). That Mg in chlorophyll prefers a coordination number 5 is probably due to the displacement of the Mg atom from the center of the macrocycle by as much as 0.5 Å (Timkovich and Tulinsky, 1969; Fischer *et al.*, 1971). With an excess of nucleophile, monomeric, fluorescent, and short wavelength chlorophyll species result.

With bifunctional ligands, the course of events may be quite different (Cotton *et al.*, 1972b). It is well established that chlorophyll *a* interacts with limited amounts of dioxane to form chlorophyll-dioxane species that have markedly red-shifted absorption spectra (Sherman and Fujimori, 1969). With a large molar excess of dioxane, monomeric short-wavelength chlorophyll·monodioxinate results. Because Mg is still available for coordination in chlorophyll dimer, bifunctional ligands such as dioxane (I), pyrazine (II), or 1,4-diazabicyclo (2.2.2) octane (III) can cross-link chlorophyll dimers to form

(I)   (II)   (III)

species listed in Table I. The orientation of the two coordination centers relative to each other is critical. Whereas 1,4-bipyridine cross-

TABLE I
CHLOROPHYLL a — BIFUNCTIONAL LIGAND ADDUCTS[a]

Ligand	Structure[b]	λ_{max} (nm)
Dioxane		
1:0.5	—ChlChl—L—ChlChl—L—ChlChl—	684, 700
1:1	—Chl—L—Chl—L—Chl—L—Chl	685, 695
Pyrazine	—ChlChl—L—ChlChl—L—ChlChl—	690
2,2'-Bipyrimidine	—ChlChl—L—ChlChl—L—ChlChl—	715
Pheophytin + H_2O	—ChlChl—H_2O—Pheo—H_2O—ChlChl—	695, 712[c]
Pyrimidine	Chl·L	665
s-Triazine	Chl · L	672
Dabco[d]	Chl—L—Chl—L—Chl—	680
Water	(Chl·H_2O)$_n$	743

[a]Dispersed in hexadecane.
[b]Structures assigned from infrared spectra and from stoichiometry of the adducts.
[c]In a hydrated film of the chlorophyll–pheophytin mixture (Norris et al., 1970).
[d]1,4-Diazabicyclo(2.2.2)octane.

links chlorophyll, 1,2-bipyridine can only use one of its nitrogen atoms for coordination to Mg because of steric reasons, and thus acts as a monofunctional ligand to disaggregate chlorophyll. Pyrimidine interacts only at one nitrogen site at room temperature, but is a cross-linking agent for chlorophyll a at low temperatures. In all cross-linked polynuclear species, red shifts in the visible absorption spectrum occur to an extent strongly affected by the geometry of the bifunctional ligand. The closer the chlorophyll rings are brought to each other, the larger the red shift. The red shift, indeed, can be correlated with the Mg-Mg distance in the adducts as determined by X-ray diffraction. A number of such chlorophyll–nucleophile adducts with their electronic transition maxima are listed in Table I. It seems reasonable to infer that the red shift in the visible absorption spectra common to the bifunctional ligand adducts must have a structural basis, and that the shift occurs to an extent determined by ring overlap in the adduct. It should not be thought that these are weak interactions, for pyrazine is capable of precipitating chlorophyll a from CCl_4 or hydrocarbon solutions. The chlorophyll-bifunctional nucleophile adducts are easily recognized to be colloidal micelles. These observations are pertinent to the question of whether there are bifunctional ligands in nature that could serve to orient chlorophyll to produce P700. There are numerous components of chloroplasts, among them proteins and pteridines, that could in principle serve such a function. In any event, many long-wavelength forms of chloro-

phyll can be produced in the laboratory but which if any have biological significance remains to be settled (Ballschmiter and Katz,
1968, 1972).

The chlorophyll–water interaction is of special importance (Katz
and Ballschmiter, 1968; Katz et al., 1968b; Ballschmiter et al., 1969a).
The older literature gives ample reason to suppose that the chlorophyll–water interaction has unusual significance. Water is a bifunctional ligand for chlorophyll because it can act as an electron donor
to Mg at its oxygen atom and is able to form one or two hydrogen
bonds simultaneously. By virtue of its small size, it appears to be a
unique nucleophile for chlorophyll. The introduction of water into a
chlorophyll a solution causes a major change in the IR spectrum in
both the $C=O$ and $O-H$ stretch regions (Fig. 3D) (Ballschmiter and
Katz, 1969). The keto $C=O$---Mg aggregation peak at 1652–1660
cm^{-1} is replaced by an intense peak at 1638 cm^{-1}, the free keto $C=O$
absorption near 1700 cm^{-1} essentially disappears, and the ester
$C=O$ absorption maxima at 1735 cm^{-1} split into two bands at 1745
and 1727 cm^{-1}. Major changes are also evident in $O-H$ stretch region. Anhydrous chlorophyll shows very little absorption in this
region. The chlorophyll–water adduct, however, has maxima at 3590,
3460, and 3240 cm^{-1}. Monomeric water itself in nonpolar media has
its antisymmetric OH fundamental ν_1 at 3615 cm^{-1}. All available
spectroscopic data can be interpreted in terms of a chlorophyll
species in which the dimer interaction is interrupted by coordination
of a water molecule to the Mg atom of one chlorophyll molecule, and
simultaneous hydrogen bonding to the two carbonyl functions of
ring V (Fig. 7C). An interpretation consistent with both the $C=O$ and
$O-H$ region spectra assigns the absorption peak at 1638 cm^{-1} to
a hydrogen bond interaction of water coordinated to Mg to the keto
$C=O$ function of another chlorophyll molecule; the ester splitting
is considered to arise from another hydrogen bond to the ester $C=O$
group in the carbomethoxy function at C-10. The three maxima in the
$O-H$ stretch region then correspond to water-coordinated to Mg,
Mg---OH_2 (3600 cm^{-1}); Mg-coordinated water hydrogen-bonded
to keto $C=O$ (3240 cm^{-1}); and Mg-coordinated water hydrogen-
bonded to ester $C=O$ (3460 cm^{-1}). The overall interaction can then
be formulated as:

$$\text{Ester} \quad C=O\cdots H-O-H\cdots O=C \quad \text{Keto}$$
$$-\overset{\vdots}{Mg}-$$

The chlorophyll–water interaction is strongly solvent and concentration dependent. In dilute solution, only the monomeric species

$Chl \cdot H_2O$ forms, but in concentrated solutions in hydrocarbon solvents, the species $(Chl \cdot H_2O)_n$ results. Ultracentrifugation shows the adduct to be very large and of colloidal dimensions. X-ray diffraction shows considerable periodicity in the adduct, with a 7.5 Å spacing, a distance close to that estimated from models for the Mg — Mg distance in a sandwich composed of two chlorophyll molecules separated by a water molecule (Katz et al., 1968b). Direct analysis indicates a 1 : 1 stoichiometry to the adduct (Cotton et al., 1970). The chlorophyll–water adduct has the largest red shift (Table I) of any chlorophyll species so far characterized. Although absorption near 740 nm has occasionally been noted in plants (Thomas et al., 1970), there is a question as to whether it is present to a significant extent in normal plants. The corresponding bacteriochlorophyll–water adduct, however, has spectral properties similar to those of living photosynthetic purple bacteria (Olson and Stanton, 1966).

VI. Photoactivity of Chlorophyll Species

We have previously (Section IV) identified antenna or bulk chlorophyll with chlorophyll oligomers $(Chl_2)_n$. The question we now consider is whether any of the other chlorophyll species we have delineated (Fig. 7) can be used to provide information about the nature of P700 chlorophyll. The characteristic feature of P700 is its red-shifted absorption maximum near 700 nm, which is reversibly photobleached to yield a photoreversible electron spin resonance (ESR) signal during photosynthesis. It becomes of interest, therefore, to examine the photoactivity of defined chlorophyll systems in terms of ESR.

The reversible ESR photosignal I in photosynthesis shows no hyperfine structure, which makes deductions about the origin of the signal very difficult. ESR signals obtained from the various chlorophyll species likewise lack hyperfine structure, and again, the conventional aids to signal assignment are not available. However, chlorophylls are now available (see Section VII) with unusual isotopic compositions; this facilitates deductions about the chemical structure of the species responsible for the ESR signal.

A. ESR OF MONOMERIC CHLOROPHYLL SPECIES

The monomeric chlorophyll species $Chl \cdot L_1$ and $Chl \cdot L_2$ yield free radicals only by chemical or electrochemical oxidation. The ESR signal shape varies only slightly with solvent, oxidant, or temperature. Table III lists the ESR and optical properties of the free radicals produced in monomeric chlorophyll species of different isotopic com-

TABLE II

OPTICAL ABSORPTION AND ELECTRON SPIN RESONANCE LINE WIDTHS OF
VARIOUS CHLOROPHYLL a SPECIES

Species	Solvent	λ_{max} (nm)	$\Delta H^{a,b}$ (gauss)
Endogamous			
Chl_2	CCl_4	665, 678	9.0 ± 0.5
$(Chl_2)_n$	$n\text{-}C_{12}H_{26}$	665, 678	9.0 ± 0.5
$(Chl_2)_n$	Film	665, 678	10.0 ± 0.5
Exogamous			
$Chl \cdot CH_3OH$	CH_3OH/CH_2Cl_2	663	9.3 ± 0.3^c
$Chl \cdot H_2O$	CCl_4	663	~ 9
$(Chl \cdot H_2O)_n$	$n\text{-}C_{12}H_{26}$	743	1–2
$(Chl_2 \cdot pyrazine)_n$	$n\text{-}C_8H_{18}$	690	9–11
$(Chl \cdot bipyrimidine)_n$	$n\text{-}C_{12}H_{26}$	715	9–11
$(Chl_2 \cdot pheophytin \cdot H_2O)_n$	$n\text{-}C_{12}H_{26}$	715–720	9–11

[a]The free radicals are produced by chemical oxidation with I_2 or $FeCl_3$.
[b]Signal width depends on oxidant concentration.
[c]Line width value for 97°K.

position. It has been shown by Borg *et al.* (1970) that the ESR signals observed in monomeric chlorophyll species are due to the π cations $(Chl \cdot L_1)^{\ddagger}$ or $(BChl \cdot L_1)^{\ddagger}$. As expected, the line widths increase in the order $\Delta H_{13_{C^{-1}H}} > \Delta H_{1_H} > \Delta H_{2_H}$. From the $^1H/^2H$ data, it can be concluded that most of the line broadening is due to interaction of the free electron spin with approximately 12 hydrogen atoms. From the ^{13}C data, it can be deduced that only a few of the carbon atoms in chlorophyll have high spin density, and that the unpaired electron is localized within the conjugated π system (Norris *et al.*, 1972).

B. ESR OF CHLOROPHYLL DIMERS AND OLIGOMERS

Free radicals in chlorophyll a dimer or oligomer can be induced only by chemical oxidation (Table II). The line widths for the ESR signals in $(Chl_2)^{\ddagger}$ and $(Chl_2)_n^{\ddagger}$ are essentially the same as those in the monomer chlorophyll species.

C. ESR OF CHLOROPHYLL–BIFUNCTIONAL LIGAND ADDUCTS

Free radicals induced in $(Chl_2 \cdot pyrazine)_n$, $(Chl \cdot bipyramidine)_n$, and $(Chl \cdot pheophytin \cdot H_2O)_n$ by chemical oxidation with iodine or ferric chloride have line widths between 9 and 11 G wide, essentially the same as those observed in $(Chl \cdot L_1)^{\ddagger}$, $(Chl_2)^{\ddagger}$, or $(Chl_2)_n^{\ddagger}$.

D. ESR OF THE CHLOROPHYLL–WATER ADDUCT, $(Chl \cdot H_2O)_n$

Of all the defined chlorophyll species, the chlorophyll–water adduct is the only one from which a reversible photo-ESR signal can be elicited with red light (> 650 nm). This highly red-shifted species (λ_{max} 743 nm) has a very narrow ESR signal (Table II) that has the

TABLE III

ELECTRON SPIN RESONANCE LINE WIDTHS (ΔH) OF
MONOMERIC CHLOROPHYLLS AT 97°K

Chlorophyll Species	λ_{max} (nm)	Oxidant	Solvent	ΔH (gauss)
^{1}H-Chl a	663	I_2 or $FeCl_3$	CH_2Cl_2/MeOH	9.3 ± 0.3
^{2}H-Chl a	663	I_2 or $FeCl_3$	CH_2Cl_2/MeOH	3.8 ± 0.2
^{13}C, ^{1}H-Chl a	663	I_2 or $FeCl_3$	CH_2Cl_2/MeOH	15.2 ± 0.5
^{1}H-BChl^a	770	I_2	Glycerol/MeOH	12.8 ± 0.5
^{2}H-BChl^a	770	I_2	Glycerol/MeOH	5.9 ± 0.2

[a]Ex. *Rhodospirillum rubrum.*

free electron g value. The unusually narrow line width is best explained by a process of spin exchange or migration involving all the chlorophyll molecules in the $(Chl \cdot H_2O)_n$ micelle. If the rate at which the spin migrates from chlorophyll to chlorophyll is sufficiently large ($> 10^9$ jumps/second), the hyperfine interactions are averaged out, and the signal collapses to a narrow line. Spin migration at a high rate is essentially equivalent to delocalization of the spin over the entire entity. Norris *et al.* (1971) have shown by second-moment analysis that under conditions of spin delocalization of the unpaired electron over N chlorophyll molecules, the line width ΔH_N is related to the line width of the monomer (ΔH_M) by the relation

$$\Delta H_N = \Delta H_M / \sqrt{N} \tag{2}$$

As ΔH_M is about 9.5 G for $(Chl \cdot L_1)^{\dot{+}}$ (Table II), delocalization of the unpaired electron over 100 chlorophyll molecules would narrow the ESR signal to ~ 1 G, the value observed in $(Chl \cdot H_2O)_n$. The width of the ESR signal in effect sets a lower limit to the size of the micelle. For our present purposes, the important point to be made is that delocalization narrows the ESR signal, and to an extent related to the number of chlorophyll molecules over which the delocalization (or its equivalent, spin migration) occurs.

The availability of chlorophylls of unusual isotopic composition provides a stringent test of the validity of Eq. (2). For $(^2H\text{-Chl } a \cdot H_2O)_n$, the narrowing of the ESR photosignal relative to $(^2H\text{-Chl} \cdot L_1)^+$ is very close to that predicted from Eq. (2). Because the signal in the ^2H systems is narrower than in ^1H-chlorophylls, the line widths can be measured with considerably greater accuracy. The isotope effect produced by ^2H substitution is an additional piece of evidence in support of the view that the unpaired electron in the free radical species does, in fact, interact with many proton nuclei. Replacement of ^1H by ^2H in chlorophyll a (Norris et al., 1971), bacteriochlorophyll (Kohl et al., 1965; McElroy et al., 1969) and Mg octaethylporphyrin (Fajer et al., 1970) in each case narrows the free radical by the same factor 2.4. This can be construed to indicate that the ESR signal originates in a chlorophyll-like compound, but cannot be used to distinguish between particular chlorophyll species.

For ^{13}C-chlorophyll species, the line shape analysis is considerably complicated by the large anisotropy associated with the unpaired electron-^{13}C spin interactions in rigid systems. This results in line shapes that are no longer Gaussian, and thus Eq. (2) does not hold for ^{13}C-chlorophyll a systems at very low temperatures. Analysis indicates that the narrowing to be expected by delocalization in a ^{13}C system is somewhat smaller than is expected from Eq. (2). This point is further elaborated when the ESR photosignal Signal I in ^{13}C-algae is discussed below (Section VII).

E. ESR OF BACTERIOCHLOROPHYLL

Although our primary concern here is with chlorophyll a, a few remarks about the rather more complex behavior of bacteriochlorophyll is in order. Anhydrous bacteriochlorophyll $(BChl)_3$ in hexane or cyclohexane solution upon oxidation with iodine or ferric chloride gives a free radical signal with a line width of 8–9 G. Hydration of such a system produces a $(BChl \cdot xH_2O)_n$ species with an absorption maximum at 865 nm. The hydrated species yields a free radical by chemical oxidation with a line width that is essentially the same as in $(BChl)_3^+$, i.e., 8–9 G. The reasons for this rather surprising behavior are not understood. The "anhydrous" bacteriochlorophyll may still retain water (bacteriochlorophyll is very difficult to dry), or the spin may be much more closely confined in the $(BChl \cdot xH_2O)_n^+$ species because hydration is not as complete as in $(Chl \cdot H_2O)_n$. More important, oxidation of either anhydrous or hydrated bacteriochlorophyll forms visible aggregates, so that there is a question as to whether monomer ESR spectra are observed in either of these systems. It is nevertheless the case that the signal width (8–9 G) generated from the species $(BChl \cdot xH_2O)_n$, which has its absorption maximum in the red at 865 nm, resembles the *in vivo* behavior of purple photosynthetic bacteria, bacterial chromatophores, or bacterial active center preparations more closely than any other *in vitro* system so far reported.

VII. ESR of *in Vivo* Active Center Chlorophyll

P700 reaction center chlorophyll yields a photoreversible ESR signal with a peak-to-peak line width of 7.0 g, the free-electron g value 2.0025, a Gaussian line shape, and no hyperfine structure. Inspection indicates at once that none of the chlorophyll species listed in Table III have both optical and ESR properties that are identical with those of reaction center chlorophyll. All of the *in vitro* ESR signals are either much broader or narrower than signal I in the plant, and have either insufficiently or excessively red-shifted optical spectra.

A major difficulty in ESR studies of chlorophyll systems *in vitro* and *in vivo* arises from the essentially featureless line shape. Absence of hyperfine structure makes structural or chemical deductions from the ESR signal very difficult. Isotopic substitution makes a valuable contribution to this end, for a different ESR spectrum arises for each of the isotopically different organisms and chlorophylls, and the isotope effect on the line shape even in the absence of hyperfine structure, considerably facilitates interpretation of ESR data. For chlorophyll systems, the important nuclei subject to isotopic substitution are ^1H by ^2H, ^{12}C by ^{13}C, ^{14}N by ^{15}N, and ^{24}Mg by ^{25}Mg. Each of these nuclei affects the ESR signal differently, and each provides different information on the nature and the environment of the chlorophyll species from which the ESR signal arises. The ability to grow organisms of unusual isotopic composition containing ^2H and ^{13}C makes it possible to use the isotope for spectral identification for both *in vivo* and *in vitro* systems (Taecker *et al.*, 1971; Flaumenhaft *et al.*, 1970).

The photo-induced ESR signal I associated with active center P700 (in plants) and P865 (purple bacteria) are presumed to arise from the photooxidized species Chl^+ and $BChl^+$ (Weaver, 1968). There are, however, serious difficulties in identifying photooxidized P700 or P865 simply as Chl^+ or $BChl^+$. First, all monomeric chlorophyll *a* or bacteriochlorophyll species in the laboratory absorb light at wavelengths considerably shorter than 700 nm or 865 nm. Second, the free radical signals from monomeric Chl^+ or $BChl^+$ produced in the laboratory are much broader than the reversible ESR photosignal observed in the plant. The anomalous features of the ESR and optical properties of reaction center chlorophyll have variously been attributed to otherwise not specified "aggregation" (Brody and Brody, 1965), chlorophyll–lipid or chlorophyll–protein interactions (Steffen and Calvin, 1970), or to perturbations in the π system of the chlorophyll resulting from unspecified changes in the environment (Borg et al., 1970). While it cannot be proved that these explanations are incorrect, tests in the laboratory provide little evidence in their support.

We have seen in Section VI that chlorophyll aggregation resulting from the chlorophyll–water interaction causes both a red shift and ESR line narrowing. The red shift in $(Chl \cdot H_2O)_n$ is much too large, the ESR signal much too narrow for P700, but can the structural features of $(Chl \cdot H_2O)_n$ be used to account for the properties of P700? The ESR of $(Chl \cdot H_2O)_n^+$ clearly establishes that spin delocalization over many chlorophyll molecules is an effective mechanism for narrowing the ESR signal. Consequently, we can restate the question we have just posed in the form, is there a value N in Eq. (2) that will provide the proper amount of narrowing for the in vivo signal I?

Table IV lists ESR line widths observed for a variety of photosynthetic organisms in a variety of isotopic compositions. Table II contains the values of ΔH_M required for the solution of Eq. (2). In column 3 of Table IV we list values of N calculated from Eq. (2). Within experimental error, N, the number of molecules of chlorophyll over which the unpaired spin must be delocalized to provide the proper degree of narrowing turns out to be 2. The in vivo ESR signal is thus considered to arise in a special pair of chlorophyll molecules oriented relative to each other with the same geometry as in $(Chl \cdot H_2O)_n$.

A comparison of the in vivo ESR spectra to the in vitro ESR spectra for rigid, nontumbling chlorophyll systems is instructive. When free radicals are mobile and tumble at sufficiently rapid rates, the anisotropic contributions to the line broadening are averaged out and the spectra are narrowed. Chlorophyll in P700 or P865 is rigid on the ESR time scale, as can be judged from the following observations: (1) frozen in vivo photosynthetic systems give line widths essentially the same as those observed at room temperature, which indicates that P700 and P865 are rigid at room temperature; (2) signal I of algae highly enriched in ^{13}C has a line shape observed for rigid $(^{13}C\text{-}Chl\ a \cdot L_1)^+$. Freely tumbling $(^{13}C\text{-}Chl\ a \cdot L_1)^+$ has a Gaussian line shape. The rigidity of in vivo chlorophyll is also deduced from the polarization of fluorescence in bacterial reaction centers (Ebrey and Clayton, 1969). Thus, all comparisons in Table IV use the data for in vitro monomeric chlorophyll species recorded near 77°K.

TABLE IV
OBSERVED AND CALCULATED LINE WIDTHS OF ELECTRON SPIN RESONANCE
SIGNAL I IN PLANTS AND BACTERIA

	$\Delta H_{in\ vivo}$[a] (gauss)	N[b]	ΔH_{calc}[c]
[1]H-*Synechococcus lividus*	7.1±0.2	1.7	6.6±0.3
[2]H-*S. lividus*	2.95±0.1	1.7	2.7±0.1
[13]C-*S. lividus*	13.0±0.5	—[d]	12.2±0.5[d]
[1]H-*Chlorella vulgaris*	7.0±0.2	1.8	6.6±0.3
[2]H-*C. vulgaris*	2.7±0.1	2.0	2.7±0.1
[1]H-*S. obliquus*	7.1±0.2	1.7	6.6±0.8
[2]H-*S. obliquus*	2.7±0.1	2.0	2.7±0.1
[1]H-HP700	7.0±0.2	1.8	6.6±0.3
[1]H-*Rhodospirillum rubrum*	9.1±0.5[e]	2.0	9.1±0.4
[1]H-*R. rubrum*	9.2±0.6	1.9	9.1±0.4
[1]H-*R. rubrum*	9.5±0.5[f]	1.8	9.1±0.4
[2]H-*R. rubrum*	4.0±0.5[e]	1.8	3.8±0.1
[2]H-*R. rubrum*	4.2±0.3[f]	1.7	3.8±0.1
[1]H-*Rhodopseudomonas spheroides*	9.6±0.2[g]	1.8	9.1±0.4

[a]From Norris *et al.* (1971), except as otherwise indicated.
[b]Calculated from $N = (\Delta H_{in\ vitro}/\Delta H_{in\ vivo})^2$.
[c]Calculated from $\Delta H_{calc} = \Delta H_{in\ vitro}/\sqrt{2}$.
[d]Calculated only for a special pair with $\Delta H_{calc} = \Delta H_{in\ vitro}/1.25$.
[e]Kohl *et al.* (1965).
[f]McElroy *et al.* (1969).
[g]Bolton *et al.* (1969).

In all systems of normal isotopic composition, the line width of a special pair of chlorophyll molecules is simply

$$\Delta H_{pair} = \Delta H_M/\sqrt{2} \qquad (2a)$$

which is the general Eq. (2) for the case $N = 2$. In systems highly enriched in ^{13}C another relationship is expected, because the line shape is no longer Gaussian. The expected line width for a special pair of ^{13}C-chlorophyll molecules is then found (Norris *et al.*, 1972) to be

$$\Delta H_{pair} \cong \Delta H_M/1.25 \qquad (3)$$

Thus, we expected that if the *in vivo* ESR has a non-Gaussian line shape, as is the case for ^{13}C-algae, that the *in vivo* signal will be narrowed relative to the *in vitro* monomer signal by the factor 1.25. From

Table IV it can be seen that results with ^{13}C systems are in good agreement with those calculated from Eq. (3).

The model we have advanced here for P700 appears to account for the *in vivo* line narrowing in a reasonable way. A simple application of the Kasha exciton formulation (Hochstrasser and Kasha, 1964) suggests that an entity (Chl H_2O Chl) is expected to have its absorption maximum near 700 nm, half way between the 664 nm maximum of monomeric Chl · H_2O and the 743 nm absorption maximum of the infinite array. Thus, the present model appears to be consistent with both the optical and ESR properties of P700.

We emphasize the importance of differentiating between the chlorophyll special pair (Chl H_2O Chl) and the chlorophyll dimer (Chl_2). Both are "aggregated" chlorophylls, but the modes of aggregation are very different, as are the physical concomitants of the aggregation processes. It should also be pointed out that water has not been proved to be an indispensable element in the chlorophyll special pair. The derivation of Eq. (2) requires the two chlorophyll molecules to be positioned in the way they are thought to be in the $(Chl \cdot H_2O)_n$ adduct, but in principle, any other bifunctional ligand or even a protein structural matrix that forces the two chlorophyll molecules to assume the proper orientation and overlap would account for the ESR line narrowing. The special chlorophyll pair might thus be written in a more general way as (Chl X Chl). However, in the laboratory, the only ligand X known to provide the proper orientation is H_2O, and that is why the formulation here is made in these more specific terms.

VIII. Chlorophyll Model for Conversion of Light

The structures suggested here for antenna chlorophyll and for reaction center chlorophyll can be combined to form a unit that possesses both light-gathering properties and photoactivity. The (Chl H_2O Chl) entity has an Mg atom available for coordination, the chlorophyll oligomer has a terminal keto $C=O$ function, so that formation of a keto $C=O$---Mg bond to form $(Chl_2)_n$ (Chl H_2O Chl) is possible. [Note that this structure is equivalent to the insertion of an occasional water molecule into the oligomer (Ballschmiter and Katz, 1968).] The chlorophyll oligomer then functions to collect light quanta and to funnel them to the (Chl H_2O Chl) moieties, where charge separation occurs. Charge separation in the special chlorophyll pair can occur by a process of hydride transfer from the coordinated water molecule to the other chlorophyll molecule in the structure shown in Fig. 7C (Garcia-Morin *et al.*, 1969). Photoinduced hydrogen atom transfer to a keto carbonyl oxygen is a well-recognized photochemical process

(Hammond and Turro, 1963). This process occurring in (Chl H_2O Chl) would produce the species

This structure may be viewed as the precursor of Chl^+ and Chl^-. Fast electron exchange must take place between the odd electron sites in this structure, and only a small motion of the proton is necessary to reconstitute the original water $O-H$ bond. The unpaired electron at the keto $C=O$ carbon atom would be expected to be delocalized into the π system of the macrocycle to form Chl^-. The electron-deficient oxygen atom is an extremely powerful oxidant, and it would abstract an electron from the chlorophyll molecule to which it is coordinated, restoring the original water molecule with the formation of $Chl^{\dagger}$. Thus, charge separation (Chl H_2O Chl^-) has occurred with energy furnished by light. It is clear that the process described here for charge separation has quite different energetics from the photolysis of water to form $H\cdot$ and $HO\cdot$. For the latter process, a very stable chemical bond must be ruptured, which requires a large amount of energy. In the hydrogen atom abstraction process described here, rupture of the $O-H$ bond in water is compensated for by formation of a new $O-H$ bond from the carbonyl oxygen atom. The energetics are therefore much more favorable. The free electron delocalized into the chlorophyll and the $HO\cdot$ radical coordinated to Mg are thus regarded as the ultimate sources of the reducing and oxidizing power for the dark reactions of photosynthesis.

Electron conduction in and out of our model photosynthetic unit is an absolute requirement for functionality. If the number of positive and negative charges are not unbalanced by electron transport, charge anihilation will occur, and the system will return to its original state, possibly with an accompanying fluorescence. Removal of the electron produces (Chl H_2O Chl)† in the active center, which is photobleached and which is the source of the ESR signal I. The system is then restored to its original state with an electron abstracted from a water molecule somewhere else in the chloroplast. The water oxidized in photosynthesis is not the water in the (Chl H_2O Chl) reaction center.

As electrons must be removed and reintroduced, the two chlorophyll molecules in the special pair can be expected to facilitate simultaneous removal and reextraction. The model system thus functions purely as an electron pump powered by light. ESR data on P865 in purple photosynthetic bacteria (Norris et al., 1971) are entirely compatible with the special chlorophyll pair hypothesis. There is thus good reason to suppose that the model advanced here is applicable to a wide range of photosynthetic organisms.

The model system described here must exist in an environment very similar in polarity to that of an aliphatic hydrocarbon solvent, and one to which water and oxygen can have only very limited access. In an environment containing a large number of nucleophiles, chlorophyll a will occur as a monomeric species; such chlorophyll will be a short-wavelength form and fluorescent. To maintain the integrity of the chlorophyll oligomers, access of water must be strictly limited, else the oligomers will be converted either to $Chl \cdot H_2O$, a short-wavelength and fluorescent form, or $(Chl \cdot H_2O)_n$, a much too red-shifted form. This suggests that the chlorophyll is on the inside of the thylakoids (Kreutz, 1970) presumed to occur in the chloroplast, in a hydrocarbon-like milieu, possibly provided by the lipids of the chloroplast. The oil-soluble electron transport agents, such as the plastoquinones, and the carotenoids, such as β-carotene, presumably accompany the chlorophyll. The water-soluble electron transport agents, the ferredoxins, cytochromes, flavoproteins, and the like are then part of the membranes surrounding the chlorophyll, and the dark reactions of photosynthesis, including oxygen evolution are then considered to occur in the aqueous phase in which the thylakoids are immersed in the chloroplasts. While the bulk of the chlorophyll in this view cannot have much contact with the proteins of the thylakoid membrane, there appears to be no reason why the special chlorophyll pair in the reaction center could not experience a more intimate interaction with the membrane.

It is obvious that many aspects of photosynthesis are not included in the proposed model. The way in which chlorophyll b and the xanthophylls might be involved is not considered at all. The relationship between the proposed model and the two photosystems schemes for photosynthesis remains to be explored. Whether the model is consistent with the fluorescence properties of photosynthetic organisms also is unsettled. Nevertheless, the model has the virtue of being explicit, and the way now appears open to the synthesis of chlorophyll systems in the laboratory structured along the lines suggested here that may have the energy transduction properties characteristic of chlorophyll in the living plant.

REFERENCES

Amster, R. L. (1969). *Photochem. Photobiol.* 9, 331.

Amster, R. L., and Porter, G. (1966). *Proc. Roy. Soc., Ser. A* 296, 38.

Anderson, A. F. H., and Calvin, M. (1964). *Arch. Biochem. Biophys.* 107, 251.

Ballschmiter, K., and Katz, J. J. (1968). *Nature (London)* 220, 1231.

Ballschmiter, K., and Katz, J. J. (1969). *J. Amer. Chem. Soc.* 91, 2661.

Ballschmiter, K., and Katz, J. J. (1972). *Biochim. Biophys. Acta* 256, 307.

Ballschmiter, K., Cotton, T. M., Strain, H. H., and Katz, J. J. (1969a). *Biochim. Biophys. Acta* 180, 347.

Ballschmiter, K., Truesdell, K., and Katz, J. J. (1969b). *Biochim. Biophys. Acta* 184, 604.

Bolton, J. R., Clayton, R. C., and Read, D. W. (1969). *Photochem. Photobiol.* 9, 209.

Borg, D. C., Fajer, J., Felton, R. H., and Dolphin, D. (1970). *Proc. Nat. Acad. Sci. U.S.* 67, 813.

Boucher, L. J., and Katz, J. J. (1967a). *J. Amer. Chem. Soc.* 89, 1340.

Boucher, L. J., and Katz, J. J. (1967b). *J. Amer. Chem. Soc.* 89, 4703.

Briegleb, G. (1961). "Elektronen-Donator-Acceptor Komplexe," pp. 5–7, Springer-Verlag, Berlin and New York.

Brody, M. (1968). *In* "The Biology of Euglena" (D. E. Buetow, ed.), Vol. 2, p. 242 *et seq.* Academic Press, New York.

Brody, S. S., and Brody, M. (1965). *Arch. Biochem. Biophys.* 110, 583.

Brown, J. S. (1963). *Photochem. Photobiol.* 2, 159.

Brown, J. S. (1972). *Annu. Rev. Plant Physiol.* 23, 73–86.

Cederstrand, C. N., Rabinowitch, E., and Govindjee, (1966). *Biochim. Biophys. Acta* 126, 1.

Chamot, C. (1967). "Integration of Gaussian Spectral Lines," Argonne Program Library, C-151. Argonne Nat. Lab., Argonne, Illinois.

Clayton, R. K. (1965). "Molecular Physics in Photosynthesis." Ginn (Blaisdell), Boston, Massachusetts.

Closs, G. L., Katz, J. J., Pennington, F. C., Thomas, M. R., and Strain, H. H. (1963). *J. Amer. Chem. Soc.* 85, 3809.

Commoner, B., Heise, J. J., and Townsend, J. (1956). *Proc. Nat. Acad. Sci. U.S.* 42, 710.

Cotton, T. M., Ballschmiter, K., and Katz, J. J. (1970). *J. Chromatogr. Sci.* 8, 546.

Cotton, T. M., Ballschmiter, K., and Katz, J. J. (1972a). Manuscript in preparation.

Cotton, T. M., Ballschmiter, K., and Katz, J. J. (1972b). To be published.

Davidon, W. C. (1966). "Variable Metric Method for Minimization," Rep. ANL-5990 (Rev. 2). Argonne Nat. Lab., Argonne, Illinois.

Dougherty, R. C., Strain, H. H., and Katz, J. J. (1965). *J. Amer. Chem. Soc.* 87, 104.

Dougherty, R. C., Strain, H. H., Svec, W. A., Uphaus, R. A., and Katz, J. J. (1970). *J. Amer. Chem. Soc.* 92, 2826.

Ebrey, T. G., and Clayton, R. K. (1969). *Photochem. Photobiol.* 10, 109.

Fajer, J., Borg, D. C., Forman, A., Dolphin, D., and Felton, R. H. (1970). *J. Amer. Chem. Soc.* 92, 743.

Fernandez, J., and Becker, R. S. (1959). *J. Chem. Phys.* 31, 467.

Fischer, M. S., Templeton, D. H., Zalkin, A., and Calvin, M. (1971). *J. Amer. Chem. Soc.* 93, 2622.

Flaumenhaft, E., Uphaus, R. A., and Katz, J. J. (1970). *Biochim. Biophys. Acta* 215, 421.

Freed, S. (1957). *Science* 125, 1248.

Freed, S., and Sancier, K. M. (1951). *Science* 114, 275.

French, C. S. (1971). *Proc. Nat. Acad. Sci. U.S.* 68, 2893.

French, C. S., and Praeger, L. K. (1969). *Progr. Photosyn. Res.* **2**, 555.
French, C. S., Brown, J. S., Wiesner, W., and Laurence, M. C. (1971). *Carnegie Inst. Wash., Yearb.* **69**, 662.
French, C. S., Brown, J. S., and Laurence, M. C. (1972). *Plant Physiol.* **49**, 421.
Garcia-Morin, M., Uphaus, R. A., Norris, J. R., and Katz, J. J. (1969). *J. Phys. Chem.* **73**, 1066.
Goedheer, J. C. (1966). *In* "The Chlorophylls" (L. P. Vernon and G. R. Seely, eds.), Chapter 6, pp. 147–184. Academic Press, New York.
Gulyayev, B. A., and Litvin, F. F. (1967). *Biophysics (USSR)* **12**, 970.
Gulyayev, B. A., and Litvin, F. F. (1970). *Biophysics (USSR)* **15**, 701.
Gurinovich, G. P., Sevchenko, A. N., and Solov'ev, K. N. (1968). "Spectroscopy of Chlorophyll and Related Compounds," p. 520. Izdatel'stvo Nauk i Tekhnika, Minsk. (Transl. No. AEC tr-7199, available from National Technical Information Service, U. S. Department of Commerce, Springfield, Virginia 22151.)
Hammond, G. S., and Turro, N. J. (1963). *Science* **142**, 1541.
Henry, M., and Leicknam, J.-P. (1970). *Colloq. Int. Cent. Rech. Sci.* **191**, 317.
Hochstrasser, R. M., and Kasha, M. (1964). *Photochem. Photobiol.* **3**, 317.
Houssier, C., and Sauer, K. (1970). *J. Amer. Chem. Soc.* **92**, 779.
Kamen, M. D. (1963). "Primary Processes in Photosynthesis." Academic Press, New York.
Katz, J. J. (1968). *Develop. Appl. Spectrosc.* **6**, 201.
Katz, J. J. (1972). *In* "Inorganic Biochemistry" (G. Eichhorn, ed.), Chapter 29. Elsevier, Amsterdam (in press).
Katz, J. J., and Ballschmiter, K. (1968). *Angew. Chem.* **80**, 283; *Angew. Chem., Int. Ed. Engl.* **7**, 286 (1968).
Katz, J. J., and Janson, T. R. (1972). *Ann. N. Y. Acad. Sci.* (in press).
Katz, J. J., Closs, G. L., Pennington, F. C., Thomas, M. R., and Strain, H. H. (1963). *J. Amer. Chem. Soc.* **85**, 3801.
Katz, J. J., Dougherty, R. C., Svec, W. A., and Strain, H. H. (1964). *J. Amer. Chem. Soc.* **86**, 4220.
Katz, J. J., Dougherty, R. C., and Boucher, L. J. (1966). *In* "The Chlorophylls" (L. P. Vernon and G. R. Seely, eds.), Chapter 7, pp. 185–251. Academic Press, New York.
Katz, J. J., Strain, H. H., Leussing, D. L., and Dougherty, R. C. (1968a). *J. Amer. Chem. Soc.* **90**, 784.
Katz, J. J., Ballschmiter, K., Garcia-Morin, M., Strain, H. H., and Uphaus, R. A. (1968b). *Proc. Nat. Acad. Sci. U.S.* **60**, 100.
Katz, J. J., Strain, H. H., Harkness, A. L., Studier, M. H., Svec, W. A., Janson, T. R., and Cope, B. T. (1972a). *J. Amer. Chem. Soc.* **94**, 7938.
Katz, J. J., Janson, T. R., Kostka, A. G., Uphaus, R. A., and Closs, G. L. (1972b). *J. Amer. Chem. Soc.* **94**, 2883.
Kohl, D. H., Townsend, J., Commoner, B., Crespi, H. L., Dougherty, R. C., and Katz, J. J. (1965). *Nature (London)* **206**, 1105.
Kok, B. (1959). *Plant Physiol.* **34**, 184.
Krasnovsky, A. A. (1969). *Progr. Photosyn. Res.* **2**, 709.
Kreutz, W. (1970). *Advan. Bot. Res.* **3**, 53–169.
Lavorel, L. (1957). *J. Phys. Chem.* **61**, 1600.
Livingston, R. (1960). *Quart. Rev., Chem. Soc.* **14**, 174.
Livingston, R., Watson, W. F., and McArdle, J. (1949). *J. Amer. Chem. Soc.* **71**, 1542.
McElroy, J. D., Mauzerall, D. C., and Feher, G. (1969). *Biochim. Biophys. Acta* **172**, 180.

Michel-Wolwertz, M. R., Michel, J. M., Brown, J. S., and Praeger, L. K. (1969). *Biochem. Soc. Symp.* **28,** 147.

Mulliken, R. S., and Person, W. B. (1969). "Molecular Complexes," Chapter 4, pp. 33–41. Wiley, New York.

Norris, J. R., Uphaus, R. A., Cotton, T. M., and Katz, J. J. (1970). *Biochim. Biophys. Acta* **223,** 446.

Norris, J. R., Uphaus, R. A., Crespi, H. L., and Katz, J. J. (1971). *Proc. Nat. Acad. Sci. U.S.* **68,** 625.

Norris, J. R., Uphaus, R. A., and Katz, J. J. (1972). *Biochim. Biophys. Acta* **275,** 161–168.

Ogawa, T., and Vernon, L. P. (1970). *Biochim. Biophys. Acta* **197,** 292.

Ogawa, T., Vernon, L. P., and Mollenhauer, H. H. (1969). *Biochim. Biophys. Acta* **172,** 216.

Olson, J. M., and Stanton, E. K. (1966). *In* "The Chlorophylls" (L. P. Vernon and G. R. Seely, eds.), p. 381. Academic Press, New York.

Rabinowitch, E. (1945a). "Photosynthesis," Vol. I, p. 412. Wiley (Interscience), New York.

Rabinowitch, E. (1945b). "Photosynthesis," Vol. I, p. 412. Wiley (Interscience), New York.

Rabinowitch, E. (1956). "Photosynthesis," Vol. II, Part 2, pp. 1501–1506. Wiley (Interscience), New York.

Rabinowitch, E., and Govindjee (1969). "Photosynthesis," p. 69, Wiley, New York.

Sauer, K., Lindsay Smith, J. R., and Schultz, A. J. (1966). *J. Amer. Chem. Soc.* **88,** 2681.

Seely, G. R. (1965). *Spectrochim. Acta* **21,** 1847.

Seely, G. R. (1966). *In* "The Chlorophylls" (L. P. Vernon and G. R. Seely, eds.), p. 91. Academic Press, New York.

Seely, G. R., and Jensen, R. G. (1965). *Spectrochim. Acta* **21,** 1835.

Sherman, G., and Fujimori, E. (1969). *Arch. Biochem. Biophys.* **130,** 624.

Steffen, H., and Calvin, M. (1970). *Biochem. Biophys. Res. Commun.* **41,** 282.

Strain, H. H., Cope, B. T., Jr., McDonald, G. N., Svec, W. A., and Katz, J. J. (1971). *Phytochemistry* **10,** 1109.

Svec, W. A., Rice, D., and Katz, J. J. (1972). Work in progress.

Taecker, R. G., Crespi, H. L., DaBoll, H. A., and Katz, J. J. (1971). *Biotechnol. Bioeng.* **13,** 779.

Thomas, J., Phondke, G. P., Tatake, V. G., and Gopal-Ayengar, A. R. (1970). *Photochem. Photobiol.* **11,** 85.

Timkovich, R., and Tulinsky, A. (1969). *J. Amer. Chem. Soc.* **91,** 4430.

Uphaus, R. A., and Katz, J. J. (1970). *Rev. Sci. Instrum.* **41,** 1515.

Weaver, E. C. (1968). *Annu. Rev. Plant Physiol.* **19,** 283.

Wiesner, W., and French, C. S. (1970). *Planta* **94,** 78.

Chemically and Physically Induced Luminescence as a Probe of Photosynthetic Mechanisms

DARRELL E. FLEISCHMAN and BERGER C. MAYNE
C. F. Kettering Research Laboratory,
Yellow Springs, Ohio

I. Introduction

In 1951 Bernard Strehler and William Arnold set out to show that illuminated chloroplasts can drive ATP formation. They illuminated a suspension of chloroplasts in the presence of ADP, phosphate, and firefly extract. If ATP were formed, it would cause the firefly extract to emit light which could be detected by a photomultiplier. Their chloroplast suspension did indeed emit light after it was illuminated. But it did so even in control experiments in which the firefly extract was omitted (Strehler and Arnold, 1951). Strehler and Arnold quickly learned that the light came from the chloroplasts themselves. It had the spectrum of *in vivo* chlorophyll fluorescence, but it could be detected for several minutes after the illumination was ended. The delayed fluorescence was most efficiently excited by light of the wavelengths and in the intensity range required for photosynthesis. It was quenched by inhibitors of photosynthesis.

Strehler and Arnold speculated that some of the early steps in the conversion of light energy to chemical energy may be partially reversible, and that regeneration of the excited chlorophyll singlet may be the end result of such a reversal.

It is now thought that every organism capable of performing photosynthesis reemits light after it has been illuminated. Ross and Calvin (1967) have pointed out that for thermodynamic reasons the primary light reaction must be able to reverse to some extent if a significant fraction of the energy of each captured photon is to be conserved in usable form (also see Knox, 1969).

In 1965 Mayne and Clayton (1966) made the discovery that if the pH of a suspension of chloroplasts is quickly raised from 4 to 8, the chloroplasts will emit a burst of light. It has subsequently been found that photosynthetic systems can be forced to re-emit light by subjecting them to any of a number of rather simple and often gentle physical or chemical perturbations. In part as a result of such experiments, our understanding of the mechanism of light emission has increased substantially.

From the moment of its discovery, it was hoped that delayed fluorescence would provide new insights into the mechanism of the early steps of quantum conversion by the photosynthetic apparatus. Luminscence studies have indeed furnished such information. But in addition, current studies indicate that delayed and induced fluorescence may provide sensitive probes of the storage of charge in photosystem II (the oxygen-evolving system of photosynthesis) and even of the state and structure of the photosynthetic membranes and of the storage of the high energy intermediates which are used to drive photophosphorylation. The mechanisms of oxygen evolution and photophosphorylation have been among the more intractable and controversial problems in photosynthesis research.

II. Luminescence Induced by an Acid–Base Transition

A. PHOSPHORYLATION RESULTING FROM AN
ACID–BASE TRANSITION

Three years after the experiment of Strehler and Arnold, Arnon *et al.* (1954) and Frenkel (1954) succeeded in showing that chloroplasts and extracts of photosynthetic bacteria can in fact drive the phosphorylation of ADP in the light. Some years later, Hind and Jagendorf (1963) and Shen and Shen (1962) were able to separate photophosphorylation into a light step and a dark step. Chloroplasts were first illuminated in the absence of ADP, phosphate, and Mg^{2+}. After an appropriate dark time, the chloroplasts were transferred, in the dark, to a solution containing these reagents. It was found that a high energy intermediate, designated X_E by Jagendorf, could be formed during the light stage and utilized for the formation of ATP during the subsequent dark stage. Since the formation of X_E was most efficient near pH 6 whereas ATP formation occurred best near pH 8, chloroplasts were routinely illuminated at low pH and then transferred to a medium of higher pH for the phosphorylation step.

In control experiments, however, it was found that a certain amount of X_E was formed by this procedure even when the chloroplasts were not illuminated (Hind and Jagendorf, 1965). Detailed study of this dark X_E formation supported the idea that during the acid stage the pH could become equilibrated across the thylakoid membrane, particularly if the buffer employed were a weak, permeant organic acid such as succinic acid. Transfer of the chloroplasts into a basic solution would then artificially create a difference in proton concentration across the thylakoid membrane. Jagendorf and his co-workers had found that chloroplasts take up protons from their suspending medium when they are illuminated (Jagendorf and Hind, 1963; Neumann and Jagendorf, 1964). Further study suggested that X_E could be identified with the proton gradient—or more properly, with the difference in proton electrochemical activity—created across the chloroplast thylakoid membrane during illumination or as the result of an acid–base transition (Jagendorf and Uribe, 1966a,b; Uribe and Jagendorf, 1967a,b; Miles and Jagendorf, 1970).

Such a conclusion seemed to provide strong evidence in favor of the chemiosmotic mechanism of phosphorylation which had been proposed by Mitchell (1961). According to Mitchell's scheme, the components of the electron transport chain are arranged anisotropically in the chloroplast thylakoid membranes. Electron flow through an alternating sequence of electron carriers (e.g., cytochromes) and hydrogen carriers (e.g., quinones) then results in a net translocation of protons into the thylakoid interior. A subsequent efflux of protons down their electrochemical gradient through a coupling factor drives ATP formation. [For the details of the chemiosmotic hypothesis, and reviews of recent developments, the reader is referred to articles by Mitchell (1966), Greville (1969), and Skulachev (1971).] Acid–base phosphorylation could also plausibly be explained, however, as the reversal of a proton "pump" driven by the chemical high energy intermediates which are postulated to be ATP precursors according to the chemical hypothesis of phosphorylation coupling (Slater, 1971).

B. Delayed Fluorescence and the High Energy Phosphorylation Intermediate

While Jagendorf and his group were discovering acid-base phosphorylation, Mayne was conducting a study of the effect of photosynthesis inhibitors upon the delayed fluorescence (3 msec delay) of chloroplasts. The results of these experiments seemed to suggest that the intensity of delayed fluorescence is somehow dependent upon the presence of the high energy phosphorylation intermediates. This conclusion was based upon the following observations (Mayne, 1967):

1. In tightly coupled chloroplasts, delayed fluorescence increases when the rate of electron flow is speeded by the addition of redox dyes such as pyocyanine or of Hill acceptors such as ferricyanide. An increased rate of electron flow would be expected to increase the rate of formation of high energy intermediates.

2. Delayed fluorescence is inhibited by phosphorylation uncouplers such as ammonia, methylamine, gramicidin D, quinacrine, and m-chlorocarbonyl cyanide phenylhydrazone (CCCP). Such uncouplers accelerate electron flow but destroy the high energy intermediates.

3. Delayed fluorescence is inhibited when ADP, phosphate, and Mg^{2+} are added, permitting high energy intermediates to be consumed in the formation of ATP. But light emission is restored to its original intensity when phlorizin or Dio-9 is added. These inhibitors are believed to block ATP formation not by destroying the high energy intermediates but by preventing their utilization at a terminal step (McCarty et al., 1965; Izawa et al., 1966). A scheme such as the following seemed to be implied:

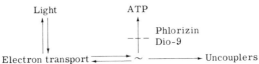

The hypothetical high energy intermediate is symbolized by $\sim$.

Similar experiments were performed with photosynthetic bacteria (Fleischman and Clayton, 1968). Oligomycin was substituted for Dio-9 or phlorizin, since it acts analogously in bacteria. The ionophore valinomycin, in association with KCl, was shown to be an efficient delayed fluorescence inhibitor. The results of the bacterial experiments were in agreement with the results of the corresponding chloroplast experiments. It appeared that energy stored in the form of high energy phosphorylation intermediates could escape again as quanta of light.

C. ACID–BASE LUMINESCENCE

Mayne and Clayton reasoned that if high energy phosphorylation intermediates are necessary for delayed fluorescence, and if such intermediates can be formed by subjecting chloroplasts to an acid-base transition, such an acid-base transition might make chloroplasts emit light.

They then repeated the experiments of Jagendorf and Uribe in front of a photomultiplier. Chloroplasts were first suspended in a solution containing 0.01 M succinic acid at a pH of about 4.5. Fifteen seconds later an equal volume of 0.1 M Tris base was injected with a hypodermic syringe, quickly raising the pH to about 8.5. A flash of light was detected by the photomultiplier (Mayne and Clayton, 1966; Mayne, 1966).

The spectrum of the emitted light was similar to that of *in vivo* chlorophyll fluorescence, indicating that the same singlet to ground transition of chlorophyll was responsible. The light emission reached maximum intensity as rapidly as the Tris could mix with the chloroplast suspension, and then decayed with a half-time of about 0.2 second. The emission of light was inhibited by desaspidin, methylamine, NH_4Cl, CCCP, and 3-(3,4-dichlorophenyl)-1,1-dimethylurea (DCMU). DCMU inhibits photosynthesis by acting specifically on photosystem II, probably by blocking electron transfer to photosystem I from Q, the primary electron acceptor of photosystem II (Bishop, 1958; Duysens and Sweers, 1963). Light emission was somewhat inhibited by the presence of the phosphate acceptor system and increased by Dio-9. It was also inhibited by ferricyanide.

The initial acid–base luminescence experiments seemed elegantly to support the prediction that light emission can be driven by a reversal of the process by which X_E, identified by Jagendorf's group as a proton gradient, is formed as a result of the absorption of light by chlorophyll. Upon further thought, though, it became apparent that this interpretation raised energetic problems. A quick calculation by Mayne (1968), using a Maxwell–Boltzmann distribution, revealed that the transfer of one proton through a pH gradient of 4.5 pH units could at best result in the emission of one quantum of chlorophyll fluorescence per 10^{26} chlorophyll molecules. The energy of the emitted light is about 40 kcal per einstein, while only about 6 kcal are available per mole of effluxing protons.

The energetic problem was resolved when it was found that chloroplasts will emit light during an acid–base transition only if they have been illuminated previously (Mayne, 1968, 1969). Fortunately, the chloroplasts used in the first experiments had inadvertently been exposed to room light long enough to activate the process.

The intensity, L, of the acid-base luminescence varied with the number, J, of photons which had been absorbed according to the relation:

$$L = L_{\max} (1 - e^{-\alpha J}) \tag{1}$$

If the absorption of photons is a random process and if one photon is sufficient to activate a luminescence unit, α becomes an estimate of the size of such a unit. The experimental value of α was found to be 195 chlorophyll molecules.

Approximately this number of chlorophyll molecules have been shown to cooperate in gathering excitation energy for each photosystem II reaction center (Duysens et al., 1961).

The action spectrum for the activation of acid–base luminescence showed that light absorbed by photosystem II pigments is the most effective. Four bits of evidence, then, suggest that photosystem II is the source of the luminescence induced by an acid–base transition:

1. The action spectra for luminescence and for photosystem II activity coincide.

2. The activation cross sections, or unit sizes, for the two processes are similar.

3. The spectrum of the light emitted during an acid–base transition is identical to the spectrum of photosystem II fluorescence.

4. Acid–base luminescence is inhibited by DCMU, a specific inhibitor of photosystem II (but see Hardt and Malkin (1972) for contrary results).

That photosystem II should be responsible for acid-base luminescence was not surprising. An accumulation of evidence of various sorts indicates that delayed fluorescence in green plants also originates almost entirely from photosystem II, although its yield and kinetics may be affected by photosystem I activity (Goedheer, 1962; Bertsch, 1962; Bertsch et al., 1967).

It is possible to measure the stability of the activated state necessary for light emission by performing the acid–base transition at various times after the illumination (Mayne, 1968). The decay of the activated state follows temperature-dependent second-order kinetics. Luminescence capacity declines to half its maximum value approximately 10 seconds after the end of illumination.

Hardt and Malkin (1971) and also Miles and Jagendorf (1969) reported a first-order decay of the high energy intermediate. Kraan (1971), on the other hand, found a second-order decay of the intermediate in the dark. The rate of this decay increased after a few seconds in the acid phase.

On the basis of the light activation studies, it was concluded that the acid–base transition provides activation energy for the light emission, and is not the sole source of the emitted energy. The increase in pH might act through the formation of a proton gradient. Alternatively, it might change the redox potential of a member of the electron transport chain, causing a reversed electron flow which could ultimately cause regeneration of the chlorophyll singlet (Mayne, 1968).

In a further study of acid–base luminescence, Miles and Jagendorf (1969) found convincing evidence that the high energy state X_E which leads to ATP production is not responsible for triggering light emission. Their evidence was the following:

1. Formation of the high energy phosphorylation precursor by an acid–base transition requires the presence of a sufficiently high concentration of a permanent organic acid anion. Glutamic acid, which is ineffective in acid–base ATP formation, works almost as well as succinic acid in luminescence experiments.

2. The pH optimum for the basic stage, in luminescence experiments, remained near 8.5, regardless of the pH during the acid stage. In phosphorylation experiments, the optimum pH in the alkaline stage shifted upward when the acid stage pH was raised.

3. In order to obtain maximal ATP yields during an acid–base transition, it is necessary to leave the chloroplasts in the acid bath for several seconds. On the other hand, acid–base luminescence is brightest when the acid incubation has been as brief as possible.

These observations seem to imply that acid–base luminescence requires only a pH increase, and that formation of a proton gradient may not be necessary.

An acid–base transition will also induce light emission from pre-illuminated chromatophores of photosynthetic bacteria (Fleischman, 1967, 1969, 1970). Chromatophores of the bacterium *Rhodopseudomonas viridis,* alone among materials we have studied, will emit delayed fluorescence even in the presence of high concentrations of phosphorylation uncouplers. We have tried to rationalize this fact in terms of the atypically low energy of the lowest excited singlet of its reaction center bacteriochlorophyll (Fleischman, 1971a). Preilluminated R. viridis chromatophores will emit light during an acid–base transition even in the presence of concentrations of gramicidin or of detergents, such as Triton X-100, which are more than sufficient to destroy a proton gradient.

For reasons such as those cited above, there now seems to be general agreement among workers in the field that the function of the acid–base transition is to induce a reverse electron flow by changing the redox levels of appropriate members of the electron transport chain.

Lavorel (1968, 1969, 1971) has proposed that luminescence is the result of a back reaction of the primary photoproducts of photosystem II:

$$Z \cdot Chl \cdot Q + h\nu \to Z^+ \cdot Chl \cdot A^- \to Z \cdot Chl \cdot Q + h\nu \qquad (2)$$

Here $Z \cdot Chl \cdot Q$ represents the system II reaction center complex. Q is the primary reductant, which will normally feed electrons to system I. Z is the primary oxidant, from which positive charges flow to water. Chl is a specialized reaction center chlorophyll, which may either sensitize or participate in the primary electron transfer. It may correspond to the chlorophyll a II described by Witt et al. (1969) and Döring et al. (1969).

Crofts and his associates (Wraight and Crofts, 1971; Crofts et al., 1971) suppose that the primary oxidant and reductant are in equilibrium with secondary donor and acceptor pools located on the inner and outer side, respectively, of the thylakoid membrane. Such an anisotropic arrangement of electron carriers would be in accordance with models proposed by Mitchell (1966) and Witt et al. (1969). The secondary donors and acceptors are postulated to be redox couples of the hydrogen carrier type. The acceptor pool, probably plastoquinone (Stiehl and Witt, 1968), would be in pH equilibrium with the external medium. The donor pool would equilibrate with the pH of the phase in the thylakoid interior. Absorption of a photon by the unit would cause a separation of charges which would migrate to the secondary donor, D, and the secondary acceptor, A:

$$DH \cdot Z \cdot Chl \cdot Q \cdot A \xrightarrow{h\nu} DH \cdot Z^+ \cdot Chl \cdot Q^- \cdot A \to H^+ + D \cdot Z \cdot Chl \cdot Q \cdot AH + OH^- \quad (3)$$

An increase in the external pH or a decrease in the internal pH would shift the redox balance between the primary and secondary acceptors in such a way that the luminescence precursor state $Z^+ \cdot Chl \cdot Q^-$ is regenerated:

$$H^+ + D \cdot Z \rightleftharpoons DH \cdot Z^+ \qquad Q \cdot AH + OH^- \rightleftharpoons Q^- A + H_2O \qquad (4)$$

interior phase   exterior phase

The proton uptake which occurs when chloroplasts are illuminated would be expected to shift the $D \cdot Z$ redox balance in such a way that the luminescence yield is increased. Wraight and Crofts (1971) have observed such a slow phase of delayed fluorescence increase, and found it to be inhibited when proton uptake is abolished by NH_4Cl, nigericin, or CCCP.

Kraan *et al.* (1970) have reported that the chloroplast fluorescence yield does not change substantially during an acid–base transition. Since the fluorescence yield is believed to be an indicator of the redox state of Q (Duysens and Sweers, 1963), these workers conclude that an acid–base transition does not increase the concentration of reduced Q. Instead, they suggest that the primary donor and acceptor are themselves hydrogen carriers, with pH-dependent midpoint potentials:

$$ZH \cdot Q \xrightarrow{h\nu} ZH^+ \cdot Q^- \qquad (5)$$
$$ZH^+ \rightleftharpoons Z + H^+ \qquad (6)$$
$$Q^- + H^+ \rightleftharpoons QH \qquad (7)$$

If ZH and Q are on the inside and outside of the thylakoid membrane, respectively, creation of a proton gradient would increase the concentration of $ZH^+ \cdot Q^-$. Light emission would then result from a reversal of reaction (5).

For an excellent and much more comprehensive discussion of luminescence induced by changes in pH and ionic strength, we recommend the thesis of Kraan (1971). We shall consider the problem further in our discussion of ferricyanide-induced luminescence and flash activation.

III. Various Other Chemiluminescences

A. OXYGEN-INDUCED LUMINESCENCE

A few days after Mayne and Clayton performed the first acid–base luminescence experiment, Fleischman predicted, on the basis of a devious and unconvincing argument, that photosynthetic bacteria would emit light if oxygen were injected into an anaerobic suspension of intact cells. A suspension of *R. viridis* cells was permitted to become anaerobic, and air was injected into the suspension with a hypodermic syringe. Surprisingly, light emission was detected (Fleischman, 1967, 1969).

The luminescence is rather weak, but appears to continue at a low level until the cell suspension has again become anaerobic. It is inhibited by uncouplers such as CCCP and quinacrine and by electron transport inhibitors such as 2-n-heptyl-4-hydroxyquinoline-N-oxide (HQNO). The light emission is dramatically enhanced in the presence of low concentrations (a few percent) of aliphatic alcohols. The effectiveness of the alcohols increases with their chain length. The spectrum of the emitted light, measured with narrow-band interference filters, is similar to the fluorescence spectrum of the bacterium. Thus, the light apparently originates in the singlet-to-ground transition of the organism's bacteriochlorophyll b. Light is emitted in two waves, and the ratio of their magnitudes is modified if the cells are pre-illuminated.

Most of the other luminescences described in this article are thought to originate in a back-reaction of products of the photosynthetic light reaction. One wonders whether light emission in the presence of oxygen may be an indication that the flow of electrons from reductants such as NADH to oxygen occurs in part through the primary electron acceptor and the reaction center chlorophyll.

B. LUMINESCENCE INDUCED BY HYDROSULFITE OR FERRICYANIDE

The fact that oxygen can cause bacteria to emit light suggested that luminescence might be evoked by other oxidants, such as ferricyanide; but reductants such as hydrosulfite could also be likely candidates. Actually both were active since Mayne showed that hydrosulfite treatment would indeed cause chloroplasts to emit light (Mayne, 1966, 1969), and Fleischman found that suspensions of chromatophores from photosynthetic bacteria would emit light upon injection of ferricyanide, or of hydrosulfite (Fleischman, 1967, 1969).

Like the acid–base luminescence, the luminescence evoked by hydrosulfite required pre-illumination of the chloroplasts or chromatophores.

Hydrosulfite-induced luminescence from chloroplasts is brightest when ferricyanide has been present in the medium during illumination. If the illumination is prolonged in the absence of ferricyanide, the capacity for chemiluminescence is lost. One might guess that the illumination generates stored positive charges which are necessary for the hydrosulfite-induced luminescence. These "holes" are slowly lost, perhaps to water, and must continuously be regenerated. But they can be regenerated only so long as there are empty electron acceptor pools. Once these have been filled, luminescence capacity will be lost unless an alternate electron acceptor such as ferricyanide is available.

It was possible to estimate the size of the endogenous electron acceptor pool by comparing the area under a plot of luminescence intensity vs time of irradiation, measured in the presence of ferricyanide, with the area under a similar plot measured in the absence of ferricyanide. There appeared to be about one electron acceptor per 100 chlorophyll molecules (Mayne, 1969).

In chloroplasts, the capacity for hydrosulfite-induced luminescence decays with second-order kinetics after illumination is ended (Mayne, 1969). In *R. viridis*, the loss of luminescence capacity parallels the reduction of a cytochrome (C558) which had become oxidized in the light (D. E. Fleishman, unpublished observations, 1972). In bacteria, then, we can tentatively identify the light-generated holes as oxidized cytochrome molecules.

It was of interest to see whether various bacterial chemiluminescences could be stimulated in succession, using the same chromatophore suspension (Fleischman, 1967) (Fig. 1). Ferricyanide luminescence is much brighter if ferricyanide injection is preceded by an acid–base transition. If ferricyanide is injected first, no other reagent injected afterward will cause light emission.

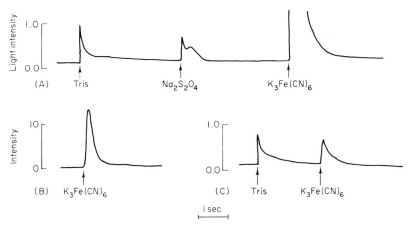

FIG. 1. Kinetics of chemically induced luminescence from chromatophores of the photosynthetic bacterium *Rhodopseudomonas viridis*. Two milliliters of chromatophores suspended in 0.05 M tris · HCl, pH 7, were first exposed to room light. One-half milliliter of 1 M $K_3Fe(CN)_6$, 1 M Tris base or 10^{-3} M sodium hydrosulfite was injected at the arrow indicated. In trace B, hydrosulfite had previously been injected. Note contracted vertical scale. Measurements were made as described by Mayne (1968).

When we injected ferricyanide after having injected hydrosulfite we thought we had discovered a chromatophore laser. A flash of light was emitted which was orders of magnitude brighter than any of the other chemiluminescences, and decayed within a fraction of a second (Fig. 1b). Light emission was evoked by this treatment even when care was taken to avoid exposure to the chromatophores to light before the chemical treatment. Such light emission from nonilluminated chromatophores has about the same intensity and time course as the light emission which accompanies the injection of ferricyanide alone into suspensions of preilluminated chromatophores. The intense, rapid component reaches maximum brightness when chromatophores have been exposed to a half-second flash of 1017 nm light of 2×10^3 erg/cm^2 sec intensity in the presence of millimolar hydrosulfite (Fleischman, 1969). The infrared absorption maximum of this bacterium is at about 1000 nm while the infrared absorption band of the reaction center bacteriochlorophyll b peaks at 985 nm (Holt and Clayton, 1965).

C. Light Emission Accompanying a Base–Acid Transition

A small amount of light emission was detected when chloroplast suspensions were acidified with succinic acid during the first step in the acid–base transition experiments (Mayne, 1968). Miles and Jagendorf (1969) found that the intensity of such acid-stimulated light emission can exceed the intensity of acid–base luminescence by a factor of almost 10 if the pH is lowered far enough. The type of acid used seems to be unimportant. The luminescence intensity increases rapidly with decreasing pH, at least down to pH 2. This type of chemiluminescence also requires a previous light activation of the chloroplasts, and is inhibited by phosphorylation uncouplers such as NH$_4$Cl and CCCP. Kraan (1971) has studied the phenomenon further and speculates that it may result from acidification of the chloroplast interior [Eq. (6)]. An alternative explanation might be that the acid-induced luminescence is a special case of salt-induced luminescence. We shall discuss this topic in a later section and cite evidence (Jackson and Crofts, 1969) that acid can duplicate the effect of salt upon changes in chromatophore absorption spectra which may be related to luminescence.

D. Luminescence Induced by Alcohols

Björn and Sigfridsson (1971) have found that *Elodea* leaves and spinach chloroplasts will emit light after they have been treated with aliphatic alcohols or aldehydes, or with certain aromatic compounds such as thymol and α-naphthol. The light emission starts seconds or minutes after alcohol addition and may reach maximum intensity as long as 45 minutes later. While the light intensity is weak, it may continue for hours, so that the integrated emission may exceed that of normal delayed fluorescence. The spectrum of the emitted light is at least roughly similar to that of prompt fluorescence from the same sample. The presence of oxygen seems not to be required. The effectiveness of alcohols in promoting the light emission increases with their chain length. This is reminiscent of the effect of alcohols in enhancing the oxygen-induced luminescence of photosynthetic bacteria.

Electron micrographs of alcohol-treated leaves indicate that there has been an extensive change in the chloroplast grana structure, and suggest that the alcohol may have dissolved some of the lipid or chlorophyll from the thylakoid membranes. Björn and Sigfridsson therefore speculate that alcohol-induced changes in interfacial energy may be the energy source for the light emission. How such changes might be coupled to the generation of chlorophyll excited singlets is not clear.

E. ENHANCEMENT OF DELAYED FLUORESCENCE BY DCMU

Clayton (1969) found that light emission from pre-illuminated spinach chloroplasts increased when he injected DCMU into the chloroplast suspension. He resisted the temptation to believe that he had found a new type of chemiluminescence. Instead, he asked whether DCMU might have increased the prompt fluorescence yield. This in turn might have been reflected as an increase in yield of delayed fluorescence. Measurement of changes in the yield of prompt fluorescence under similar conditions confirmed this suspicion. Clayton further pointed out that since treatment with hydrosulfite also increases the prompt fluorescence yield, such an effect might provide a trivial explanation for hydrosulfite-induced luminescence and perhaps for other chemiluminescences.

Butler (1966) and Lavorel (1968, 1969, 1971) have noted that both prompt and delayed fluorescence originate from singlet excitation quanta in the chlorophyll associated with system II in green plants or in the light-harvesting chlorophyll of photosynthetic bacteria. Consequently, factors influencing the yield of prompt fluorescence should influence the yield of delayed fluorescence in a similar way. Lavorel

(1969) suggests that the intensity of delayed fluorescence, L, should obey the relation

$$L = \Phi J \tag{8}$$

where Φ is the prompt fluorescence yield and J is the rate of the chemical reaction, e.g., Eq. (2), which generates quanta of chlorophyll excitation.

At this point it would perhaps be appropriate to consider the relationship between prompt and delayed fluorescence and photochemical trapping in more detail. We shall restrict the discussion to photosynthetic bacteria, because here the mechanism is the most clearly defined (Clayton, 1966b; Duysens, 1966, 1971).

A photon absorbed by the light-harvesting chlorophyll of a photosynthetic bacterium will wander or become delocalized in the chlorophyll aggregate as a singlet exciton (Pearlstein, 1966; Robinson, 1966) until it experiences one of three fates. It may be reemitted as fluorescence or nonradiatively degraded to heat. Or it may reach a specialized photochemically active bacteriochlorophyll. Here it will probably be consumed within 10^{-11} second (Zankel et al., 1968) when the excited reaction center chlorophyll, P, donates an electron to an acceptor, A:

$$(\text{BChl}) \cdot P \cdot A + h\nu \rightarrow (\text{BChl})^\circ \cdot P \cdot A \rightarrow (\text{BChl}) \cdot P^\circ \cdot A \rightarrow (\text{BChl}) \cdot P^+ \cdot A^- \tag{9}$$

where (BChl) represents the light-harvesting bacteriochlorophyll aggregate.

Such photochemical trapping competes effectively with fluorescence for the excitons in the light-harvesting chlorophyll. Therefore, the fluorescence yield will be strongly influenced by the availability of reaction centers in the trapping state, PA. Reaction centers in the states P^+A^-, P^+A, or PA^- cannot perform photochemistry, so they are much less efficient as fluorescence quenchers.

In practice it is usually found that a part of the fluorescence yield, termed the live fluorescence, does respond to changes in the state of the photochemical traps. Another portion of the fluorescence, the "dead" fluorescence, does not. The chlorophyll responsible for the dead fluorescence is believed not to be in contact with the reaction centers. It is generally believed that the excitations responsible for delayed fluorescence originate in the reaction center chlorophyll and then migrate to the associated light-harvesting chlorophyll (Clayton, 1969; Lavorel, 1971; Duysens, 1971). Therefore, Clayton (1969) points out, the probability that such chemically generated excitons will be emitted as delayed fluorescence should depend only upon the live fluorescence yield, not upon the total fluorescence yield.

Duysens (1966) and Clayton (1966a) recognize that each reaction center might have an associated cluster of light-harvesting chlorophyll molecules which can exchange excitation energy with that reaction center and no other. At the opposite extreme, excitation energy might be able to migrate freely between reaction centers. A photosynthetic unit in which an exciton has just arisen by a reversal of reaction (9) clearly always will have its reaction center in the trapping state, PA. Therefore, the delayed fluorescence yield will obey Eq. (8) only if such an exciton almost always escapes from the vicinity of the reaction center of its origin. Clayton (1966b) has presented evidence that excitons are able to migrate between reaction centers in a number of photosynthetic bacteria. Nevertheless, there well may be instances in which they cannot. In such cases the delayed fluorescence intensity would fortuitously parallel the prompt fluorescence yield simply because both are dependent upon the number of reaction centers in the P^+A^- state.

Fluorescence yields are influenced by factors other than the state of the photochemical traps (Bonaventura and Myers, 1969; Papageorgiou, 1968; Mayne, 1965). These include the presence of cations (Murata *et al.*, 1970) and proton uptake (Wraight and Crofts, 1970; Cohen and Sherman, 1970). Such factors would be expected to have an identical effect on the yields of prompt and delayed fluorescence.

IV. Thermoluminescence

A. GLOW CURVES FROM PLANTS

In their initial study, Strehler and Arnold (1951) noticed that algae release stored energy as delayed fluorescence more slowly at lower temperatures. Later, Arnold and his co-workers found that algae and leaves can trap light energy in a stable chemical form when they are illuminated at temperatures below $-100°C$. When the materials are subsequently warmed in the dark, some of the light is reemitted (Arnold and Sherwood, 1959). If algae are illuminated while frozen and then heated at a constant rate of 3°C per second, light is emitted in a series of four waves, or glow peaks, having intensity maxima at $-155°$, $-6°$, $+30°$, and $+52°C$. A broad, oxygen-dependent emission occurs between $+30°$ and $+100°C$ (Arnold, 1966; Arnold and Azzi, 1968). Rubin and Venediktov (1969) have performed very similar experiments.

Both groups believe that after the primary light-induced charge separation, the electrons and holes move to acceptors, or traps. Plastoquinone might, for example, serve as an electron trap. The carriers between the system II reaction center and water could serve as hole traps. Light emission is thought to occur when the electrons and holes return to chlorophyll and annihilate. In a semiconductor model suggested by Arnold and Azzi (1968), the electrons and holes would return to the chlorophyll aggregate at separate points and migrate through the aggregate until an electron and a hole arrive simultaneously at the same chlorophyll molecule. Bertsch (1969) has described further details of such a semiconductor model. Alternatively the electron-hole annihilation could occur by reversal of reaction (9).

Arnold assumed that the rate of charge recombination luminescence is proportional to the rate at which electrons (or holes) can escape from the traps and return to chlorophyll. The luminescence intensity, L, would then obey the relation (Randall and Wilkins, 1945; Arnold and Azzi, 1968):

$$L = -\frac{dN}{dt} = NFe^{-E/kT} \tag{10}$$

N is the number of trapped electrons. F includes an entropy of activation factor and a factor related to the probability that an electron will tunnel through the potential barrier separating the chlorophyll and the trap. E is the activation energy and is related to the trap depth. T is the absolute temperature, and k is Boltzmann's constant.

Because of the exponential term, electrons or holes which are trapped during irradiation at low temperatures may not be able to escape from the traps and return to chlorophyll. As the chloroplasts are heated, however, the rate of untrapping increases. Arnold and Azzi and Rubin and Venediktov believe that the glow curve peaks correspond to the escape of charges from traps of different depths. From the shape of the glow curves, they have been able to calculate a trap depth and an excitation cross section corresponding to each glow peak (Arnold and Azzi, 1971).

It has long been known that the delayed fluorescence decay curve includes several components (Tollin et al., 1958). Shuvalov and Litvin (1969) have attempted to establish a one-to-one correspondence between glow peaks and components of the delayed fluorescence decay.

Only the glow peak at $+30°C$ remains in chloroplasts which have been treated with DCMU (Arnold and Azzi, 1968). Bennoun (1970) has presented evidence that the delayed fluorescence which remains in the presence of DCMU corresponds to the reoxidation of reduced Q by a direct reversal of the photoreaction. Hydroxylamine, which feeds electrons into the donor side of photosystem II, inhibits both the reoxidation of Q and the accompanying delayed fluorescence.

Jursinic and Govindjee (1972) have obtained thermoluminescence from algae by injecting warm water into a pre-illuminated algal suspension which contains DCMU. They have clearly shown that the increase in light emission which accompanies the temperature jump is due to an increase in the rate of reoxidation of Q^- and a resulting increase in the intensity of delayed fluorescence. By factoring out the fluorescence yield [Eq. (8)], they have measured the rate of the chemical back reaction and have calculated its activation energy from an Arrhenius plot of the measured second-order rate constants.

B. Glow Curves and Delayed Fluorescence from Bacteria

When chromatophores of the photosynthetic bacterium R. *viridis* are frozen in the dark and then illuminated at temperatures between -10 and $-100°C$, two cytochrome molecules and one chlorophyll molecule become oxidized (Fleischman and Cooke, 1971). The chlorophyll recovers rapidly when illumination is ended.

$$C^{+2} \cdot C^{+2} \cdot P \cdot A \cdot B \cdot D \xrightarrow{h\nu} C^{+3} \cdot C^{+3} \cdot P^+ \cdot A^- \cdot B^- \cdot D^- \xrightarrow{K} C^{+3} \cdot C^{+3} \cdot P \cdot A \cdot B^- \cdot D^- \quad (11)$$

C represents cytochrome, P is reaction center chlorophyll, A, B, and D are unidentified electron acceptors. The first-order rate constant K varies from 53 sec^{-1} at $-40°C$ to 76 sec^{-1} at $-198°C$ (D. E. Fleischman, unpublished observations, 1972).

Delayed fluorescence decaying with the same first-order constant accompanies the chlorophyll recovery. As the temperature is lowered, the rate of chlorophyll recovery and decay of delayed fluorescence increases, but the intensity of the delayed fluorescence diminishes.

During a prolonged illumination at low temperatures, the reaction centers become converted to the form $P^+ \cdot A \cdot B^-$. The conversion follows first-order kinetics, and the rate is temperature dependent. Delayed fluorescence disappears as conversion to the $P^+ \cdot A \cdot B^-$ state proceeds. The rate constant for the burnout of delayed fluorescence coincides at each temperature with the rate constant for the reaction center conversion.

After illumination is ended, the reaction centers relax to the state $P \cdot A \cdot B$, again by a temperature-dependent first-order process. If the chromatophores are heated in the dark, a glow peak can be observed (Fleischman, 1971b). The intensity of the glow is directly proportional to the number of reaction centers still in the state $P^+ \cdot A \cdot B^-$ at the start of light emission.

The following conclusions may be drawn:

1. Delayed fluorescence accompanies the donation of an electron from A^- to P^+, i.e., the direct reversal of the primary light reaction. The

glow peak results from the return of an electron from the secondary acceptor B^- to P^+.

2. The return of an electron from A^- to P^+ has no measurable activation energy, and in fact becomes faster as the temperature is lowered. The accompanying delayed fluorescence does, however, require activation energy. The most plausible mechanistic conclusion is that most of the electrons tunnel nonradiatively from A^- into the chlorophyll ground state. Only a small fraction return by a radiative route through the chlorophyll singlet. At least in bacteria then, the activation energy E [Eq. (10)] is the activation energy for the transfer of an electron from A^- into the lowest excited singlet of P, rather than for electron untrapping.

V. Ferricyanide-Induced Luminescence

When potassium ferricyanide is injected into a pre-illuminated suspension of bacterial chromatophores, light is emitted (Fig. 1) (Fleischman, 1967, 1969). This chemiluminescence has the following requirements in *R. viridis.*

1. Before the pre-illumination, the cytochrome 558 and the reaction center bacteriochlorophyll, P985, must be in the reduced form.

2. The activating flash must contain enough quanta to oxidize some of the cytochrome, but not enough quanta to oxidize all of the P985.

3. If ferricyanide is injected at various times after the activating flash, the luminescence intensity is found to be proportional to the amount of cytochrome which was oxidized during the flash and has not yet recovered (Fig. 2).

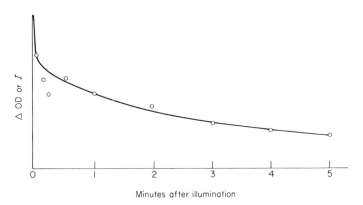

FIG. 2. Line: reduction of cytochrome 558 following photooxidation, measured as ΔA 418 nm–ΔA 422 nm in an Aminco-Chance double-beam spectrophotometer. Circles: intensity of ferricyanide induced luminescence as a function of time after activating flash. Taken from Fleischman (1969).

In summary, the luminescence intensity is proportional to the number of reaction centers in which P985 is in the reduced form, but at least one electron acceptor has been photochemically reduced and has not yet lost its electron at the time of ferricyanide injection.

We have suggested that ferricyanide first oxidizes the P985. Light emission then accompanies the return of an electron to P985$^+$ from the acceptor.

The time course of the light emission (Fig. 1) is similar, over a wide temperature range, to that of a delayed fluorescence component. This suggests that both emissions result from the same recombination.

The luminescence becomes much more intense as the pH is increased (D. E. Fleischman, unpublished observations, 1972), reaching half maximum at about pH 8.5. Chance *et al.* (1970) have reported a fast flash-induced proton binding by *Chromatium* chromatophores. Its half-time (400 μsec) would be compatible with a model in which the tertiary electron acceptor, D, takes up a proton from the medium when it accepts an electron. At higher pH, the midpoint potential of D might be shifted upward, so that it would no longer be able to accept an electron from the secondary acceptor. We therefore propose the following scheme:

$$C^{+2} \cdot P \cdot A \cdot B \cdot D \xrightarrow{h\nu} C^{+3} \cdot P \cdot A \cdot B^- \cdot D + H^+ \rightleftharpoons C^{+3} \cdot P \cdot A \cdot B \cdot DH$$
$$\downarrow \quad {\scriptstyle K_3Fe(CN)_6} \qquad\qquad\qquad (12)$$
$$C^{+3} \cdot P \cdot A \cdot B \cdot D + h\nu \leftarrow C^{+3} \cdot P^+ \cdot A \cdot B^- \cdot D$$

Such a scheme clearly could account for acid-base luminescence as well.

The extremely fast, bright luminescence which is observed when chromatophores have been illuminated in the presence of hydrosulfite before ferricyanide injection may result from the return of electron from A$^-$ to P$^+$.

The light emission obtained when hydrosulfite and ferricyanide are added in succession in the dark is especially interesting. The tail of the decay curve perfectly parallels the light emission obtained when ferricyanide alone is added to preilluminated chromatophores (compare Fig. 1A and 1C). It would appear that hydrosulfite has reduced the physiological acceptor. In effect, the experiment is a reconstitution of delayed fluorescence, and in fact of the primary light reaction itself, chemically in the dark.

VI. Salt-Induced Luminescence

Shortly after the discovery of acid–base luminescence, Peter Mitchell visited the Kettering Laboratory. While attempting to relate luminescence to the chemiosmotic hypothesis, Mitchell commented that the acid–base phosphorylation experiments really should not have worked. The protonmotive force across a thylakoid membrane includes two terms, he explained, a diffusion term and an electrical term (Mitchell and Moyle, 1968):

$$\Delta p = \Delta \psi - Z \, \Delta pH \tag{13}$$

where Δp is the protonmotive force, $\Delta \psi$ is the membrane potential, ΔpH is the pH difference across the membrane, and Z is a constant. The first few protons to leak from the thylakoids after an acid–base transition should leave behind a net negative charge. This should have prevented further proton efflux, and, according to the chemiosmotic hypothesis, should have prevented ATP synthesis. Perhaps, Mitchell suggested, the proton efflux may have been balanced by a counterflow of other ions.

Except for dilute buffer, there was no salt in the medium in which we had measured acid–base luminescence with bacterial chromatophores. Therefore, the experiment was repeated in the presence of KCl. Substantially more light was emitted. Further reflection suggested that if the salt were in fact canceling a negative electrostatic contribution to the protonmotive force, it should do so equally well if the salt were added after the base injection. Therefore, KCl was injected into a chromatophore suspension after Tris injection, and, as predicted, a second burst of light resulted (Fleischman, 1967, 1969). Miles and Jagendorf (1969) found that salt injection would cause light emission from chloroplast suspensions. They showed that such luminescence requires prior illumination of the chloroplasts, and that the emitted light has the spectrum of chlorophyll fluorescence. Salt injection would not drive ATP formation. Miles and Jagendorf suggested that the salt treatment in some way lowers an energy barrier to accelerate the recombination of stored electrons and holes.

Strehler and Lynch (1957) had noticed that delayed fluorescence in certain respects parallels a light-induced absorbance change at 515 nm in chloroplasts. Junge and Witt (1968) have presented evidence that this absorbance change may be an indicator of chloroplast membrane potential. Baltscheffsky (1967) found that the carotenoid absorbance bands of *Rhodospirillum rubrum* chromatophores would undergo a red shift in the presence of Mg^{2+} and ATP or pyrophosphate. It was also found that the light-induced red shift of the carotenoid bands of *Rhodopseudomonas spheroides* was inhibited by phosphorylation uncouplers and electron transport inhibitors (Fleischman and

Clayton, 1968). The absorbance change and delayed fluoresence seemed to be affected in a parallel fashion by a number of these reagents. The effect of several uncouplers and ionophores on the kinetics of the carotenoid shift could be explained in a qualitative way if it, like the 515 nm change in chloroplasts, was a membrane potential indicator (Greville, 1969).

Jackson and Crofts (1969) elegantly demonstrated that shifts of the carotenoid bands of R. *spheroides* chromatophores can be induced when K^+ or H^+ diffusion potentials are generated across the chromatophore membranes. Chromatophores were first treated with valinomycin, an ionophoretic antibiotic which specifically increases the K^+ permeability of membranes. KCl was then injected into the chromatophore suspensions, and a red shift of the carotenoid absorbance bands was observed.

After such a salt injection, but before equilibrium is reached, the membrane potential, $\Delta\psi$, which is induced should obey the relation (Goldman, 1943; Barber and Varley, 1972; see also Dilley, 1971):

$$\Delta\psi = \frac{RT}{F} \ln \frac{P_c[C]_o + P_a[A]_i}{P_c[C]_i + P_a[A]_o} \tag{14}$$

where R, T and F are the gas constant, the absolute temperature, and the Faraday constant, respectively. P_c and P_a are the membrane permeability coefficients for the cation and the anion. $[C]_o$, $[A]_o$, $[C]_i$ and $[A]_i$ are the outside and inside concentrations of the cation and anion.

Jackson and Crofts find that the magnitude of the carotenoid shift induced by KCl injection is linearly related to the calculated value of the membrane potential. Strichartz and Chance (1971) have obtained similar results in a study of the 515 nm change in chloroplasts.

A portion of the light-induced carotenoid change in bacteria has a rise time of less than 10^{-7} second (Baltscheffsky, 1969). Crofts *et al.* (1971) suggested that the reaction center bacteriochlorophyll may lie near the inner surface of the chromatophore membrane and the primary acceptor may lie near the outer surface (Fig. 3). The fast carotenoid change may then occur in response to the transmembrane dipole created by the primary electron transfer. Crofts also recognized the parallelism between the carotenoid change and delayed fluorescence. If the primary donor and acceptor were oriented as suggested in the membrane, he pointed out, a membrane potential (inside positive) would facilitate the return of an electron from the acceptor to the donor. Such an effect would be expected to lower the

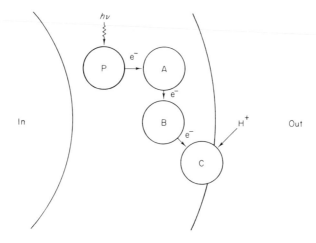

FIG. 3. Proposed arrangement of electron carriers in the membranes of bacterial chromoatophores. P is reaction center chlorophyll; A, B, and C are electron acceptors. Arrows indicate direction of normal electron flow.

activation energy for the transfer of an electron from the acceptor into the excited singlet of the chlorophyll, and Eq. (10) may be modified as follows (Fleischman, 1971a) (Fig. 4):

$$L = \Phi NFe^{-(E - \Delta\psi)/kT} \tag{15}$$

Independently, Barber and Kraan (1970) found that the KCl-induced light emission from chloroplasts is stimulated severalfold by valinomycin. The dependence of luminescence intensity upon the amount of

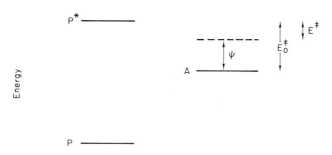

FIG. 4. Proposed effect of membrane potential on the activation energy for light emission. P and P° are the ground and lowest excited singlet levels of reaction center chlorophyll. A is the highest filled level of the reduced primary acceptor, A. $E_o^{\ddagger}$ is the activation energy for light emission in the absence of a membrane potential, ψ. $E^{\ddagger}$ is the actual activation energy.

KCl injected reveals that the luminescence intensity is proportional to the exponential of the induced membrane potential. Barber and Kraan suggested that the membrane potential reduces the activation energy for light emission. Kraan *et al.* (1970) independently proposed a delayed fluorescence model similar to that of Crofts. A relation similar to Eq. (15) is now generally accepted by the workers cited in this paragraph.

Crofts *et al.* (1971) have expanded the equation further to include the effect of a pH gradient explicitly.

Barber and Varley (1972) have performed a very careful study of the relationship between light emission and the membrane potential induced by salt injection. The predicted exponential relation is obeyed

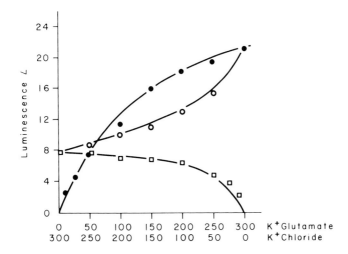

FIG. 5. Initial luminescence intensity induced by various concentrations of potassium chloride (open squares) and potassium glutamate (filled circles). The curves have been drawn according to the equations given below and correspond to $P_{Cl}/P_k = 0.11$ and $P_{Gl}/P_k = 0.03$. The third set of points (open circles) show the luminescence induced by adding mixtures of potassium chloride and glutamate keeping the external K^+ concentration constant at 300 mM. The curve was drawn for this mixture experiment according to the equation given. Taken from Barber and Varley (1972).

Equations: K^+ glutamate $\quad L = \dfrac{[K]_o}{5 + 0.03 \, (Glu)_o}$

Mixture $\qquad\quad L = \dfrac{300}{5 + 0.11 \, [Cl]_o + 0.03 \, [Glu]_o}$

K^+ chloride $\qquad L = \dfrac{(K)_o}{5 + 0.11 \, [Cl]_o}$

for a number of potassium salts. The diffusion potential resulting from the addition of a mixture of salts can be calculated with the use of a generalized form of Eq. (14). Barber and Varley find that light emission accompanying the injection of salt mixtures has the behavior that is predicted from the permeability coefficient ratios measured in experiments with the individual salts (Fig. 5). Experiments in which potassium benzoate is included do not conform to this pattern, however. It appears that benzoate has an additional affect which is not yet understood.

VII. Flash Activation of Luminescence

The study of photosynthesis (oxygen production) following a small number of short flashes, in contrast to the study of the integrated rate during flashing light such as that of Emerson and Arnold (1932), started with the work of Allen and Franck (1955). They reported no oxygen production following a single flash, but that oxygen was produced by a pair of flashes. This work has been extended by a number of the workers, the most recent being Joliot *et al.* (1971) and Kok *et al.* (1970). Forbush *et al.* (1971) showed that oxygen production is a cyclic function of the flash number. The period of the cycle is 4 flashes and the maximum yield of oxygen production occurs with flash 3.

Kok *et al.* (1970) postulated a scheme to explain the results of their investigation of flash activation of oxygen evolution. Diagrammatically the scheme is as follows:

$$S_0 \xrightarrow{h\nu} S_1 \xleftarrow{\quad} \xrightarrow{h\nu} S_2 \xleftarrow{\quad} \xrightarrow{h\nu} S_3 \xleftarrow{\quad} \xrightarrow{h\nu} S_4 \longrightarrow O_2$$

where the different S's are different oxidation states of a precursor of oxygen. S_1 is very stable. Therefore, approximately 75% of S will be in the S_1 state following a period of time in the dark.

Barbieri *et al.* (1970), Joliot *et al.* (1971), and Zankel (1971) have investigated delayed fluorescence as a function of flash number. The Paris group studied the delayed fluorescence of *Chlorella*, measuring light emission at delay times greater than 30 msec. They found that delayed fluorescence was an oscillatory function of the flash number with a period of 4. The peak delayed fluorescence occurred following flashes 2 and 6. Measuring delayed fluorescence at shorter times (milliseconds and shorter), Zankel (1971) found that the delayed fluorescence peaked following flashes 3 and 7.

Joliot *et al.* concluded that states S_2 and S_3 were involved in the delayed fluorescence they measured, but that the "oscillations in whole algae are mainly due to the very rapid deactivation of S_3."

We have extended this type of study to the flash number dependence of chemically induced light emission. All the chemically induced luminescence studies — pH jump, reduction with dithionite, and salt induced — follow the same flash activation pattern as the delayed fluorescence of *Chlorella* measured at this time, the peak light emission following flash 2 (Mayne and Hobbs, 1971a,b) (Figs. 6 and 7).

In an endeavor to obtain a chemically induced luminescence in a system which showed oscillations of delayed fluorescence with flash number, Mayne and Hobbs (1971b) found that the injection of a sodium benzoate solution into a *Chlorella* suspension caused an increase in the light emission. In agreement with Joliot *et al.* (1971), our chloroplasts do not show a consistent pattern in their flash activation of delayed fluorescence, measured with a delay time of seconds. This increase in light emission appears to be an integration of the remaining potential for delayed light emission. This luminescence follows the same oscillation pattern, frequency and phase, as delayed fluorescence measured at this time.

Owing to the similarity of the phase relation between delayed fluorescence and chemically induced luminescence, we conclude that the same S states are probably the source of the oxidation reduction potential necessary to excite the chlorophyll to the excited singlet state in both cases.

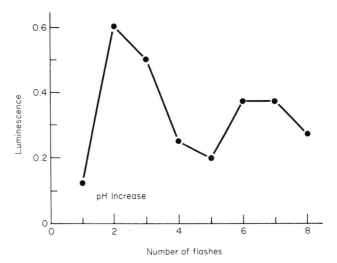

FIG. 6. pH increase induced luminescence of spinach chloroplasts as a function of flash number. One milliliter of a chloroplast suspension containing 21 μg of chlorophyll, 0.05 M tricine, pH 7.4, and 0.01 M KCl was exposed to the indicated number of flashes from an EG&G FX 12-.25 flash lamp operated at 1000 V and 2 μf. Five seconds after the last flash, 0.5 ml of 0.04 M succinic acid was injected; 5 seconds later, 1 ml of 0.2 M Tris base.

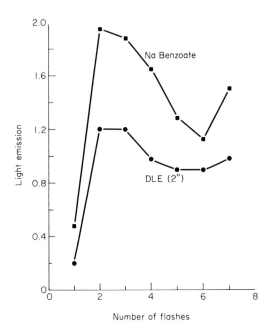

FIG. 7. Delayed fluorescence and sodium benzoate-induced luminescence. The illumination conditions were the same as in Fig. 6. One milliliter of a 1.5 M sodium benzoate solution was injected into 1 ml of a suspension of *Chlorella pyrenoidosa* 2 seconds after the last flash. The delayed fluorescence was measured 2 seconds after the last flash. The delayed fluorescence and benzoate-induced luminescence are not on the same scale.

VIII. Conclusion

It is perhaps appropriate to end as we began, with an experiment of William Arnold. Arnold and Azzi (1971) reported that delayed fluorescence from spinach chloroplasts becomes as much as 60 times brighter if electrodes are placed in the cuvette and a voltage is applied. The light intensity increases roughly as the cube of the voltage in the region from 0 to 200 V/cm. If an alternating voltage is used, the effect disappears at frequencies greater than 2×10^4 cycles/second.

The reason for the effect has not been firmly established. Perhaps a significant fraction of the total voltage drop appears across the thylakoid membranes. If a membrane potential can indeed be so induced by an externally applied field, it could provide a powerful new tool for the study not only of light emission, but of the entire range of interactions between electron transport and membrane potential.

ACKNOWLEDGMENTS

This work was partially supported by a National Science Foundation Grant GB1756. We wish to thank Mrs. R. Roper and Mrs. S. Miller for their excellent secretarial help in the preparation of this manuscript.

C. F. Kettering Research Laboratory Contribution No. 465.

REFERENCES

Allen, F. L., and Franck, J. (1955). *Arch. Biochem. Biophys.* **58**, 124.

Arnold, W. (1966). *Science* **154**, 1046.

Arnold, W., and Azzi, J. R. (1968). *Proc. Nat. Acad. Sci. U.S.* **64**, 211.

Arnold, W., and Azzi, J. R. (1971). *Photochem. Photobiol.* **14**, 233.

Arnold, W., and Sherwood, H. (1959). *J. Phys. Chem.* **63**, 2.

Arnon, D. I., Allen, M. B., and Whatley, F. R. (1954). *Nature (London)* **174**, 394.

Baltscheffsky, M. (1967). *Nature (London)* **216**, 241.

Baltscheffsky, M. (1969). *In* "Progress in Photosynthesis Research," p. 1306. Laupp, Tübingen.

Barber, J., and Kraan, G. P. B. (1970). *Biochim. Biophys. Acta* **197**, 49.

Barber, J., and Varley, W. J. (1972). *J. Exp. Bot.* **23**, 216.

Barbieri, R., Delosme, R., and Joliot, P. (1970). *Photochem. Photobiol.* **12**, 197.

Bennoun, P. (1970). *Biochim. Biophys. Acta* **216**, 357.

Bertsch, W. F. (1962). *Proc. Nat. Acad. Sci. U.S.* **48**, 2000.

Bertsch, W. F. (1969). *In* "Progress in Photosynthesis Research," p. 996. Laupp, Tübingen.

Bertsch, W. F., Azzi, J. R., and Davidson, J. B. (1967). *Biochim. Biophys. Acta* **143**, 129.

Bishop, N. I. (1958). *Biochim. Biophys. Acta* **27**, 205.

Björn, L. O., and Sigfridsson, B. (1971). *Physiol. Plant.* **25**, 308.

Bonaventura, C., and Myers, J. (1969). *Biochim. Biophys. Acta* **189**, 366.

Butler, W. L. (1966). *Curr. Top. Bioenerg.* **1**, 49.

Chance, B., Crofts, A. R., Nishimura, M., and Price, B. (1970). *Eur. J. Biochem.* **13**, 364.

Clayton, R. K. (1966a). *Brookhaven Symp. Biol.* **19**, 62.

Clayton, R. K. (1966b). *Photochem. Photobiol.* **5**, 807.

Clayton, R. K. (1969). *Biophys. J.* **9**, 61.

Cohen, W. S., and Sherman, L. A. (1970). *FEBS Lett.* **16**, 319.

Crofts, A. R., Wraight, C. A., and Fleischman, D. E. (1971). *FEBS Lett.* **15**, 89.

Dilley, R. A. (1971). *Curr. Top. Bioenerg.* **4**, 237.

Döring, G., Renger, G., Vater, J., and Witt, H. T. (1969). *Z. Naturforsch. B* **24**, 1139.

Duysens, L. N. M. (1966). *Brookhaven Symp. Biol.* **19**, 71.

Duysens, L. N. M. (1971). *Proc. Eur. Biophys. Congr., 1st, 1971* Vol. IV, p. 13.

Duysens, L. N. M., and Sweers, H. E. (1963). *In* "Studies on Microalgae and Photosynthetic Bacteria," p. 353. Jap. Soc. Plant Physiol., Tokyo.

Duysens, L. N. M., Amesz, J., and Kamp, B. B. (1961). *Nature (London)* **190**, 510.

Emerson, R., and Arnold, W. (1932). *J. Gen. Physiol.* **16**, 19.

Fleischman, D. E. (1967). *Abstr. Biophys. Soc., 11th Annu. Meet.* WE7.

Fleischman, D. E. (1969). *In* "Progress in Photosynthesis Research," p. 952. Laupp, Tübingen.

Fleischman, D. E. (1970). *Abstr. Biophys. Soc., 14th Annu. Meet.* FAM-E8.

Fleischman, D. E. (1971a). *Photochem. Photobiol.* **14**, 177.

Fleischman, D. E. (1971b). *Photochem. Photobiol.* **14**, 65.
Fleischman, D. E., and Clayton, R. K. (1968). *Photochem. Photobiol.* **8**, 287.
Fleischman, D. E., and Cooke, J. A. (1971). *Photochem. Photobiol.* **14**, 159.
Forbush, G., Kok, B., and McGloin, M. P. (1971). *Photochem. Photobiol.* **14**, 307.
Frenkel, A. (1954). *J. Amer. Chem. Soc.* **76**, 5568.
Goedheer, J. C. (1962). *Biochim. Biophys. Acta* **64**, 294.
Goldman, D. E. (1943). *J. Gen. Physiol.* **27**, 37.
Greville, C. D. (1969). *Curr. Top. Bioenerg.* **3**, 1.
Hardt, H., and Malkin, S. (1971). *Photochem. Photobiol.* **14**, 483.
Hardt, H., and Malkin, S. (1972). *Biochem. Biophys. Res. Commun.* **46**, 668.
Hind, G., and Jagendorf, A. T. (1963). *Proc. Nat. Acad. Sci. U.S.* **49**, 715.
Hind, G., and Jagendorf, A. T. (1965). *J. Biol. Chem.* **240**, 3195.
Holt, A. S., and Clayton, R. K. (1965). *Photochem. Photobiol.* **4**, 829.
Izawa, S., Winget, G. D., and Good, N. E. (1966). *Biochem. Biophys. Res. Commun.* **22**, 223.
Jackson, J. B., and Crofts, A. R. (1969). *FEBS Lett.* **4**, 185.
Jagendorf, A. T., and Hind, G. (1963). *Nat. Acad. Sci. — Nat. Res. Counc. Publ.* **1145**, 599.
Jagendorf, A. T., and Uribe, E. (1966a). *Brookhaven Symp. Biol.* **19**, 215.
Jagendorf, A. T., and Uribe, E. (1966b). *Proc. Nat. Acad. Sci. U.S.* **55**, 170.
Joliot, P., Joliot, A., Bouges, B., and Barbieri, R. (1971). *Photochem. Photobiol.* **14**, 287.
Junge, W., and Witt, H. T. (1968). *Z. Naturforsch. B* **23**, 244.
Jursinic, P., and Govindjee (1972). *Photochem. Photobiol.* **15**, 331.
Knox, R. S. (1969). *Biophys. J.* **9**, 1351.
Kok, B., Forbush, B., and McGloin, M. (1970). *Photochem. Photobiol.* **11**, 457.
Kraan, G. P. B. (1971). Ph.D. Thesis, University of Leiden, Leiden, The Netherlands.
Kraan, G. P. B., Amesz, J., Velthuys, B. R., and Steemers, R. G. (1970). *Biochim. Biophys. Acta* **223**, 129.
Lavorel, J. (1968). *Biochim. Biophys. Acta* **153**, 727.
Lavorel, J. (1969). *In* "Progress in Photosynthesis Research," p. 883. Laupp, Tübingen.
Lavorel, J. (1971). *Photochem. Photobiol.* **14**, 261.
McCarty, R. E., Guillory, R. J., and Racker, E. (1965). *J. Biol. Chem.* **240**, 4822.
Mayne, B. C. (1965). *Biochim. Biophys. Acta* **109**, 59.
Mayne, B. C. (1966). *Brookhaven Symp. Biol.* **19**, 460.
Mayne, B. C. (1967). *Photochem. Photobiol.* **6**, 189.
Mayne, B. C. (1968). *Photochem. Photobiol.* **8**, 107.
Mayne, B. C. (1969). *In* "Progress in Photosynthesis Research," p. 947. Laupp, Tübingen.
Mayne, B. C., and Clayton, R. K. (1966). *Proc. Nat. Acad. Sci. U.S.* **55**, 494.
Mayne, B. C., and Hobbs, L. J. (1971a). *Abstr. Biophys. Soc., 15th Annu. Meet.* TPMD16.
Mayne, B. C., and Hobbs, L. J. (1971b). *Abstr. Amer. Soc. Plant Physiol. Meet., 1971* p. 31.
Miles, C. D., and Jagendorf, A. T. (1969). *Arch. Biochem. Biophys.* **129**, 711.
Miles, C. D., and Jagendorf, A. T. (1970). *Biochemistry* **9**, 429.
Mitchell, P. (1961). *Nature (London)* **191**, 144.
Mitchell, P. (1966). *Biol. Rev. Cambridge Phil. Soc.* **41**, 445.
Mitchell, P., and Moyle, J. (1968). *Eur. J. Biochem.* **7**, 471.
Murata, N., Tashiro, H., and Takamiya, A. (1970). *Biochim. Biophys. Acta* **197**, 250.
Neumann, J. S., and Jagendorf, A. T. (1964). *Arch. Biochem. Biophys.* **107**, 109.
Papageorgiou, G. (1968). Ph.D. Thesis, University of Illinois, Urbana, Illinois.

Pearlstein, R. M. (1966). *Brookhaven Symp. Biol.* **19**, 8.

Randall, J. T., and Wilkins, M. H. F. (1945). *Proc. Roy. Soc., Ser. B* **184**, 372.

Robinson, G. W. (1966). *Brookhaven Symp. Biol.* **19**, 16.

Ross, R. T., and Calvin, M. (1967). *Biophys. J.* **7**, 595.

Rubin, A. B., and Venediktov, P. S. (1969). *Biofizika* **14**, 107.

Shen, Y. K., and Shen, G. M. (1962). *Sci. Sinica* **11**, 1097.

Shuvalov, V. A., and Litvin, F. F. (1969). *Mol. Biol.* **3**, 45.

Skulachev, V. P. (1971). *Curr. Top. Bioenerg.* **4**, 127.

Slater, E. C. (1971). *Quart. Rev. Biophys.* **4**, 35.

Stiehl, H. H., and Witt, H. T. (1968). *Z. Naturforsch. B* **23**, 220.

Strehler, B. L., and Arnold, W. (1951). *J. Gen. Physiol.* **34**, 807.

Strehler, B. L., and Lynch, V. H. (1957). *Res. Photosyn., Pap. Discuss. Gatlinburg Cont., 1955* p. 89.

Strichartz, G., and Chance, B. (1971). *Biochim. Biophys. Acta* **256**, 71.

Tollin, G., Fujimori, E., and Calvin, M. (1958). *Proc. Nat. Acad. Sci. U.S.* **44**, 1035.

Uribe, E. G., and Jagendorf, A. T. (1967a). *Plant Physiol.* **42**, 697.

Uribe, E. G., and Jagendorf, A. T. (1967b). *Plant Physiol.* **42**, 706.

Witt, H. T., Rumberg, B., Junge, W., Döring, G., Stiehl, J., Weikard, J., and Wolff, C. (1969). *In* "Progress in Photosynthesis Research," p. 1361. Laupp, Tübingen.

Wraight, C. A., and Crofts, A. R. (1970). *Eur. J. Biochem.* **17**, 319.

Wraight, C. A., and Crofts, A. R. (1971). *Eur. J. Biochem.* **19**, 386.

Zankel, K. L. (1971). *Biochim. Biophys. Acta* **245**, 373.

Zankel, K. L., Reed, D. W., and Clayton, R. K. (1968). *Proc. Nat. Acad. Sci. U.S.* **61**, 1243.

The Reducing Side of Photosystem I[1]

JAMES SIEDOW,[2] CHARLES F. YOCUM,[3] and ANTHONY SAN PIETRO
Department of Plant Sciences,
Indiana University,
Bloomington, Indiana

"In order to reach the Truth, it is necessary,
once in one's life, to put everything in doubt."
Descartes

I. Introduction

Some years ago, Martin Kamen associated the various time eras of photosynthesis with a corresponding "level of ignorance" (cf. Fig. 1, Kamen, 1963). To set into proper focus the material which follows, we have borrowed this approach to provide in Fig. 1 a "redox spectrum of knowledge." There is a great deal of information available concerning the electron carriers functional in the intermediate regions of the redox scale, i.e., approximately -0.42 V (ferredoxin) to $+0.43$ V (P700).

[1]Part of the research described herein was supported by research grant GM 16314 (to A.S.P.) from the National Institutes of Health, United States Public Health Service.
[2]Present address: Department of Biophysics, University of Michigan, Ann Arbor, Michigan.
[3]Present address: Department of Biochemistry and Molecular Biology, Cornell University, Ithaca, New York.

In the extreme regions (< -0.42 V and $> +0.4$ V), we are less knowledgeable concerning reaction mechanisms and cofactors involved as indicated by the decreased height of the shaded area in the figure. It is well established that illuminated chloroplasts have the capacity to reduce electron acceptors with redox potentials more negative than -0.42 V (Kok *et al.*, 1965; Zweig and Avron, 1965; Black, 1966; Brune and San Pietro, 1970). Within the past several years a multiplicity of factors have been cast sequentially in the role of the natural,

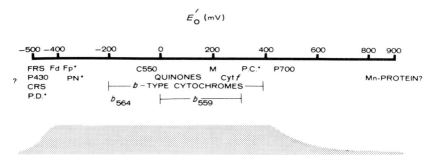

FIG. 1. Redox spectrum of knowledge. The ordinate of the shaded area is "index of knowledge" and the abscissa is redox potential. The height of the shaded area denotes knowledge, CRS, cytochrome reducing substance; Fd, ferredoxin; Fp, Fd-NADP reductase; FRS, ferredoxin reducing substance; PC, plastocyanin; PD, photoredoxin; PN, pyridine nucleotides.

low potential (< -0.42 V) primary acceptor for photosystem I of photosynthesis. This is the topic under consideration herein. The evidence to date; namely, low-temperature EPR spectroscopy (Malkin and Bearden, 1971, 1972; Leigh and Dutton, 1972) and kinetics of repetitive flash spectrophotometry (Hiyama and Ke, 1971a,b), best supports the view that the natural acceptor is a bound nonheme iron protein.[4]

In a similar vein, at the oxidizing end of the redox scale (Fig. 1), little is known of the mechanism of oxygen evolution. There is good evidence for the involvement of manganese in this process (Cheniae, 1970), but the intimate details for the extraction of four electrons from water to release molecular oxygen is completely unknown. Interestingly, a similar correlation can be made for mitochondria solely at the

---

[4]The various notations used for the bound nonheme iron protein are: bound nonheme iron protein (Malkin and Bearden, 1971); P430 (Hiyama and Ke, 1971a); and photoredoxin (P. L. Dutton, personal communication, 1972).

positive end of the redox scale where the reverse reaction occurs, namely, a four-electron reduction of molecular oxygen to yield water.

II. FRS, ORS, and S_{L-ETH}

Yocum and San Pietro (1969, 1970) found that vigorous sonication of osmotically shocked chloroplasts produced chloroplast fragments with low rates of NADP reduction. These fragments, fractionated by density-gradient centrifugation or gel filtration, showed higher rates of NADP reduction when supplemented with a factor termed "ferredoxin reducing substance" (FRS). A rate vs concentration plot of FRS gave rise to saturation kinetics, suggesting that FRS was acting catalytically in the assay system. Under anaerobic conditions, substrate amounts of photoreduced FRS were capable of reducing ferredoxin added in a succeeding dark step. Photoreduction of methyl viologen was not observed with FRS-depleted subchloroplast fragments, but this activity was restored by adding FRS to the fragments. Cytochrome reducing substance (CRS; see below), like FRS, enhanced viologen reduction but did not stimulate NADP reduction when added back to FRS-depleted fragments. These studies indicated that FRS and CRS act at, or near the level of, the primary electron acceptor for photosystem I.

Subsequent studies done in collaboration with Drs. T. Hiyama and B. Ke of the C. F. Kettering Research Laboratory, showed that FRS-depleted chloroplast fragments retained a P700 photooxidation signal (Yocum, 1971). This spectral change can be separated into two kinetically distinct phases, one fast and one slow. The fast phase represents presumably the return of an electron from the primary acceptor, X^-, to $P700^+$ (Rumberg, 1964), and the slow phase arises from donation of electrons to $P700^+$ from the oxidizing side of the photoact. In the FRS-depleted fragments, addition of ferredoxin decreased the extent of the fast recovery phase, indicating an efficient electron acceptor function for ferredoxin. In contrast, addition of both ferredoxin and ferredoxin-NADP reductase was without effect; i.e., the extent of the fast recovery phase was the same as that observed with particles alone. It appeared that ferredoxin together with ferredoxin-NADP reductase did not enhance loss of electrons from the photoact possibly because a complex was formed between ferredoxin and ferredoxin-NADP reductase which was a poor electron acceptor. However, when all three factors were provided, namely, FRS, ferredoxin, and ferredoxin–NADP reductase, the extent of the fast-recovery phase was again decreased. This latter result indicates most probably that FRS could serve as an electron-transfer component mediating electron flow from the photoact to the complex between ferredoxin and ferredoxin–NADP reductase.

Chemical characterization of FRS indicated that it consists of a prosthetic group (perhaps an isoflavone molecule) and a small peptide. The molecular weight of FRS, as estimated by gel filtration, is about 5000.

The principal difficulty encountered in studies of FRS has been the method of extraction, namely sonication. While chloroplast fragments prepared by this procedure retain normal physiological properties (i.e., requirements for plastocyanin, ferredoxin, and ferredoxin–NADP reductase), basal rates of NADP reduction from an ascorbate–DPIP donor system have been extremely variable, and it must be concluded that sonication is not a reproducible method for extraction of FRS. Alternative methods of extraction using chemical procedures have so far been unsuccessful. Until a reproducible method is found for extraction of FRS without the concomitant destruction of chloroplast function, it is impossible to define unequivocally the exact site of action of FRS on the reducing side of photosystem I.

Honeycutt and Krogmann (1970, 1972) examined an oxygen reducing system present in the blue-green alga *Anabaena variabilis*, and isolated the factor, termed oxygen reducing substance (ORS), responsible for catalysis of this activity. By careful study of oxygen uptake in the presence of the artificial electron donor system $TCIPH_2$, it was shown that two donor sites exist in the algal electron transport chain. One site, operative at low donor concentrations, required plastocyanin or algal cytochrome c and was more sensitive to temperature and pH than the second site, which was functional at higher donor concentrations and not dependent on the presence of plastocyanin or cytochrome c. It was further shown that oxygen reduction proceeded only when $TCIPH_2$ was present as the electron donor. Electrons from water (photosystem II) could not serve for oxygen reduction.

Later studies on oxygen reduction by intact algal lamellae showed that the factor catalyzing this reaction was present in a concentration of 10 equivalents per chlorophyll molecule. Extraction of lamellae by the procedure used to release CRS liberated the factor (ORS) responsible for oxygen uptake. Extracted lamellae exhibited depressed rates of oxygen and methyl viologen reduction, and both activities were stimulated by addition of ORS. Particles depleted of ORS showed a low extent of photooxidation of endogenous cytochrome f. This photooxidation was not restored by methyl viologen, but added

ORS restored it to the level observed in non-ORS-depleted lamellae. The estimated molecular weight of ORS is between 3000 and 4000.

Regitz *et al.* (1970) showed that when chloroplast fragments were injected into rabbits, antibodies against various photosystem I elec-

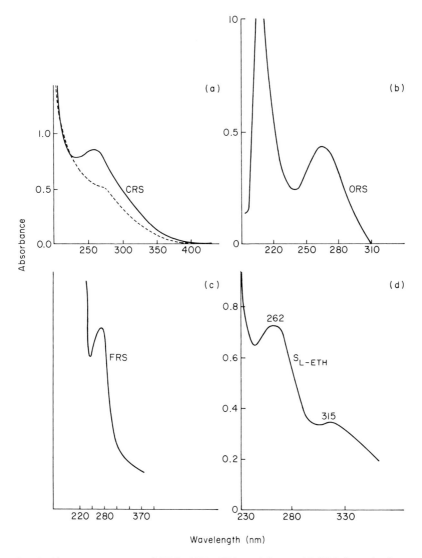

FIG. 2. Absorption spectra of CRS, ORS, FRS, and $S_{L\text{-ETH}}$. (a) CRS from *Anabaena*. From Fugita and Myers (1966a). Solid line, without borohydride; dotted line, with borohydride. (b) ORS from *Anabaena*. From Honeycutt (1971). (c) FRS from spinach. From Yocum and San Pietro (1970). (d) $S_{L\text{-ETH}}$ from spinach. From Regitz *et al.* (1970).

tron transport activities were elaborated. Using anthroquinone photo-reduction as the assay system, they were able to isolate a water-soluble factor (S_{L-ETH}) from lyophilized, ether-treated chloroplasts which reversed the inhibition of anthroquinone reduction caused by the antibody preparation designated as [11]C_{10}. Tests by Yocum and San Pietro (1970) and Honeycutt and Krogmann (1970) indicated that [11]C_{10} inhibition was common to their systems, and either FRS or ORS reversed the antibody inhibition of photoactivity (NADP or oxygen reduction). These results strongly suggest that FRS, ORS, and S_{L-ETH} (perhaps also CRS) have a common identity. For purposes of comparison, the absorption spectra of these four factors are presented in Fig. 2.

III. CRS

The existence of a cytochrome reducing substance (CRS) was suggested originally by Fugita and Myers (1966a) from studies of cytochrome c (mammalian) redox reactions in lamellar fragments of the blue-green alga *Anabaena cylindrica*. They observed that under anaerobic conditions the lamellar fragments were capable not only of oxidizing ferrocytochrome c in the light but, more surprisingly, could reduce the photoproduced ferricytochrome c back to its original redox level in the subsequent dark period. This light–dark reversibility was taken as evidence for the presence of a "pool" of redox substance(s) associated with the reducing side of photosystem I. A detailed kinetic analysis of this system (Fugita and Murano, 1967) revealed that the chlorophyll a : CRS ratio was about 5, assuming CRS to be a single electron carrier. The association with photosystem I was based on two observations: (1) the lamellar fragments were devoid of Hill reaction activity with DPIP as an electron acceptor; and (2) the cytochrome c redox reactions were insensitive to DCMU (Fugita and Myers, 1966b).

Initial attempts to isolate CRS suggested that it was rather tightly bound to the membrane system since neither repeated washing, sonication, detergent treatment, nor extraction with nonpolar solvents released the factor. Extraction of CRS from the membranes was achieved finally through the use of polar solvents, such as acetone.

Chemically, CRS was characterized as a heat-stable, water-soluble component of molecular weight approximately 3000–4000. It exhibited a single absorbance maximum at 260 nm which was bleached temporarily by borohydride (Fugita and Myers, 1966c). No attempts to characterize further CRS have been reported. In addition to *Anabaena*, fractions with CRS activity have also been isolated from red algae, green algae, and spinach chloroplasts (Fugita and Myers, 1966c).

Extraction of CRS from *Anabaena* yielded lamellar fragments whose ability to catalyze cytochrome *c* redox reactions was greatly reduced but could be restored upon addition of purified CRS (Fugita and Myers, 1966b). The reconstituted activity (in either direction) was linear with respect to the amount of CRS added. Likewise, under aerobic conditions, only the oxidation of the ferrocytochrome *c* was observed and this activity was dependent on the presence of CRS. It should be noted that both the extent and rate of the cytochrome *c* redox reactions were enhanced by the addition of CRS to depleted lamellar fragments.

In addition to the reactions described above, CRS stimulated pseudocyclic photophosphorylation catalyzed by isolated spinach chloroplasts (Fugita and Murano, 1967), but no direct evidence for the participation of CRS in photosynthetic electron transport was ever presented. However, Fugita and Murano (1967) made the interesting observation that when CRS was extracted from spinach chloroplast membranes, there resulted a marked inhibition of NADP photoreduction but only a minimal inhibition of methyl viologen-mediated oxygen uptake. Attempts to restore NADP reduction by the readdition of purified CRS, however, were unsuccessful.

IV.   P430, Bound NHI, and Photoredoxin

Hiyama and Ke (1971a,b) have described a new spectral species, termed P430, based on its spectral minimum (light minus dark difference spectrum). This new component of the photosynthetic electron transport chain was detected by a kinetic analysis of the biphasic nature of the dark recovery of photooxidized P700. Two kinetically separable and distinct recovery phases (P700$^+$ reduction) were clearly evident: the rapid phase (presumably P700$^+$ reduction by P430$^-$; P430$^-$ + P700$^+$ → P430 + P700) was affected (decreased by the presence of an electron acceptor, such as methyl viologen; the slower phase (presumably the reduction of P700$^+$ by an electron donor other than P430$^-$) was affected (increased) by the presence of an electron donor, such as TMPD.

An isosbestic point at 444 nm in the spectrum for P700 photooxidation facilitated the study of P430 kinetics. Direct measurements of P430 showed that increasing concentrations of acceptors, such as methyl viologen, increased the rate of P430 dark decay. More notably, spinach ferredoxin was effective in stimulating the dark decay of P430. Light minus dark kinetic difference spectroscopy has revealed the presence of P430, observable as a broad negative absorption band, in several photosynthetic organisms (Fig. 3c). Extension of these spectra farther into the red has failed to detect any other spectral changes attributable to P430. The chemical nature of P430 remains unknown, although its midpoint potential has been estimated to be -0.47 V (Ke, 1972).

Malkin and Bearden (1971) demonstrated by chemical analysis the presence of large amounts of bound NHI protein (1 per 75 chloro-

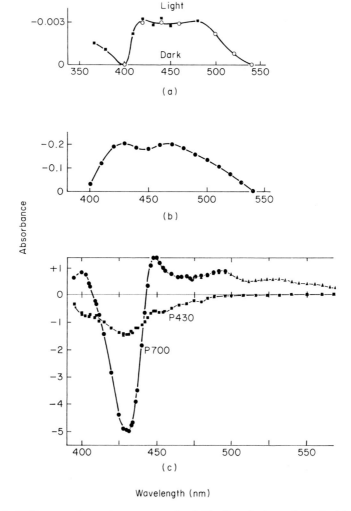

Wavelength (nm)

FIG. 3. Difference absorption spectra of soluble ferredoxin and P430. (a) and (b) Soluble ferredoxin, light minus dark and reduced minus oxidized difference absorption spectra, respectively. From Chance and San Pietro (1963). (c) Light minus dark difference absorption spectrum of P430. From Hiyama and Ke (1971b).

phylls) in chloroplasts freed of soluble ferredoxin. Upon illumination of chloroplasts at 77°K and subsequent cooling to 25°K, an EPR signal with g values of 2.05, 1.94, and 1.86 was obtained; the $g = 1.94$ signal is characteristic of nonheme iron proteins (Fig. 4a and b). Initially,

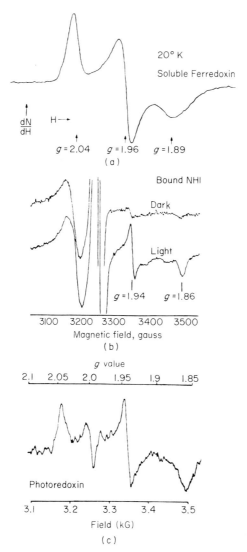

FIG. 4. EPR spectra of soluble ferredoxin, bound NHI, and photoredoxin[4]. (a) Reduced, soluble spinach ferredoxin. From Malkin and Bearden (1971). (b) Light-induced spectrum of bound NHI in washed, broken spinach chloroplasts. From Malkin and Bearden (1971). (c) Light minus dark spectrum of photoredoxin in spinach chloroplasts. From Leigh and Dutton (1972).

the illumination time required to produce this signal was 20 minutes. An estimation of the redox potential of this bound NHI protein was obtained by chemical reduction with either dithionite or Cleland's reagent and subsequent low-temperature electron paramagnetic resonance (EPR) spectroscopy. The signal appeared only with di-thionite as the reductant, indicating that chloroplast-bound NHI has a potential below that of Cleland's reagent (−0.33 V).

In a later study (Malkin and Bearden, 1972), the EPR signal was evident after a much shorter illumination period (< 100 msec), the limitation on accurate estimation of this parameter being the rise time of the EPR spectrometer. Furthermore, the signal could be generated by illumination with either long (715 nm) or short (645 nm) wave-length light. It was observed both with photosystem (PS) II and PS I enriched subchloroplast particles prepared by digitonin treatment of whole chloroplasts.

Leigh and Dutton (1972) have also observed light-induced low temperature EPR spectra attributable to bound NHI (photoredoxin[4]) in preparations from *Chromatium* D and spinach chloroplasts (Fig. 4c). By redox poising of the *Chromatium* system, the potential of the bound NHI in this organism was estimated to be −0.28 V. The corre-sponding value for the chloroplast system is < −0.42 V (P. L. Dutton, personal communication).

To summarize thus far (Sections II–IV), it is evident that two differ-ent (chemically and physically) but functionally related groups of electron carriers have been identified. Their sequential role in elec-tron transfer on the reducing side of photosystem I (of photosynthesis) may be depicted as follows:

$$
P700 \xrightarrow{\text{PS I}} \left\{ \begin{array}{l} \text{Bound NHI} \\ \text{P430} \\ \text{Photoredoxin} \end{array} \right\} \longrightarrow \left\{ \begin{array}{l} \text{FRS} \\ \text{ORS} \\ \text{CRS} \\ \text{S}_{\text{L-ETH}} \end{array} \right\} \longrightarrow \text{Fd}
$$

Clearly those compounds which have been isolated from chloro-plasts (FRS, ORS, $S_{\text{L-ETH}}$, and possibly CRS; Fig. 2) share a common identity with regard to reversal of antibody inhibition, general chemical and physical properties, and site of action, namely, the re-ducing side of PS I. They all appear to be tightly bound to the chloro-plast membrane as evidenced by the drastic procedures required for their release. Organic extraction (CRS, ORS, and $S_{\text{L-ETH}}$) destroys the usefulness of the extracted membranes for subsequent assay of NADP photoreduction activity, and attempts at extraction with retention of this activity (FRS) led to problems with regard to reproducibility.

The discovery of a light-induced EPR signal attributable to a reduced bound NHI suggests that this type protein may serve as the primary acceptor. It is reasonable to assume further that the absorbance change at 430 nm (P430) may reflect reduction of a bound NHI. The difference absorption spectra of soluble ferredoxin and P430 are presented in Fig. 3. The molar difference extinction coefficient (oxidized minus reduced) of P430 is reported to be about 12,000 assuming equal concentrations of P430 and P700 in the chloroplast. This value is much too high (about 2.5 times) by comparison to that reported for soluble ferredoxin (Fry and San Pietro, 1963). This may, however, be an unwarranted and premature comparison since neither the mode of binding of the NHI protein nor the effect of binding on the properties of the NHI protein can be evaluated at this time. It is obvious that the nature and identity of the primary acceptor for PS I remains a fruitful topic for further investigation.

V. "310" Factor

Recently, Siedow and San Pietro (1972) reported the isolation and purification of a factor which showed a pronounced ability to inhibit NADP photoreduction catalyzed by isolated spinach chloroplasts. The factor was released from the chloroplasts upon sonication (in dilute pyridine) of osmotically shocked chloroplasts.

As noted initially, the factor inhibited NADP photoreduction when either ascorbate or water served as the electron donor. Kinetically, this inhibition was shown to be competitive with respect to ferredoxin suggesting that the factor acts at or near the site of ferredoxin reduction in the photosynthetic electron transport pathway. In this regard, the ferredoxin-mediated reductions of both nitrite and mammalian cytochrome c are inhibited as well by the factor. This could mean simply that the factor can serve to direct electrons to oxygen. However, of further interest as regards nitrite reduction is the observation that the factor is inhibitory even under anaerobic conditions. This latter observation could mean that the factor can mediate a cyclic electron flow around PS I.

The factor also stimulates the basal rate of mammalian cytochrome c reduction catalyzed by illuminated chloroplasts in the absence of any added ferredoxin. Studies utilizing polylysine, a specific inhibitor of photosystem I (Brand et al., 1971), have established the fact that this basal rate of cytochrome c reduction is PS I mediated. In addition, like the chromophore of Wu and Myers' D-2 factor (1970) (see below), the "310" factor stimulates the rate of pseudocyclic photophosphorylation catalyzed by spinach chloroplasts.

The purified factor has an absorption spectrum (maximum at 310 nm) essentially the same as the purified chromophore of Wu and Myers' D-2 factor (1970). Similar fluorescence spectra, pH behavior, and chemical properties strongly suggest that the two factors represent the same compound. Analysis by gel filtration and mass spectrometry reveal the molecular weight to be about 200. In addition, none of the physiological activities are affected by either heat (100°C) or treatment with proteolytic enzymes, and there would appear to be no requirement for the presence of a protein moiety in the action of the factor. As with the D-2 chromophore, the chemical identity of the factor is unknown.

All this would seem to indicate that the factor acts on the reducing side of PS I at or prior to the site of ferredoxin. What its physiological role might be has yet to be elucidated. However in light of the observed inhibition of nitrite reduction, under anaerobic conditions, by the factor, it is tempting to speculate that it may play a role in mediating some form of cyclic electron flow associated with PS I. There is at present no substantial evidence to support this hypothesis, however.

VI. D-2 Factor

In 1969 Wu and Myers reported the isolation of a blue fluorescent protein factor from spinach chloroplasts which they called simply the D-2 factor. It stimulated not only pseudocyclic photophosphorylation (analogous to the Saltman and Gee protein factor and phosphodoxin), but also the chloroplast-mediated photoreduction of NADP. It was further noted that treatment of the D-2 factor with 70% acetone led to the release of a chromophore from the peptide from which it could be conveniently separated by chromatography on Sephadex G-25 (Wu and Myers, 1970). The chromophore exhibited a single absorption maximum at 310 nm and a marked fluorescence in the blue (440 nm). The absorption at 310 nm underwent a reversible shift to 355 nm upon treatment with alkali suggestive of some form of deprotonation. It was further shown that the chromophore itself was capable of stimulating photophosphorylation in a manner analogous to the holo D-2. No mention was made of the effect, if any, of the chromophore on NADP reduction.

Of even more interest, however, was the finding that the chromophore contained covalently bound phosphorus and that, in the presence of illuminated chloroplasts and $^{32}P_i$, there was incorporation of $^{32}P_i$ into the chromophore. Based on this latter result, Wu and Myers (1970) suggested a direct involvement of the D-2 factor in photophosphorylation. Unfortunately, the exact chemical nature of the chromophore was not determined.

of the 315 nm bleaching leaves open the possibility that something other than electron transport is responsible for this change.

To summarize, there are rather marked similarities in the spectral (see Fig. 5) and chemical characteristics of the "310" Factor (Siedow and San Pietro, 1972), the D-2 factor (Wu and Myers, 1969), phosphodoxin (Black *et al.*, 1963) and the protein factor (Saltman and Gee, 1966) all of which stimulate pseudocyclic photophosphorylation.

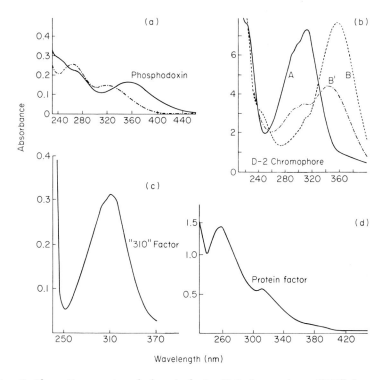

FIG. 5. Absorption spectra of phosphodoxin, D-2 chromophore, "310" factor, and protein factor. (a) Phosphodoxin from spinach. From Black *et al.* (1963). Solid line, 0.1 N NaOH; dashed line, 0.1 N HCl. (b) D-2 chromophore from spinach. From Wu and Myers (1970). Curve A, 0.1 N HCl; curve B, immediately after dissolving in 0.1 N NaOH; curve B', after 24 hours in 0.1 N NaOH. (c) "310" factor from spinach. From Siedow and San Pietro (1972). (d) Protein factor from spinach. From Saltman and Gee, (1966).

There are some differences, however: (1) With three of the factors, the small molecular weight chromophoric group alone is capable of stimulating photophosphorylation while the isolated chromophore of the protein factor (Saltman and Gee, 1966) is not. This result is rather surprising in light of the marked similarity of the four factors; (2) in addition, the molecular weight of the protein factor (15,000) is much higher than that of the D-2 factor (5,000) or phosphodoxin and the "310" factor (probably below 500). These differences may simply be the result of the varied isolation techniques employed, and it is tempting to speculate that the active component of all four factors is the same compound (or type of compound) and that the protein moiety either (1) represents merely a convenient site of attachment of the active factor or (2) is fragmented differentially by the various isolation techniques such that varying size species of a single larger component remain.

IX. Concluding Remarks

To conclude as begun, some years ago electron transport on the reducing side of photosystem I seemed rather straightforward. One could write simply

$$PS\ I \longrightarrow \text{"X"} \longrightarrow Fd$$

and therein hide our ignorance within the confines of the symbolic temple of the unknown, "X." The intervening years have witnessed increased information concerning this pathway as evidenced by the multiplicity of new factors described herein. The pathway is now so overcrowded with factors that is perhaps resembles more the proverbial training maze used by psychologists. We might ask: Has our knowledge or our ignorance or both increased during this time? Perhaps it is more the latter, and we can conclude that "Knowledge Begets More Questions."

ACKNOWLEDGMENT

The authors thank Mr. Richard A. Halverson for preparing the figures. Figures 2–5 are reprinted with permission of the publishers and authors.

REFERENCES

Black, C. C. (1966). *Biochim. Biophys. Acta* **120**, 332.
Black, C. C., and San Pietro, A. (1963). *In* "Bacterial Photosynthesis" (H. Gest, A. San Pietro, and L. P. Vernon, eds.), p. 227. Antioch Press, Yellow Springs, Ohio.
Black, C. C., San Pietro, A., Limbach, D., and Norris, G. (1963). *Proc. Nat. Acad. Sci. U.S.* **50**, 37.
Black, C. C., San Pietro, A., Norris, G., and Limbach, D. (1964a). *Plant Physiol.* **39**, 279.
Black, C. C., Heise, J., and San Pietro, A. (1964b). *Biochim. Biophys. Acta* **88**, 57.
Brand, J., Baszynski, T., Crane, F. L., and Krogmann, D. W. (1971). *Biochem. Biophys. Res. Commun.* **45**, 533.
Brune, D., and San Pietro, A. (1970). *Arch. Biochem. Biophys.* **141**, 371.

Chance, B., and San Pietro, A. (1963). *Proc. Nat. Acad. Sci. U.S.* **49**, 633.

Cheniae, G. M. (1970). *Annu. Rev. Plant Physiol.* **21**, 467.

Commoner, B., Heise, J. J., and Townsend, J. (1956). *Proc. Nat. Acad. Sci. U.S.* **42**, 710.

Fry, K., and San Pietro, A. (1963). *Nat. Acad. Sci.–Nat. Res. Counc., Publ.* **1145**, 252.

Fugita, Y., and Murano, F. (1967). *Plant Cell Physiol.* **8**, 269.

Fugita, Y., and Myers, J. (1966a). *Plant Cell Physiol.* **7**, 599.

Fugita, Y., and Myers, J. (1966b). *Arch. Biochem. Biophys.* **113**, 730.

Fugita, Y., and Myers, J. (1966c). *Arch. Biochem. Biophys.* **113**, 738.

Gee, R., Kylin, A., and Saltman, P. (1970). *Biochem. Biophys. Res. Commun.* **40**, 642.

Hiyama, T., and Ke, B. (1971a). *Proc. Nat. Acad. Sci. U.S.* **68**, 1010.

Hiyama, T., and Ke, B. (1971b). *Arch. Biochem. Biophys.* **147**, 99.

Honeycutt, R. C. (1971). Ph.D. Dissertation, p. 140, Purdue University, Lafayette, Indiana.

Honeycutt, R. C., and Krogmann, D. W. (1970). *Biochim. Biophys. Acta* **197**, 267.

Honeycutt, R. C., and Krogmann, D. W. (1972). *Biochim. Biophys. Acta* **256**, 467.

Kamen, M. D. (1963). "Primary Processes in Photosynthesis." Academic Press, New York.

Ke, B. (1972). *Arch. Biochem. Biophys.* **152**, 70.

Kok, B., Rurainski, H. J., and Owens, O. V. H. (1965). *Biochim. Biophys. Acta* **109**, 347.

Leigh, J. S., and Dutton, P. L. (1972). *Biochem. Biophys. Res. Commun.* **46**, 414.

Malkin, R., and Bearden, A. J. (1971). *Proc. Nat. Acad. Sci. U.S.* **68**, 16.

Malkin, R., and Bearden, A. J. (1972). *Biochem. Biophys. Res. Commun.* **46**, 1299.

Regitz, G., Berzborn, R., and Trebst, A. (1970). *Planta* **91**, 8.

Rumberg, B. (1964). *Z. Naturforsch. B* **19**, 707.

Saltman, P., and Gee, R. (1966). *In* "Symposium on the Use of Isotopes in Plant Nutrition and Physiology," sm 77/25. IAEA, Vienna.

Siedow, J. N., and San Pietro, A. (1972). *Fed. Proc., Fed. Amer. Soc. Exp. Biol.* **31**, 461.

Wu, M., and Myers, J. (1969). *Arch. Biochem. Biophys.* **132**, 430.

Wu, M., and Myers, J. (1970). *Arch. Biochem. Biophys.* **140**, 391.

Yocum, C. F., and San Pietro, A. (1969). *Biochem. Biophys. Res. Commun.* **36**, 614.

Yocum, C. F., and San Pietro, A. (1970). *Arch. Biochem. Biophys.* **140**, 152.

Yocum, C. F. (1971). Ph.D. Dissertation, p. 55, Indiana University, Bloomington, Indiana.

Zweig, G., and Avron, M. (1965). *Biochem. Biophys. Res. Commun.* **19**, 347.

The Chemistry of Vertebrate and Invertebrate Visual Photoreceptors

Edwin W. Abrahamson and Roger S. Fager
Department of Chemistry,
Case Western Reserve University,
Cleveland, Ohio

I. Introduction

Vision is unique among the sensory processes in that molecules in the sensory cell membranes which actually receive the primary stimulus, i.e., the absorption of visible light, have very singular spectral properties. Being long-chain conjugated polyenes of high extinction and polarizability, their spectra serve as sensitive probes of their microenvironments. Furthermore, changes in their native spectra initiated by the absorption of light give us considerable insight into the sequence of molecular changes in the visual pigments themselves as well as their membrane milieux. The fact that these spectral changes can now be measured precisely on a time scale of the order of milliseconds and less, concomitant with early electrophysiological events, points to the imminent possibility of directly relating molecular and neural events in sensory membranes. In addition, visual photoreceptor membranes and their constituent pigments can be obtained conveniently in large quantity and in high purity. This ready biochemical accessibility of visual pigments and the sensitivity, specificity, and comparative ease of their mensuration clearly make visual pigment membranes an ideal prototype system not only for the study of sensory processes but for membrane processes in general.

In this review we focus attention on the comparative properties of vertebrate and invertebrate photoreceptor pigments and their membranes. The value of such a direct comparison is that it points up the major similarities and differences of the two systems and in so doing underscores those characteristics intrinsic to the visual process.

II. The Structure of Visual Photoreceptor Cells

Visual photoreceptor cells in the animal kingdom are of two basic types, the ciliary cell of vertebrates and allied phyla and the rhabdomeric cell of the invertebrate phyla (Eakin, 1965, 1972). Both types of cells possess an inner and outer segment. The inner segment contains the cell nucleus, mitochondria, and synthetic machinery while the outer segment contains the visual pigment embedded in tightly packed membranes.

A. CILIARY PHOTORECEPTORS

Typical of the ciliary photoreceptors is the vertebrate rod cell associated with low light level black and white vision (Figs. 1A, 1B, and 1C). The outer segment consists of a stack of unitary pancakelike membranes called saccules or discs, which contain the visual pigment, rhodopsin. These discs, which typically number about 500, enclose an aqueous region and the entire stack is itself sheathed by a plasma membrane. The outer segment, therefore, is partitioned into two internal aqueous regions, the intradiscal enclosed by the disc, and the

FIG. 1A. Schematic view of a vertebrate rod cell. OS, outer segment; CC, connecting cilium; MIT, densely packed mitochondria; NUC, nucleus; SYN-synaptic terminal.

intracellular enclosed by the plasma membrane. Of the two regions the intracellular has, by far, the larger total volume.

The function of the two aqueous compartments is not known. It is clear, however, that the tight stacking of the discs (repeat distance 320 Å) provides a very large surface area containing a high concentration of visual pigment molecules, which by virtue of their high absorbancy and quantum yield of photobleaching (Section V) affords a great sensitivity to light. In fact, the eye is sensitive to as few as 5 quanta (Hecht *et al.*, 1942), which would indicate that the rod cell is essentially a quantum counter.

The inner and outer segments of the rod cell are connected by a modified cilium (Fig. 1C). Very recent studies in our own laboratory suggest that for the bovine rod the cilium consists of nine peripheral tubules surrounding a central structure of the axis (Mason *et al.*, 1973c).

The cone cell which is associated with color vision in some vertebrates has much the same structure as the rod cell. So few cones are

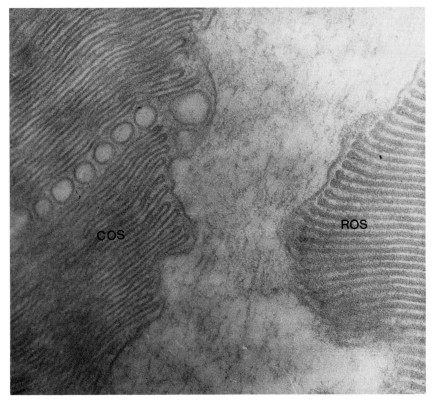

FIG. 1B. Adjacent bovine rod and cone outer segments. Note the looseness of the cone discs relative to that of the rods. The line of vesicles in the cone cell may represent the mechanism by which new disc membranes are formed or else by which the membranes are catabolized ($\times 74{,}580$). From Mason *et al.* (1973c).

present in the visual vertebrate retina compared to rods ($\sim 1{:}25$ in the bovine retina, Fig. 1B, 2) that their isolation is difficult, and hence the properties of their pigments and pigment membranes are not nearly as well known as those of rods.

B.   RHABDOMERIC PHOTORECEPTORS

The rhabdomeric photoreceptor cells of invertebrates, like the ciliary photoreceptor cells, have an inner and outer segment, but unlike them, possess no cilium. There is only a single internal aqueous compartment along the axis of the outer segment which is surrounded by a tightly packed cluster of fingerlike projections of the plasma membrane (microvilli), oriented perpendicular to the axis (Figs. 3A, 3B, and 4A). The walls of the microvilli appear to contain the visual

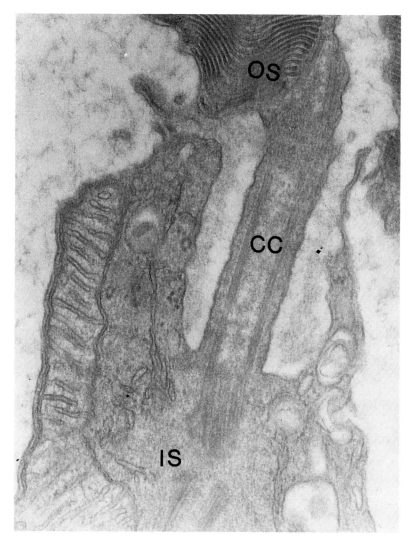

FIG. 1C. The narrow neck connecting the inner and outer segments of a bovine rod cell. OS, outer segment; IS, inner segment; CC, connecting cilium. From Mason *et al.* (1973c).

pigment molecules and presumably function as the sensory membrane. Several such cells are organized into clusters called rhabdomes.

III. Properties of Visual Pigments and Their Membranes

A. THE COMPOSITION OF OPSIN

Rhodopsin is extracted from rod outer segments with aqueous de-

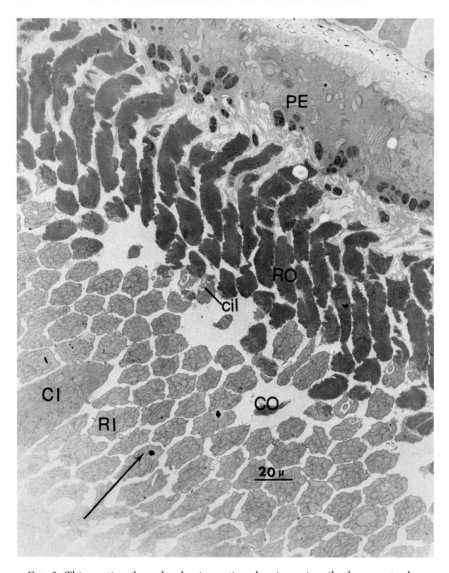

FIG. 2. Thin section through a bovine retina showing primarily the receptor layer. RO, rod outer segment; CO, cone outer segment; Cil, connecting cilium; CI, cone inner segment; RI, rod inner segment; PE, pigment epithelium. Arrow indicates approximate direction of incident light. In the inner segments note the dense packing of mitochondria. From Mason *et al.* (1973c).

tergents as a conjugated lipoprotein. The protein moiety stripped of chromophore and lipid has traditionally been called *opsin*. The amino acid composition and molecular weight of this protein after purification by various techniques is reported in Tables I and II. One

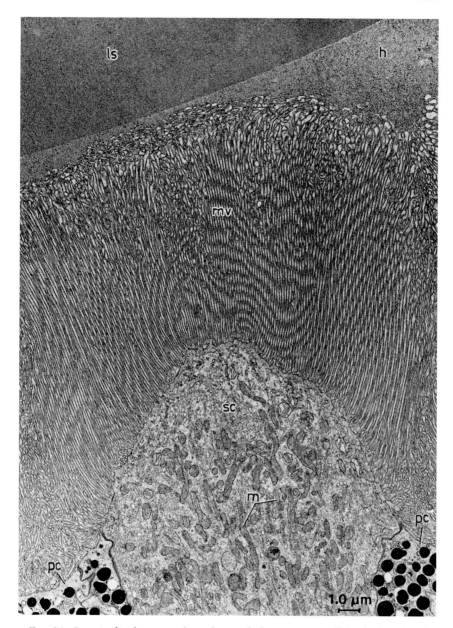

FIG. 3A. Longitudinal section through tip of photosensory cell (psc) of snail *Helix aspersa*. h, humor; ls, lens; mv, microvilli; pc, pigmented cells; m, mitochondria. Eakin and Brandenberger, from Eakin (1968).

notes that the amino acid compositions and molecular weights are roughly the same ($\sim$ 28,000) for all vertebrate opsins with the excep-

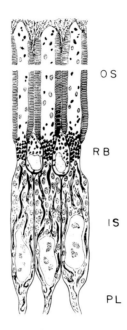

FIG. 3B. Sketch by Zonana (1961) based on a thin sectioning study of the squid retina. OS, outer segment, in this case facing toward the light; RB, rod base; IS, inner segment; PL, plexiform layer.

tion of the latest one for frog opsin (Robinson *et al.*, 1972), although in this case the mole fractions of the constituent amino acids are in harmony with the earlier determination (Heller, 1969). In contrast the molecular weight of squid opsin is about twice that of vertebrate opsin.

All the determinations of rhodopsin composition point to it as being highly hydrophobic, with approximately 50% hydrophobic amino acid residues. Recently Reporter and Reed (1972) have reported that several amino groups in the lysine side chains are methylated, further enhancing its hydrophobic character.

The hydrophobic character is particularly prominent in the region of the chromophore binding site in illuminated rhodopsin. Bownds (1967) found a highly hydrophobic decapeptide containing the chromophore after reducing illuminated rhodopsin with NaBH$_4$ and hydrolyzing with pronase. In our laboratory, P. G. Millar (unpublished observations, 1967) found a highly hydrophobic chromophore-containing peptide having 26 amino acids purified from tryptic hydrolyzates. Still another peptide, actually a glycopeptide, was isolated and se-

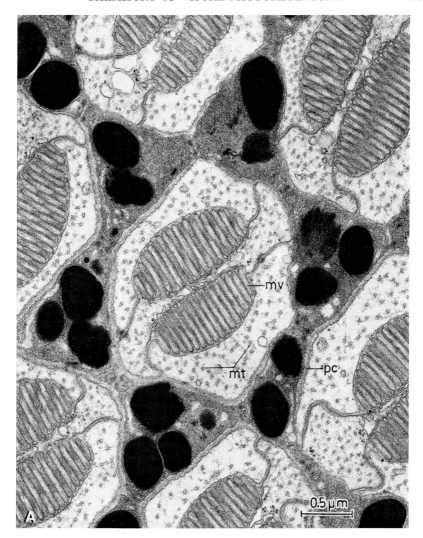

FIG. 4A. Cross section of several retinal units in anterolateral eye of jumping spider, *Phidippus johnsoni*. mt, Microtubules; pc, pigmented cell. Eakin and Brandenberger, from Eakin (1972).

quenced by Heller and Lawrence (1970) from enzymatic hydrolyzates. They suggested that it might function to orient the molecule in the membrane.

We have determined the composition of the squid rhodopsin (Kimbel *et al.*, 1973) and also find it to have a highly hydrophobic

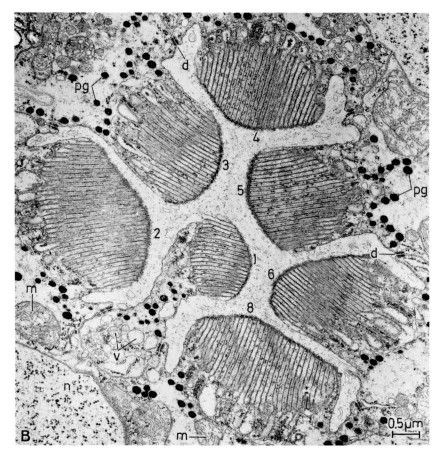

FIG. 4B. Cross section of rhabdom of fruit fly, *Drosophila melanogaster*. The numbering indicates the eight individual cells or rhabdomeres which make up the rhabdom;
d, demosomers; m, mitochondria; n, nucleus; pg, pigment granules; and v, pinocytotic
vesicles.

opsin moiety with about the same proportion of hydrophobic residues (50%) as vertebrate opsin. However, the detailed composition is
greatly different; all but four of the mole fractions of amino acids differ
from vertebrate rhodopsin by greater than 20%.

B. The Lipid Composition of Visual Pigment Membranes

Since rhodopsin is an integral part of a membrane, it is of interest
to know what the physical properties of that membrane are. Chemically, evidence can be obtained as to the rigidity or fluidity of the
membrane by analysis of its lipid composition. The presence of

TABLE I

AMINO ACID COMPOSITIONS OF VISUAL PIGMENTS (RHODOPSINS)
EXPRESSED AS RESIDUES PER MOLE

	Bovine rhodopsin			Rat	Frog		Squid
	a	b	c	d	d	e	f
Asp	18	15	19	16	15	27.7	50
Thr	20	17	25	18	16	25.2	22
Ser	17	12	15	13	17	21.7	44
Glu	21	21	25	21	20	24.7	71
Gly	19	16	21	16	15	23.7	49
Tyr	11	11	10	11	13	19.5	28
Lys	13	10	8	10	10	15.6	34
His	6	4	4	4	4	6.8	7
Arg	10	6	6	6	6	9.0	16
Pro	19	13	16	14	14	19.5	60
Ala	22	20	25	19	18	29.1	67
1/2Cys	6	5	6	6	6	18.0	9
Val	20	20	15	18	18	24.4	27
Met	8	8	8	9	9	14.5	30
Ile	14	13	13	13	15	21.6	44
Leu	22	20	20	20	19	27.9	38
Phe	21	19	22	18	18	29.0	32
Trp	6	6	–	4	4	12.0	10
MW	28,600	27,707	27,700	27,769	28,023	41,200	70,200

[a]Shields et al., 1967.
[b]Heller, 1968a.
[c]Shichi et al., 1969.
[d]Heller, 1969.
[e]Robinson et al., 1972.
[f]Kimbel et al., 1973.

largely saturated fatty acids in the phospholipid side chains enables close packing and gives rise to a rigid matrix, whereas membranes with a high proportion of polyunsaturates cannot pack as well because of the kink in the molecule formed by the double bonds, and consequently such a membrane is much more fluid in nature. Cholesterol is a component which tends to lend rigidity to the membrane structure.

Several laboratories have studied the lipid composition of bovine rod outer segments and are in fundamental agreement (Table III). The total lipid is approximately 40% by dry weight. The membrane lipids are predominantly phospholipids, and phosphatidylcholine and phosphatidylethanolamine together make up 70–80% of the phospho-

TABLE II

AMINO ACID COMPOSITION OF VISUAL PIGMENTS
ON A MOLE FRACTION BASIS

	Bovine rhodopsin				Rat	Frog		Squid
	a	b	c	d	e	e	f	g
Asp	6.6	6.7	6.4	7.3	6.8	6.3	6.3	7.9
Thr	7.3	7.6	7.2	9.6	7.6	6.8	6.9	3.4
Ser	6.2	1.7	5.1	3.9	5.5	7.2	6.0	6.9
Glu	7.7	12.2	8.9	9.6	8.9	8.4	6.3	11.2
Gly	7.0	8.0	6.8	8.0	6.8	6.3	6.5	7.7
Tyr	4.0	4.6	4.7	4.8	4.7	5.5	5.4	4.4
Lys	4.8	2.5	4.2	3.1	4.2	4.2	4.3	5.3
His	2.2	1.3	1.7	1.6	1.7	1.7	1.9	1.1
Arg	3.7	2.5	2.6	2.3	2.5	2.5	2.5	2.5
Pro	7.0	6.3	5.5	6.1	5.9	5.9	5.2	9.4
Ala	8.1	8.8	8.5	9.6	8.0	7.6	8.0	10.5
1/2Cys	2.2	1.7	2.1	2.3	2.5	2.5	4.9	1.4
Val	7.3	7.2	8.5	5.7	7.6	7.6	6.7	4.2
Met	2.9	3.4	3.4	3.1	3.8	3.8	4.0	4.7
Ile	5.1	5.6	5.5	3.8	5.5	6.3	5.9	6.9
Leu	8.1	8.4	8.5	7.7	8.5	8.0	7.6	5.9
Phe	7.7	8.8	8.1	8.4	7.6	7.6	8.0	5.0
Trp	2.2	2.9	2.1	–	1.7	1.7	3.3	1.6

[a]Shields et al., 1967.
[b]Azuma and Kito, 1967.
[c]Heller, 1968a.
[d]Shichi et al., 1969.
[e]Heller, 1969.
[f]Robinson et al., 1972.
[g]Kimbel et al., 1973.

lipids, with smaller amounts of phosphatidylserine, sphingomyelin, and phosphatidylinositol. The percentage of cholesterol is very small. An interesting observation is that on silica gel plates and on columns the phosphatidylcholine could be resolved into two distinct fractions; it is unclear what the functional significance of these two resolvable components might be (Nielsen et al., 1970).

The fatty acid composition of the bovine rod outer segments shows a striking concentration of long-chain, polyunsaturated fatty acids and the most singular characteristic is the presence of an extremely high proportion of docosahexenoic acid (22:6). It occurs in highest proportion in phosphatidylethanolamine (see Table IV). Recently in this laboratory we have determined the lipid fatty acid composition of frog photoreceptors (Mason et al., 1973c). They appear to have a

TABLE III

LIPID COMPOSITION OF PHOTORECEPTOR OUTER SEGMENTS

Component	Bovine								Frog i	Squid j
	a	b	c	d	e	f	g	h		
Total lipid	37.3	39.0	38.9	38.8	—	—	—	48.0	40.6	49.4
Phospholipid	25.8	31.5	—	31.5	—	28	27.8		26.6	38.0
Retinal	0.10	0.14	—	—	.098	—	—		—	—
Cholesterol	—	3.1	—	0.9	—	—	—		1.7	10.1
Triglyceride										13.1
Glycolipid	—	—	—	—	—	—	—		9.5	—
Total protein	62.7	61.0	61.1	61.2	—	70	—		59.4	51.6
Rhodopsin as a lipoprotein	14.0	19.6	—	—	14.0	—	—		—	0
Protein portion only	9.0	12.6	—	—	9.0	—	—		50.0	22.0
Phosphatidylethanolamine	37.5	39.2	—	51.0	—	—	38.6	47.2	25.2	50.2
Phosphatidylserine	7.3	11.2	—	11.7	—	—	13.3	13.8	9.5	3.6
Phosphatidylcholine	51.3	36.4	—	31.0	—	—	40.2	38.8	49.4	32.1
Phosphatidylinositol	—	—	—	—	—	—	2.3	1.7	—	trace
Sphingomyelin	1.5	1.0	—	6.3	—	—	3.6	1.5	1.8	10.0
Other phospholipids	2.5	8.6	—	—	—	—	2.1	1.7	9.2	2.2

[a] Poincelot and Zull, 1969; Poincelot and Abrahamson, 1970b.
[b] Borggreven et al., 1970.
[c] Adams, 1967.
[d] Sjöstrand, 1959.
[e] Hubbard, 1953.
[f] Collins et al., 1952.
[g] Anderson and Maude, 1970.
[h] Nielsen et al., 1970.
[i] Eichberg and Hess, 1967.
[j] Mason et al., 1973a.

TABLE IV

FATTY ACID COMPOSITION OF PHOTORECEPTORS

	Total lipid			Rho-dopsin	Bovine rod outer segments						Squid rhabdome		
					Phosphatidyl-ethanolamine		Phosphatidyl-choline		Phosphatidyl-serine		Phos-phatidyl-ethanolamine	Phos-phatidyl-choline	Sphingo-myelin
	a	b	c	a	a	d	a	d	a	d	e	e	e
12:0	Trace	—	—	Trace	Trace	—	Trace	—	0.4	—	1.4	2.8	4.6
13:0	—	—	—	—	—	—	—	—	—	—	3.9	1.5	4.9
14:0	0.2	(<16.0)	(<16.0)	0.5	0.5	Trace	0.5	1.6	1.7	2.0	6.7	8.7	10.6
15:0	Trace	—	—	0.5	0.5	Trace	0.5	1.6	1.7	2.0	6.7	8.7	10.6
16:0	18.6	19.4	13.1	10.1	15.3	10.3	26.2	32.3	11.8	3.3	3.0	3.9	2.5
16:1	0.1	0.8	0.5	0.3	0.2	0.7	2.3	2.3	3.7	2.3	—	—	—
16:1	—	—	0.2	—	—	—	—	—	—	—	1.2	3.5	5.7
17:0	Trace	0.6	—	0.3	0.3	Trace	0.2	1.4	2.1	—	4.3	1.2	0.6
17:1											10.6	11.9	7.6
18:0	23.5	23.1	18.9	19.9	19.4	21.9	22.7	17.7	14.3	19.2	4.7	6.3	1.8
18:1	7.6	6.4	4.4	9.9	6.4	6.1	8.9	10.7	8.5	5.4	4.0	4.5	5.2
18:2	0.8	1.4	0.5	1.6	1.0	2.2	0.9	1.8	1.2	1.9	6.4	5.4	4.7
18:3	0.2	—	0.2	0.4	1.4	—	1.6	—	1.4	—	0.8	0.1	0.7

Fatty acid	1	2	3	4	5	6	7	8	9	10	11	12	13
19:0	—	—	—	—	—	—	—	—	—	—	—	—	—
20:0	0.2	—	—	0.4	1.7	0.9	0.3	0.8	2.5	1.3	—	—	—
20:1	0.2	—	—	Trace	Trace	1.1	Trace	0.4	0.8	1.0	5.3	1.8	0.7
20:2	3.2	—	—	0.2	Trace	1.1	Trace	Trace	0.4	0.5	5.6	7.4	3.8
20:3	1.0	—	—	0.5	1.1	1.1	0.3	0.6	0.4	1.3	5.8	1.2	4.2
20:4	7.0	6.0	8.4	8.3	9.4	5.0	8.2	4.3	4.7	3.0	8.2	2.1	1.1
20:5	—	—	—	—	—	Trace	—	—	—	1.7	—	5.4	1.9
21:0	0.6	—	—	0.4	0.7	—	Trace	—	0.8	—	—	1.3	—
22:0	0.3	—	—	0.6	Trace	—	1.0	—	0.4	—	5.9	—	—
22:1	0.4	—	—	0.8	Trace	—	0.9	—	12.8	—	—	4.0	4.2
22:2	—	—	—	—	—	3.4	—	1.1	—	6.8	3.7	—	—
22:4	—	1.5	3.6	—	—	5.7	—	2.0	—	5.6	3.8	2.4	11.0
22:5	—	1.2	—	—	—	—	—	—	—	—	—	1.2	12.8
22:6	22.6	34.3	37.2	25.7	29.3	31.7	16.6	20.6	16.8	31.8	—	2.0	—
24:0	1.5	—	—	0.3	Trace	24:x1.4	Trace	24:xtr	1.2	24:x10.0	—	—	—
24:1	5.0	—	—	3.4	3.9	—	2.3	—	2.3	—	—	—	—
24:2	6.7	—	—	5.1	8.0	—	5.7	—	3.6	—	—	—	—
un-	0.2	4.71	11.2	1.0	10.9	—	0.0	—	6.8	—	—	—	—

[a] From Poincelot and Abrahamson, 1970b.
[b] Borggreven et al., 1970.
[c] Nielsen et al., 1970.
[d] Anderson and Maude, 1970.
[e] Mason et al., 1973a.

typically fluid composition, i.e., a low cholesterol content and a high percentage of long chain polyunsaturated fatty acids. These fatty acids, however, differ significantly in composition from those found in bovine photoreceptors. While no other isolated mammalian photo-receptors have been analyzed for fatty acid composition, Anderson has determined the fatty acid composition of whole retinas of human, rabbit, rat, pig, and dog (Anderson, 1970). He finds that docosahexanoic acid is a prominent component in all of them and occurs in the highest proportion in phosphatidylethanolamine. The saturated fatty acids of the bovine rod are almost entirely stearic (18:0) and palmitic (16:0) acids.

The phosphatidylcholine component is somewhat more tightly bound to the bovine rod since extraction of lyophilized rods with hexane removes phosphatidylethanolamine preferentially and leaves the rods richer in phosphatidylcholine (Poincelot and Abrahamson, 1970b; Borggreven et al., 1970). Other membranes show similar behavior.

Confirmation of the fluidlike character of the pigment-containing membranes of frog rods comes from Blasie and Worthington's study of the temperature dependence of their low angle X-ray diffraction pattern. The diffraction maxima broaden in a way that suggests increased temperature brings a greatly increased thermal motion of the proteins in the membrane — something that would be expected in a liquidlike membrane (Blasie et al., 1969; Worthington, 1971).

A problem which merits greater study is the nature of the glyco-lipid components of the retinal rods, since the sugar chains from these glycolipids probably have a significant influence on the surface properties of the membrane. Eichberg and Hess (1967) report that 26% of the frog rod lipids are glycolipids. In this laboratory, we have recently determined that glycolipids make up 19% of the bovine mem-brane lipids and 27% of the frog membrane lipids (Mason et al., 1973c; W. T. Mason and R. S. Fager, unpubl. results).

The lipid composition of squid outer segments, which has recently been studied in this laboratory, differs from bovine outer segments (Tables III and IV). The fatty acid composition differs in that the overall level of unsaturation is significantly less. Similarly docosa-hexenoic acid is present in less than half of its proportion in verte-brate outer segments. Furthermore the unsaturation is spread over a much larger range of chain lengths. Whereas there are virtually no fatty acids in the bovine rod with fewer than 16 carbons, about 20% of the squid fatty acids are in this class. There are also major differ-ences in the relative proportions of the lipid classes present. Tri-glycerides and cholesterol, which are almost absent from bovine outer segment lipids, are found in large quantity in the squid rhabdomes.

The two together amount to over 20% of the total lipids. Sphingomyelin is somewhat higher and phosphatidylserine is somewhat lower than in the vertebrate outer segments. As in vertebrate outer segments, phosphatidylcholine and phosphatidylethanolamine are the dominant phosphatides and, again, between them make up approximately 80% of the total phospholipid content (Mason *et al.*, 1972a). Our most recent studies have shown squid photoreceptor glycolipid to be approximately 50% of membrane lipid.

It is clear from the differences in fatty acid and cholesterol composition that the squid invertebrate photoreceptor membrane is significantly more rigid than that of the vertebrates.

C. Rhodopsin as a Lipoprotein

Studies by Broda (1941) and Krinsky (1958) showed clearly that rhodopsin in aqueous detergent suspensions behaved as a lipoprotein. The lipid molecules could not be completely removed by prolonged electrodialysis or by hexane extraction of the dried micelles.

If dark-adapted, lyophilized rods are exhaustively extracted with petroleum ether, exposed to light, and then reextracted, an additional amount of lipid is released (Ishimoto and Wald, 1946; Krinsky, 1958). This also demonstrates that the rhodopsin molecule interacts significantly with phospholipid of the membrane. Poincelot and Abrahamson (1970b) carried the same procedure further; namely, they showed that if the rhodopsin is extracted at the metarhodopsin$_{478}$I stage, 4 extra moles of phospholipid per mole of rhodopsin (i.e., 4 moles/mole greater than in the dark) are released, and if the reaction is allowed to proceed to metarhodopsin$_{380}$II an additional 8 extra moles of phospholipid per mole of rhodopsin are released. Recently, in our laboratory, a similar pattern of phospholipid release has been observed to occur in squid rhabdomes (Mason *et al.*, 1973b).

Since the molecular function of rhodopsin is not known, there is a problem in defining precisely the native state of this visual pigment. So far the only acceptable criterion has been the integrity of the 500 nm absorption band of the spectrum. The visible spectrum of vertebrate rhodopsin is unchanged by solubilization in a variety of detergents and by treatments which remove a large proportion of the phospholipids, such as phospholipase treatment or chromatography on Sephadex G-200 (Heller, 1969a; Borggreven *et al.*, 1971).

Recently evidence has been assembled that phospholipids should be regarded as an integral part of native vertebrate rhodopsin and that the maintenance of the 500 nm band may not be an adequate parameter by which to assess the condition of rhodopsin. It has now been found that, whether or not it is possible to completely remove rhodopsin phospholipids and maintain the integrity of the visible spectrum, phospholipids are essential to the rhodopsin integrity (Shichi, 1971a,b). Thus when the lipids have been removed from rhodopsin by either phospholipase treatment or organic solvent extraction, the normal behavior of rhodopsin alters in two important properties, its regenerability and its circular dichroism spectrum after illumination.

When rhodopsin in digitonin solution is bleached by light and 11-cis-retinal is added, the 500 nm band gradually returns as the 11-cis-retinal is incorporated into its structure (Wald and Brown, 1950). However, Zorn (1971) and Shichi (1971a) demonstrated that in lipid-stripped preparations this regeneration does not take place but can be restored by the addition of phospholipid. Shichi has studied the circular dichroism spectrum of rhodopsin and its changes on light exposure (Shichi, 1971a,b). He finds that at wavelengths less than 240 nm, where the circular dichroism spectrum reflects changes in protein conformation, there is very little change on exposure to light for rhodopsin in membrane fragments or in digitonin micelles with rod phospholipids present. If lipid has been removed, however, he finds a marked change in the circular dichroism spectrum on light exposure.

The above criteria can conceivably be used to decide which detergent optimally maintains rhodopsin in a state comparable to that in the membrane. Thus, it is found that while these properties are maintained with digitonin as the solubilizing agent, they are lost with Triton X-100, Emulphogene BC-720, and CTAB (Shichi, 1971a,b).

As we shall see in Section V, there is a possible third criterion for assessing the condition of rhodopsin, namely, the rates of its intermediate reactions. Comparable studies on the lipoprotein nature of invertebrate rhodopsins have not been reported in the literature.

D.   Size and Shape of the Rhodopsin Molecule

Rhodopsin is a lipoprotein which cannot be solubilized directly in its native condition. One can, however, bring it into a monodispersed aqueous suspension as a detergent micelle and it is only as an aqueous suspension of these micelles that the physical measurements of molecular weight and shape can be made. But one must be cognizant of the fact that these micelles contain a substantial and perhaps variable amount of associated lipid as well as detergent which must be taken into account in assessing such measurements.

1. The Molecular Weight of Rhodopsin

Hubbard (1953) made the first estimation of the molecular weight of frog rhodopsin from sedimentation studies in the ultracentrifuge.

Correcting for the digitonin molecules complexed to the parent rhodopsin she concluded that rhodopsin micelles were monodispersed, having one chromophore per molecule and a molecular weight of approximately 40,000.

Shields *et al.* (1967) were first to determine the molecular weight of rhodopsin by an essentially chemical method. Assuming one chromophore per molecule and knowing the amino acid composition, they determined the molecular weight of bovine rhodopsin to be 28,600. By using the known mole fractions of the amino acids and the number of peptides produced by specific cleavage with trypsin and with cyanogen bromide, Millar *et al.* (1969) calculated the molecular weight to be 28,000. Heller (1968a) measured the outflow volumes of a series of standard proteins on an agarose column in aqueous CTAB solution to establish a calibration curve. The outflow volume of bovine rhodopsin fell in the molecular weight range of 27,000–28,000.

From disc electrophoresis methods, somewhat higher molecular weights have been obtained for vertebrate rhodopsins. Cavanaugh and Wald (1969) using SDS electrophoresis obtained a molecular weight of 35,000 (bovine), and Robinson *et al.* (1972) (frog) and Heitzmann (1972) (bovine) have found values (around 40,000) by the same method.

In our laboratory we have recently used the disc electrophoresis method of Hedrick and Smith (1968) for molecular weight determinations wherein one varies the acrylamide concentration and measures the variation of the R_f (the ratio of the protein migration to that of a small molecular weight marker dye). The log R_f is then plotted against acrylamide concentration and approximately linear plots result. Making a secondary plot of the slopes of the log plot versus molecular weight, one obtains an approximately linear calibration curve for standard proteins. Using this curve and the slope for bovine rhodopsin, we estimate 35,000 as the molecular weight.

An advantage of this method and calibrated column chromatography over the somewhat easier sodium dodecyl sulfate (SDS) electrophoresis method, is that rhodopsin may be run in native form (the electrophoresis is carried out in the dark), and therefore one determines not only the molecular weight but also whether rhodopsin is monomeric or polymeric—an important question in deciding whether there is a possibility of cooperative interactions between protein molecules.

While it is possible that acrylamide electrophoresis methods may overestimate the rhodopsin molecular weight somewhat, it nonetheless clearly indicates that there is one chromophore per molecule of rhodopsin in solution. SDS electrophoresis does, however, furnish an important complementary piece of information in that there is only one band in an SDS gel of purified rhodopsin, and hence only one peptide chain in the rhodopsin molecule.

In our laboratory we have also carried out experiments of a similar kind on squid rhodopsin. For squid rhodopsin purified by a variety of methods, the molecular weight per chromophore determined by amino acid analysis is approximately 70,000 (Kimbel *et al.*, 1973). By the acrylamide gel electrophoresis method of Smith and Hedrick described above, we estimate native squid rhodopsin to have a molecular weight of 76,000 (Fager *et al.*, 1971). When squid rhodopsin is purified by preparative disc electrophoresis and the purified protein is run on an SDS gel, it moves as a single band of 70,000 molecular weight (Fager *et al.*, 1973c). Therefore, the molecular weight of squid rhodopsin is more than twice that of vertebrate rhodopsin, but like vertebrate rhodopsin, it is monomeric, having a single chromophore per molecule, and a single peptide chain per monomer unit.

While SDS electrophoresis is unquestionably the method of choice for molecular weight determinations for proteins in the molecular weight range of rhodopsin and while molecular weight calibrations of well characterized proteins made by this method are impressively good, nonetheless, some caution must be exercised in the use of this method for determining the molecular weight of membrane lipoproteins. It is not clear what the precise mechanics of the SDS method are, but it is evident from the fact that charged groups on the protein have little influence on its electrophoretic mobility that the charge on the migrating micelle stems largely from SDS molecules somehow loosely associated with the protein. Such an association can logically be expected to depend on the degree of hydrophobicity of a protein molecule. The percentage of hydrophobic side chains is significantly greater in rhodopsin than those of the hydrophilic proteins for which the SDS calibration curves are made. While typical hydrophilic proteins have 25–35% hydrophobic residues, both vertebrate and invertebrate rhodopsins possess approximately 50% hydrophobic residues as do other membrane proteins. Therefore, SDS molecular weight determinations, where possible, should be compared with those obtained by other methods.

2. The Shape of Rhodopsin

Several points of evidence suggest a globular form for vertebrate rhodopsin. One type of evidence is derived from various electron micrographs, both on osmium-stained thin sections and on discs, negatively stained with phosphotungstate. When vertebrate photoreceptor membranes are examined in this manner, globular subunits of approximately 40 Å diameter are seen, suggesting that the rhodopsin molecule is spherical (Fernández-Morán, 1961; Nilsson, 1965; Blasie and Worthington, 1969). However, it is difficult to say at this point whether these workers were actually seeing rhodopsin molecules because there are several ways by which concentrated areas of the heavy metal stain may arise.

The idea of a globular, and hence spherical, vertebrate rhodopsin molecule has been challenged by Wu and Stryer (1972) on the basis of their measurement of the time of transfer of electronic excitation energy from the borohydride reduced retinyl group (after light exposure) to a synthetic acceptor chromophore attached to a thiol group of the rhodopsin. Their estimation of the distance between the two chromophores is 72 Å, and on this basis they suggested that native rhodopsin is a long thin molecule capable of traversing the entire membrane. However, the accuracy of such a measurement depends on the relative orientation of the two chromophores, and, particularly, on how accurately the fluorescence-absorption overlap integral of the two chromophores *in situ* is known. It is doubtful that reliable values for these parameters are known so that their estimated values could be in considerable error.

The idea of rhodopsin passing through the membrane not only disagrees with the earlier measurements mentioned above, but also is inconsistent with the X-ray diffraction measurements of Worthingtion (1971) which are now refined to give the electron density of a disc membrane to better than 8 Å. In the center of the membrane, there is an electron density which he feels can be consistent only with hydrocarbon chains of lipid molecules (C. R. Worthington, personal communication, 1972).

Recently, in our laboratory we have been using a different approach for the determination of the shape of visual pigment molecules, namely, electron microscopy of micelles of vertebrate and invertebrate rhodopsin (Mason *et al.*, 1973f; Fager *et al.*, 1973e). In order to determine whether the micelle shape of molecules reflects the shape of the protein contained within, we carried out studies on several hydrophilic proteins of known shape in digitonin solution and found that micrographs of shadowed micelles reflected the known structure of the protein. Shown is a micelle preparation of catalase, a protein known to have a hexagonal subunit structure (see Fig. 5A). It is not clear

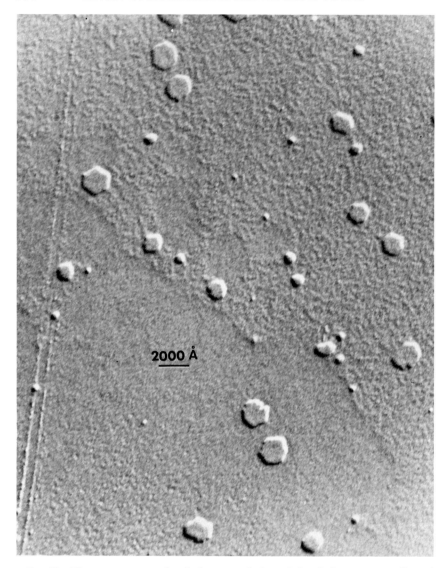

FIG. 5A. Electron micrograph of platinum shadowed dried digitonin micelles of catalase, showing the hexagonal structure of the protein. From Mason *et al.* (1973f).

as to why this should be true, for as the micelle dries on the grid, it spreads out to a dimension many times that of the protein at its core, but nonetheless, the micelle shape reflects the shape of the core protein for proteins of known shape.

Micelles of bovine rhodopsin as seen by platinum shadowing are symmetrical flattened domes (see Fig. 5B). This tends to confirm the

FIG. 5B. Electron micrograph of platinum shadowed dried digitonin micelles of bovine rhodopsin. Note that the cross section is circular; there is no evidence of asymmetry. From Fager *et al.* (1973e).

picture derived from the earlier studies, namely, that vertebrate rhodopsin is monomeric and globular since an estimation of the volume of the dried micelles agrees with the ultracentrifuge data (Hubbard, 1953) and with the elegant study by Bridges (1957) on the stoichiometry of digitonin molecules to rhodopsin molecules during extraction of visual pigments.

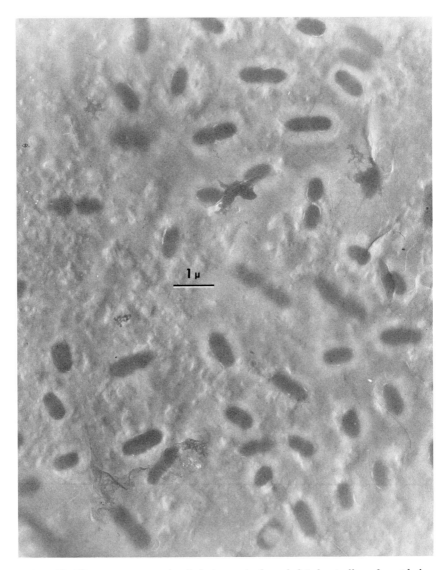

FIG. 5C. Electron micrograph of platinum-shadowed dried micelles of squid rhodopsin (*Loligo pealii*). Note that the micelles are highly asymmetric and very different in appearance from the micelles of bovine rhodopsin seen in Fig. 6. From Fager *et al.* (1973e).

In contrast, squid rhodopsin micelles, when viewed after platinum shadowing, appear highly asymmetric with an axial ratio of approximately 2.3. They are larger and more electron dense than bovine rhodopsin micelles. A consistent finding is an electron transparent region surrounding each rhodopsin micelle suggesting that the drying micelle draws material from the adjacent solution. Extensive controls were run to rule out bacterial contamination and other sources of artifact. Digitonin solutions alone, digitonin solutions of photoreceptor phospholipids, and blank preparations showed no micelles of the type seen. Mixing two different proteins produced micrographs with the two types of micelles present together. Finally, phosphotungstic acid staining of vertebrate and invertebrate visual pigment micelles, a method in which the principle of visualization is quite different, yields the same picture, i.e., symmetrical micelles for bovine rhodopsin and highly asymmetric ones for squid (see Figs. 6A and 6B).

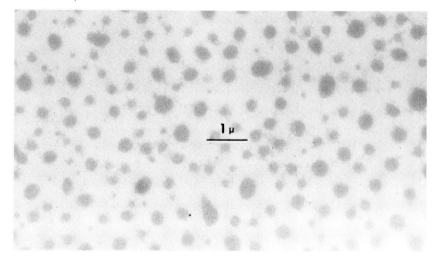

FIG. 6A. Bovine rhodopsin as visualized for electron microscopy by phosphotungstic acid staining. From Fager *et al.* (1973e).

In the phosphotungstic acid staining procedure there is not as thorough drying as in the shadowed preparations. Therefore, the micelles do not flatten and spread to quite the dimensions of those visualized by shadowing and consequently appear somewhat smaller. The ratio of the dimensions of the shadowed preparation to those of the phosophotungstate-stained preparation is the same for vertebrate

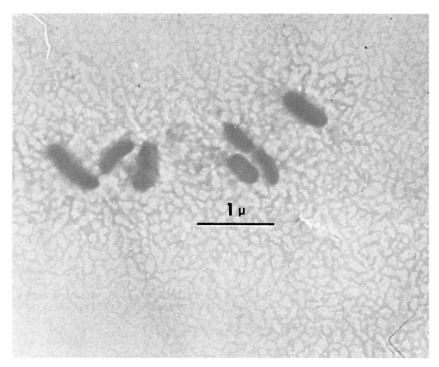

FIG. 6B. Squid rhodopsin as visualized for microscopy by phosphotungstic acid staining. From Fager *et al.* (1973e).

rhodopsin as for squid rhodopsin and the axial ratio of squid rhodopsin is the same by both techniques. Therefore the large differences in appearance of vertebrate and invertebrate rhodopsin micelles are consistent with the differences in the biochemistry of vertebrate and invertebrate visual pigments.

There are, in addition, significant differences between the visual pigment micelles and those of hydrophilic protein micelles. Visual pigment micelles are larger and more electron dense. They are relatively constant in size and appearance regardless of digitonin concentration, whereas hydrophilic protein micelles increase in size readily as the detergent concentration increases. (No difference has been observed between micelles dried in the dark and in the light for either the vertebrate or the invertebrate rhodopsin.)

Since the bovine and squid rhodopsin are not only the best studied of their respective classes of visual pigments, but also among the best characterized of all membrane proteins, the above approach may provide insight into the size and shape of other membrane proteins.

E. The Organization of Rhodopsin in the Photoreceptor
Membrane

Two important questions to be answered about photoreceptor membranes are the precise organization of the pigment molecules in the
membrane and how light affects this organization.

From thin sectioning with permanganate or osmium staining, the
inner surface of a disc membrane of a vertebrate retinal rod appears
to be little different from the outer surface. However, by low angle
X-ray diffraction several laboratories have shown a pronounced
assymmetry (Blasie *et al.*, 1965; Gras and Worthington, 1967; Blaurock and Wilkins, 1969; Worthington, 1971). The model of Worthington and Blasie has two electron dense regions surrounding a central
region of electron density so low that they conclude that it is almost
entirely fatty acid side chains of the lipids. The inner surface of the
disc has an electron density significantly greater than on the outer
surface. On this basis, C. R. Worthington (personal communication,
1972) suggests that the rhodopsin is localized on the internal surface
of the disc membrane. On exposure to light the electron density pattern changes, the maximum moving slightly toward the center of the
membrane; this Blasie (1972) interprets as rhodopsin sinking slightly
into the membrane. Dratz (1972) concluded rhodopsin was in the
hydropholic phase since it was inaccessible to water-soluble reagents;
however, more recent work from the same laboratory (E. A. Dratz and
S. Schwartz, personal communication) has shown the hydrophilic
groups of membrane-bound rhodopsin are available for substitution.

As mentioned earlier, both lipid composition and temperature
broadening of X-ray diffraction maxima suggest that there is appreciable translational mobility in the plane of the disc. Recent studies on
dichroism induced by bleaching and its rapid thermal decay (Brown,
1972; Cone, 1972) show rotational mobility as well; i.e., the transition
dipole rotates around axes perpendicular to the plane of the disc.
Despite this great mobility in the plane of the rod, membrane rhodopsin is oriented with the transition dipole of its 500 nm band parallel to the plane of the disc (Schmidt, 1938; Liebman, 1972). This could
be explained if the molecule had, on one end, a highly hydrophilic
group and, on the other, a highly hydrophobic one.

Freeze fracture electron microscopy is ideally suited to the study
of a problem such as this. In this method a sample is very rapidly
frozen in liquid Freon just above its melting point to prevent the
formation of ice crystals. The sample is then placed in a high vacuum
at liquid nitrogen temperatures and fractured with a knife. On raising
the temperature to approximately −100° the surface is etched − i.e.,

ice is sublimed away to expose additional uncleaved membrane surface. The exposed surface features are visualized for electron microscopy by platinum shadowing.

Recently in this laboratory we (Mason *et al.*, 1973d) have applied this method to the study of frog photoreceptor membranes. Two distinct types of surfaces can be seen: hydrophilic surfaces which can be identified by a relatively smooth contour and hydrophobic cleavage surfaces which can be identified by a rippled appearance.

There are three possible sites at which the rhodopsin molecules might be located: (1) in the hydrophobic interior of the membrane, (2) on the intradisc hydrophilic phase facing the disc lumen, and (3) on the extradisc surface, i.e., the one facing away from the disc lumen. Particles, which we believe to be rhodopsin molecules, can be clearly seen on some of the surfaces. The appearance of the particles and the change of this appearance provides insight into the role rhodopsin may be playing in the visual process.

Before light exposure of the membranes the rippled hydrophobic surfaces show no evidence of particles identifiable as rhodopsin (see Fig. 7). Therefore, in the native condition the rhodopsin molecules

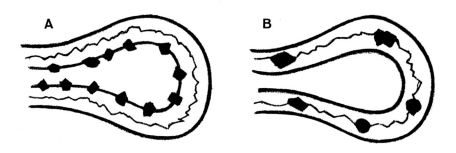

FIG. 7. Schematic view of the surfaces in a disc membrane before (A) and after (B) light. Before light, particles are located on the inner hydrophilic surface only. After light they sink deeper into the membrane and appear on the rippled hydrophobic surface on which cleavage takes place. The featureless surfaces represent the imaginary junction between hydrophobic and hydrophilic layers while the structured surfaces represent actual cleavage surfaces (Mason *et al.*, 1973d).

appear not to be buried in the hydrophobic interior of the membrane. They must, then, be on one or both hydrophilic surfaces. In viewing the hydrophilic surfaces one sees two very different types. The first is free of particles. The second (Fig. 9) is densely studded with particles, about 50 Å in diameter, with a density of approximately one

FIG. 8. Rippled hydrophobic layer exposed by cleavage of dark-adapted frog rods. The surface is free of particles. From Mason *et al.* (1973d).

per 5400 Å², consistent with estimates from microspectrophotometry (Liebman, 1972) and X-ray diffraction (Worthington, this volume) for the density of rhodopsin molecules, assuming the molecules were localized on a single surface. One can conclude, therefore, that all the rhodopsin molecules are on only one of the two hydrophilic faces.

From observing the curvature of the periphery of the disc one can see that the hydrophilic surface facing away from the disc lumen is smooth and that the particle-covered surface is the one on the inside of the disc.

On the particulated hydrophilic surface (see Fig. 9) the particles,

FIG. 9. Smooth hydrophilic face on the inside of a dark-adapted frog disc studded with particles (viewed by freeze/etch microscopy). ($\times$72,000.) Mason *et al.* (1973d).

presumably rhodopsin molecules, are arranged in an interesting short-range order, i.e., in strings of particles with branching strings roughly perpendicular. This conclusion as to the identity of the two hydrophilic surfaces is further strengthened by the fact that on samples which have been etched only and not cleaved, only smooth surfaces are visible, as would be expected since there is no fracturing of the disc membrane to expose the inner surface.

After exhaustive light exposure, the picture changes dramatically. All hydrophilic surfaces are now largely smooth, and particles are seen on the rippled hydrophobic surfaces (Fig. 10). It would appear, therefore, that rhodopsin has migrated into the hydrophobic phase. The density of particles is somewhat less than that seen before light and the individual particles are much larger, suggesting that the

FIG. 10. Rippled hydrophobic cleavage face of a light-exposed frog membrane. Particles, presumably rhodopsin, have appeared on this surface after light exposure. (× 112,000.) Mason *et al.* (1973d).

individual rhodopsin molecules have aggregated into clusters of 4–8 molecules. There is no trace of the ordered strings in the intradisc surface as seen before light exposure.

This picture of the photodynamic behavior of rhodopsin is consistent with the results from low angle X-ray diffraction of oriented frog rod preparations (Worthington, 1971; Blasie, 1972), but possess the advantage that the rods can be frozen seconds after light exposure, whereas a much longer period is required for X-ray diffraction measurements. However, some uncertainty still exists in identification of the surfaces.

Figure 7 shows a schematic view of the process based on our observations. Before light exposure the particles are on the inner hydrophilic surface (A). After exposure to light they migrate so as to appear on the median hydrophobic surface (B). At no time do they appear on the external hydrophilic surface. Smooth surfaces depict the noncleavable interfaces of hydrophobic and hydrophilic layers. Earlier studies (Clark and Branton, 1968; Leeson, 1970) had demonstrated two types of cleavable surfaces but had shown no light effect.

The question of where the photopigment is located in the invertebrate photoreceptor has not been investigated in the same degree of detail. However, on the basis of what is known, some interesting speculations can be made. The surface of the cell is convoluted into a series of tightly packed fingerlike microvilli (Zonana, 1961) about 1 μ in length and 0.1 μ in diameter. For any one cell all the microvilli are quite accurately parallel. This structure and the lipid composition suggest that the squid membranes may be much more rigid than those of vertebrates although this has not been approached experimentally by physical methods. Since, on the basis of the electron micrographs of dried micelles, squid rhodopsin is a long thin molecule, we suggest that its long axis may be oriented parallel to the long axes of the microvilli. If, in addition, the transition dipole of the chromophore is oriented parallel to the long molecular axis of rhodopsin then each cell would have a unique direction of greatest polarization. This is consistent with the observation that the squid apparently can distinguish between light of the same intensity but differing polarization (Waterman et al., 1969; Hays and Goldsmith, 1969). Preliminary work by Liebman and Hagins (P. A. Liebman, personal communication, 1972) has indicated that the chromophore in squid photoreceptors may be sufficiently dichroic to be consistent with such a model, but microspectrophotometry by Goldsmith (1962) on crustacean rhabdomes suggests a somewhat lesser degree of orientation. Our estimated dimensions of squid rhodopsin, i.e.,

100 Å × 40 Å (Fager *et al.*, 1973e) are consistent with a molecule that could traverse the membrane were its thickness comparable to the disc membrane of the frog.

F. LIGHT-INDUCED CHEMICAL CHANGES IN RHODOPSIN AND PHOTORECEPTOR MEMBRANES

1. Reactivity of Sulfhydryl Groups

Wald and Brown (1952) reported that exposure of rhodopsin to light uncovered two moles of sulfhydryl groups per mole of rhodopsin, which had been inaccessible to titration in native rhodopsin. The stoichiometry held for bovine, frog, and squid rhodopsin. They further found that PCMB titration of these liberated thiol groups prevented regeneration of rhodopsin, but, when PCMB was competitively removed by glutathione, regenerability returned.

Work in this laboratory was carried out to ascertain at which step in sequence of intermediates the thiol groups were uncovered by light when exposed. The conclusion reached by Ostroy *et al.* (1966b) was that between one and two thiol groups were exposed after the formation of metarhodopsin$_{380}$II.

Recently, Zorn and Futterman have carried out detailed studies of the reactivity of rhodopsin thiols after various chemical treatments (Zorn and Futterman, 1971; Zorn, 1971). Their findings were that the thiols can be divided into three categories on the basis of their chemical reactivity. One mole of thiol per mole of rhodopsin can be titrated in native rhodopsin solubilized by detergents. An additional two thiol groups are accessible at 35°C after incubation in 2 M urea or after stripping off the bulk of the phospholipid, two treatments which do not bleach rhodopsin. A final two thiols are uncovered upon light exposure after these pretreatments, consistent with the earlier work. W. Hubbell (personal communication, 1972) finds that the availability of thiol groups to titration differs, depending on the detergent used to micellate rhodopsin.

Although it is hightly suggestive that two thiols are uncovered in both vertebrate and invertebrate rhodopsin, which are very dissimilar in other ways, it is not possible to say whether those thiols uncovered by light exposure are involved in the rhodopsin function. There is, however, reason to believe that these groups interact closely with the chromophore binding site since they are only uncovered by light exposure and since blocking them prevents regeneration. No cysteine appears in the retinyl peptide Bownds (1967) isolated, so the thiols may be close to the chromophore binding site in the three dimensional structure of rhodopsin but remote in the primary sequence.

2. Light-Induced Changes in Phosphatases and Kinases

McConnell and Scarpelli (1963) presented evidence for a light-stimulated ATPase in the rod outer segments, but other laboratories have failed, as yet, to reproduce these results.

Bitensky *et al.* (1971) and Miller *et al.* (1971) have found a very high level of activity of adenyl cyclase (called adenylate cyclase in IUPAC nomenclature) which catalyzes the conversion of ATP to 3′5′-cyclic AMP in retinal rods, Eq. (1). This appears to be the largest activity found for any tissue on a per milligram protein basis.

$$\text{ATP} \xrightarrow[\text{adenyl cyclase}]{\text{Mg}^{2+}} 3',5' \text{ cyclic AMP} + \text{pyrophosphate} \tag{1}$$

$$3',5'\text{-cyclic AMP} \xrightarrow[\text{phosphodiesterase}]{\text{Mg}^{2+}} 5'\text{-AMP} \tag{2}$$

The significance of this finding is that, for an organelle as simple as the rod and as specialized for a single purpose, it follows that a component present in such quantities must somehow be related to the visual function. The prime evidence that this adenyl cyclase activity is associated with vision is that its activity is reported to be large in the dark but to disappear on light exposure. Miller *et al.* (1971) have reported that the disappearance of adenyl cyclase is proportional to the amount of rhodopsin bleached, and on this basis, they suggest that cyclic AMP acts directly on a receptor molecule which controls the sodium permeability of the cell membrane. They (Bitensky *et al.*, 1972) further find that various conditions which disrupt the rod membranes (e.g., exposure to digitonin or homogenization) cause a loss of the light control of the cyclase activity. They find cyclase activity in ground squirrel cones and invertebrate rhabdomes of lobsters but with no light control.

3. Light-Induced Exposure of the Chromophore Linkage

In both vertebrate and invertebrate rhodopsin, before light exposure the chromophoric linkage is inacessible to reduction by sodium borohydride at room temperature whereas after light exposure, reduction proceeds rapidly (Bownds and Wald, 1965). Hydroxylamine, which has no effect on either vertebrate or invertebrate rhodopsin before light exposure, rapidly extracts the chromophore and forms retinal oxime after light exposure. This appears to indicate that the chromophore of native rhodopsin is sequestered in a hydrophobic pocket of the molecule and cannot be reached by small water-soluble molecules.

4. Exposure of Ionizable Groups on Illumination

Radding and Wald (1955) titrated digitonin-solubilized vertebrate rhodopsin and showed that after light exposure the number of titratable groups, both acid and basic, increased by approximately 20%. McConnell et al. (1968) and Downer and Englander (1972) showed rapid hydrogen ion uptake and exchange in disc membranes on light exposure. Matthews et al. (1963) and Ostroy et al. (1966a) showed a pH dependence of the equilibrium between metarhodopsin $_{478}$I and metarhodopsin$_{380}$II. On the basis of the observed pK of 6.5, Matthews suggested that the protonation of an imidazole group was involved. As would be expected the rate of the metarhodopsin$_{478}$I → metarhodopsin$_{380}$II process is markedly enhanced at lower pH (Ostroy et al., 1966a; Rapp, 1970; Emrich, 1971).

The changes in exposure of ionizable groups are probably related to rapid conductance changes on light exposure in rhodopsin solutions seen by Hara (1958) and Hara (1963), in photoreceptor suspensions by Falk and Fatt (1966), and membrane potentials across dialysis membranes in which rhodopsin is confined to one side (Ostroy, 1971).

While there is no reasonable doubt that such changes in the exposure of ionizable groups occur, it is not possible to say whether they are the source of or merely accompany absorption-excitation coupling.

G. THE CHROMOPHORE BINDING SITE

A considerable amount of chemical (Morton and Pitt, 1955; Hubbard, 1969) and spectroscopic evidence (Abrahamson and Ostroy, 1967; Abrahamson and Wiesenfeld, 1972; Rimai et al., 1971) points to the 11-cis-retinal derived chromophore as being bound to an amino group on the lipoprotein opsin in the form of a protonated Schiff base. As both phospholipid and the pigment-associated protein have available amino groups, there is a question whether the chromophore is bound to one of about 40 available amino groups in phosphatidylethanolamine and phosphatidylserine of the bovine rod outer segments or the 10–13 epsilon amino groups furnished by the lysine units.

Bownds and Wald (1965) reported that, upon illumination, bovine rhodopsin in micelles could be reduced by aqueous NaBH$_4$. Subsequent alkaline hydrolysis of the reduced lipoprotein showed the retinylidene chromophore to be attached to a lysine unit of the protein (Bownds, 1967; Akhtar et al., 1967). Somewhat later Poincelot et al. (1969, 1970) found that extraction of dried bovine rod outer segments or digitonin micelles of rhodopsin with dry methanol $10^{-3.5}$ M in HCl gas yielded quantitative amounts of the lipid complex, N-retinylidene phosphatidylethanolamine (NRPE). As model Schiff bases of retinal appeared to be stable to transimination (transfer of the cabonyl moiety to different amino groups) under these conditions, this suggested a phosphatidylethanolamine (PE) binding site for the chromophore in unilluminated rhodopsin. This idea was reinforced by the fact that the $NaBH_4$ reduction of an aqueous suspension of rod outer segments or rhodopsin micelles in the dark at temperatures near 60°C yielded N-retinylphosphatidylethanolamine (NRH_2PE) as the only identifiable product. Further experiments of similar kind on the intermediate metarhodopsin$_{480}$I yielded the same results, i.e., a PE binding site. At the metarhodopsin$_{380}$II stage, however, the chromophore could be clearly identified as attached to lysine, in agreement with the earlier findings (Bownds, 1967; Akhtar *et al.*, 1967). It seemed therefore that the chromophore was undergoing a thermal transimination in the metarhodopsin$_{480}$I $\rightarrow$ metarhodopsin$_{380}$II process (Poincelot *et al.*, 1969; Kimbel *et al.*, 1970).

In contrast to the evidence supporting a lipid binding site in native vertebrate rhodopsin, there have been recent reports countering this notion. Hall and Bachrach (1970) injected frogs with ^{32}P-labeled phosphate and purified and examined the visual pigments after periods of 3 and 6 days. Assuming the turnover rate of ^{32}P in all rod outer segment lipids to be the same, they estimated that there was less than 1 mole of phospholipid per mole of rhodopsin and concluded, therefore, that the chromophore in rhodopsin could not be bound to a phospholipid. While this undoubtedly argues against the NRPE hypothesis, the argument would fail if the lipids associated with the binding site turned over at the same rate as rhodopsin (50–60 days) while the membrane lipids had a much more rapid turnover. Anderson and Maude (1970) and Anderson (1972) demonstrated under a variety of conditions that the chromophore of unilluminated bovine rhodopsin was solubilized and precipitated concomitant with the associated protein. He did not, however, chemically identify the binding site. Hirtenstein and Akhtar (1970) revised their earlier conclusion (Akhtar and Hirtenstein, 1969) favoring PE as the native binding site, and in the later paper stated that the proportion of NRH_2PE and N-retinyllysine found in the reduction of rhodopsin in the presence of high concentrations of trichloroacetic acid varied from experiment to experiment and suggested that the chromophore might oscillate between the two binding sites in the native state. Zorn (1971) and Girsch and Rabinovitch (1972) independently found, in the presence of urea and $NaBH_4$, variable proportions of lipid and protein-bound chromophore, depending on the conditions of the reduction. Zorn concluded that this probably indicated a lysine binding site, and Girsch and Rabinovitch suggested that their results supported the Akhtar hypothesis of two binding sites. Stronger evidence against a PE binding site has been reported from the Nijmegen laboratory, which found that phospholipase treatment of bovine rod outer segments reduces the lipid ethanolamine:rhodopsin ratio to somewhat less than unity (Borggreven et al., 1971).

Very recently we have reinvestigated the question of the chromophore binding site in bovine rhodopsin using a new reducing agent, sodium cyanoborohydride (Fager et al., 1972). This reagent has the advantage, aside from being more lipophilic and more specific for Schiff bases than $NaBH_4$, of being much more stable at neutral and acid pH values. Cyanoborohydride reacts directly with an unilluminated rhodopsin in a controlled fashion at temperatures as low as 3°C. At pH = 5.0 and 3°C, conditions under which rhodopsin is stable, cyanoborohydride reduces rhodopsin micelles in a period of less than 48 hours, yielding N-retinyllysine as the sole product. At pH = 7, where the reducing power of cyanoborohydride is minimal, the 500 nm absorption maximum of rhodopsin is stable, indicating that there is no nonspecific denaturation of the rhodopsin molecule by cyanoborohydride and this is further borne out by our still more recent studies of the kinetics of the reduction process (Fager et al., 1973b). It appears most probable that in these experiments the chromophore linkage is reduced directly without denaturing the protein. This is the strongest evidence to date favoring a protein (lysine) binding site for the chromophore in vertebrate visual pigments. However, a word of caution is in order, at this time when certainly the weight of evidence now favors the conclusion relative to the native chromophore binding site reached some five years ago on the basis of the experiments on illuminated rhodopsin. The experience of this laboratory, in particular, underscores the subtlety of the chemical problem of determining the chromophore binding site and the ease with which the chromophore can migrate. We feel that the only evidence which can be unequivocal as regards the chromophore binding site is that based on an appropriate physical measurement on rhodopsin in situ.

We have also carried out chemical studies of the chromophore binding site in unilluminated squid rhodopsin (Fager et al., 1971, 1973d). When either lyophilized native squid rhabdomes or lyophilized digitonin micelles of native squid rhodopsin were extracted with methanol which is 10^{-2} M in anhydrous HCl, the chromophore was quantitatively brought into solution as an orange colored, protonated Schiff base of denatured rhodopsin. The solution was stable for varying periods of time depending on the temperature. Eventually, however, the chromoprotein precipitated, essentially free of lipid.

On addition of solid sodium borohydride to the solution of the chromolipoprotein the chromophoric Schiff base linkage was reduced and the chromoprotein precipitated quantitatively leaving the lipids in the supernatant. Subsequent alkaline hydrolysis of the chromo-protein yielded up to 45% of the chromophore as N-retinyllysine. Thin-layer chromatography in three solvent systems run against standards showed a single spot containing the chromophore as identi-fied by fluorescence and the antimony trichloride (Carr-Price) color test. The spot also showed the ninhydrin test for primary amines. The HCl concentration used in this case was 3×10^{-2} M and therefore sufficient to prevent transimination.

The results of studies on illuminated rhabdomes and squid rho-dopsin micelles were identical to those obtained for unilluminated preparations. This supports the notion that the chromophore in native invertebrate squid rhodopsin is bound to a protein and, furthermore, remains on the protein after light exposure. The problem is being studied further in our laboratory using cyanoborohydride.

IV.   The Chromophore of Visual Pigments

A.   Retinals and Their Properties

All visual pigments whose chromophores have been chemically identified are derived from two basic polyene aldehydes, retinal, and its 3-dehydro derivative (Wald, 1953). Although there are six known isomers of the retinals (Fig. 11) in all cases it appears to be the 11-*cis*-retinal and its 3-dehydro derivative from which the physio-logical active native pigments are formed (Oroshnik *et al.*, 1956). X-ray structure determinations (Gilardi *et al.*, 1971; Hamanaka *et al.*, 1972) show the 11-*cis* and *trans* isomers of retinal to have the struc-tures (III) and (I), respectively.

The stable crystalline form of the 11-*cis* isomer is s-*cis* with respect to the C_6-C_7 and C_{12}-C_{13} formal single bonds of the polyene chain. Both isomers are nonplanar to a marked extent. In the 11-*cis* isomer the ring torsion about the C_6-C_7 single bond is 40°, and the chain segment from atoms 6 to 13 is essentially planar; the rotation angles about the C_8-C_9, C_9-C_{10} and C_{11}-C_{12} bonds being 8°, 4°, 0°, and 3°, respectively. This agrees with the prediction of Patel (1969), based on NMR studies in solution, that the environment about the C_{10}-C_{11} single bond is planar. About the C_{12}-C_{13} single bond there is a marked

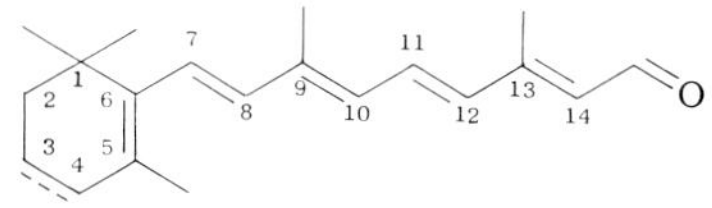

FIG. 11. Structural formulas for isomers of retinal and 3-dehydroretinal (---). All isomers are shown in the 6-s-*cis* form, although this is known experimentally only in the case of (I) and (III). (I) *trans*, 6-s-*cis*; (II) 9-*cis*, 6-s-*cis*; (III) 11-*cis*, 6,12-s-di-*cis* (X-ray structure); (IV) 12-*cis*, 6-s-*cis*; (V) 11,13 di-*cis*, 6-s-*cis*; (VI) 9,13 di-*cis*, 6-s-*cis*.

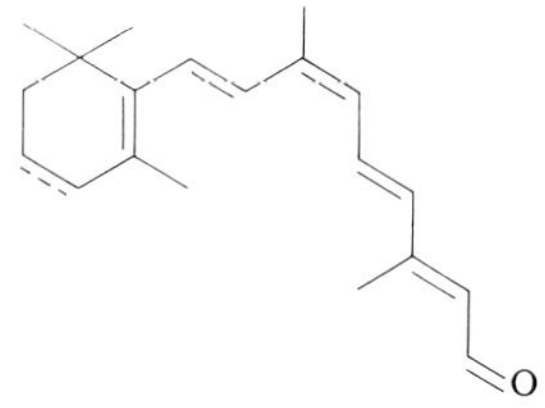

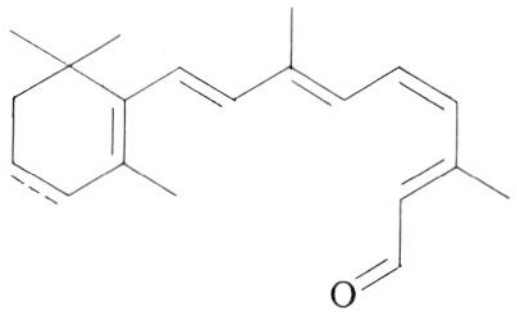

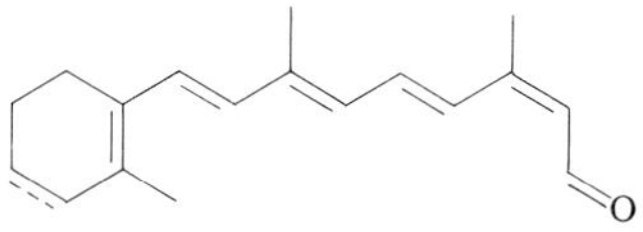

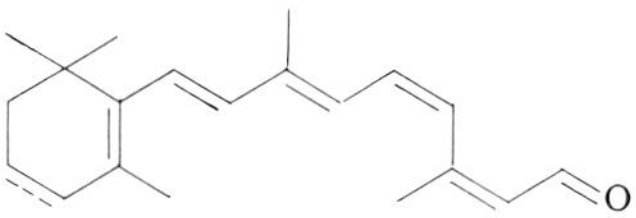

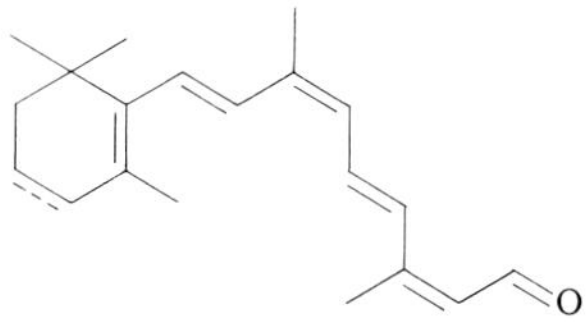

torsion of 39° from the s-*cis* conformation, such that the C_{13}-C_{14} double bond and the carbonyl group are directed well out of the plane of the carbon chain.

Like the 11-*cis* isomer the crystalline *trans* isomer, by X-ray evidence, is s-*cis* about the C_6-C_7 single bond with the torsion angle between ring and chain considerably larger than for the *cis* isomer; 59° as reported by Gilardi *et al.* (1971) and 62° as reported by Hamanaka *et al.* (1972).

2. Spectra

The visible and near ultraviolet spectra of 5 of the 6 known isomers of retinals are shown in Fig. 12. They are generally characterized by a

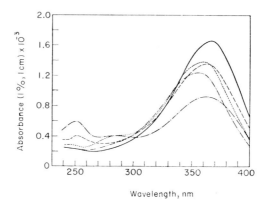

Wavelength, nm

FIG. 12. Absorption spectra of isomers of retinal. ——, all-*trans*; ---, 13-*cis*; — · —, 11-*cis*; · · · ·, 9-*cis*; — - —, 9,13-di-*cis*. (Hubbard, 1956.)

principal long wavelength absorption band of high extinction (368–381 nm) and one or two weaker absorption bands (in the case of the *cis* isomers) lying at shorter wavelengths. The molar absorbances of the principal absorption bands in ethanol are given in Table V.

TABLE V
MOLAR ABSORBANCE OF THE PRINCIPAL ABSORPTION BAND IN
RETINALS AND 3-DEHYDRORETINALS IN ETHANOL[a]

Isomer	Retinal λ_{max} (nm)	3-Dehydroretinal		
		ϵ_{max} (liter cm^{-1}mole^{-1})	λ_{max} (nm)	ϵ_{max} (liter cm^{-1}mole^{-1})
trans	381	43,400	401	41,500
9-*cis*	373	36,100	391	34,100
11-*cis*	376.5	24,900	393	24,900
13-*cis*	375	35,800	395	33,300
11,13-di*cis*	373	19,900	386	27,200
9,13-ci*cis*	368	32,400	—	—

[a]Morton and Pitt (1957); von Planta *et al.* (1962).

In polyene aldehydes one can usually observe two types of electronic transitions in the long wavelength region of the spectrum; $^1(\pi,\pi^*) \leftarrow G$ and $^1(n,\pi^*) \leftarrow G$. The former which is the principal absorption band, arises from the optical promotion of an electron from the highest energy occupied delocalized π molecular orbital to the lowest energy unoccupied π molecular orbital. The latter has usually a very low extinction ($\epsilon \sim 50$), appearing as a satellite peak on the long wavelength shoulder of the principal band and arises from the optical promotion of an electron from a lone pair localized in an atomic p orbital on the carbonyl oxygen atom to the lowest energy unoccupied π orbital. This $^1(n,\pi^*) \leftarrow G$ transition is clearly visible in the absorption spectrum of polyene aldehydes having a lesser degree of conjugation than retinal (Blout and Fields, 1948). In retinal, however, it appears to lie so close to the absorption maximum of the principal band as to be obscured by it.

A point of some interest is the anomalous behavior of the spectrum of the 11-*cis* isomer. At room temperature the spectrum has a much lower absorbance than the other isomers of retinal with the exception of the 11,13-di*cis* isomer. But at low temperatures ($-188°C$) its molar absorbance increases by over 60% and the peak narrows considerably relative to the "normal" behavior of the *trans* isomer.

Honig and Karplus (1971) offer a quite plausible explanation for the anomalous spectral behavior of the 11-*cis* isomer based on a theoretical calculation of the torsional potential about the C_{12}-C_{13} single bond. This shows two minima, one displaced 60° from the planar 12-s-*trans* conformation and the other displaced about 50° from the planar 12-s-*cis* conformation. The latter minimum is not too different from that found for the crystalline 11-*cis* isomer, i.e., 139° from the 12-s-*trans* planar conformation, and lies, according to their calculations, 0.8 kcal lower than the minimum of the hindered 12-s-*trans* conformation. This clearly favors the 12-s-*cis* conformation and a calculation in our laboratory by D. Cross (unpublished observations, 1972) of the ratio of oscillator strengths for the principal absorption bands of the hindered (139°) 11-*cis*, 6,12-s-di*cis* to the *trans*, 6-s-*cis* isomer yields 0.72, which compares favorably with the reported value of 0.78 for the ratio of molar absorbances of the 11-*cis* to *trans* isomer at $-196°C$ (Becker *et al.*, 1971a).

The C_{12}-C_{13} torsional potential surface of Honig and Karplus (1971) shows only a 1.1 kcal barrier between the two minima. Furthermore the hindered s-*trans* minimum lies at a more torsionally distorted position than does the s-*cis*, i.e., 60° as opposed to 50°, which points to a smaller oscillator strength for the hindered s-*trans* isomer. In fact, Honig and Karplus (1971) suggest that "at room temperature the molecule would be expected to undergo transitions from vibrational levels with contributions from a wide range of geometries in the neighborhood of the s-*trans* as well as the s-*cis* minimum. There would be clearly a broad absorption peak, which could become significantly narrower and more intense at lower temperature when the molecule is trapped in the appropriate minimum energy conformation."

In the last few years a number of semiempirical molecular obrital calculations have appeared dealing with the energies of the ground and excited states of retinal isomers. Wiesenfeld and Abrahamson (1968), Inuzuka and Becker (1968), Becker *et al.* (1971a,b), Langlet *et al.* (1969) and Pullman *et al.* (1969) have used various versions of the Pariser, Parr, Pople-self consistent field (PPP-SCF) method to treat the absorption spectra of retinal isomers. This method deals with the π electron system alone in an assumed constant potential field of the σ carbon–hydrogen framework. In general one can obtain reasonable agreement with experimental absorption maxima and oscillator strengths using this method by appropriate adjustments of the values of the empirical coulomb and resonance integrals.

Some insight can be gained using the PPP-SCF method as to the approximate torsional potential surfaces on rotation about formal single and double bonds providing that changes in the σ potential are not significant. The method, however, appears inappropriate by itself to deal with cases involving steric hindrance or other sources which change the σ core potential appreciably. Thus the earlier predictions of our laboratory based on the π electron energy calculations (Abrahamson and Ostroy, 1967; Wiesenfeld and Abrahamson, 1968) regarding the relief of steric hindrance in the 11-*cis* isomer of retinal by predominant torsion above the C_{11}-C_{12} bond have not been confirmed by experiment. The NMR evidence of Patel (1969) suggests the major relief is achieved by torsion about the C_{12}-C_{13} single bond in solution, and this is borne out unequivocally in the crystal (Gilardi *et al.*, 1971). Calculations which include variations in the σ as well as π potential are in qualitative agreement with experiment (Nash, 1969; Honig and Karplus, 1971; Pullman *et al.*, 1969; Langlet *et al.*, 1969).

The fluorescence of *trans*-retinal was first seen by Dawson (1962) on flash excitation of *trans*-retinal in an ether:isopentane:ethanol (8:3:5) rigid glass solution at $-196°C$. More recently Balke and Becker (1967) and Becker *et al.* (1971a) have studied the fluorescence of retinal isomers in some detail. They find the fluorescence yield of *trans*-retinal to be relatively high at $-196°C$, approaching 0.7 at longer wavelengths, while the 9-*cis* isomer is considerably less (~ 0.16). At room temperature the fluorescence yield is so low in all isomers of retinal studied, i.e., *trans*, 9-*cis*, 13-*cis*, and 11-*cis*, that it is undetectable. Of the isomers studied, only the physiologically active 11-*cis* isomer shows no fluorescence, i.e., a fluorescence yield < 0.001, even at $-196°C$.

Phosphorescence has not been observed in any of the retinals so that direct measurements of the energy of their lowest triplet states have not been made. Evans (1960) has observed population of the lowest triplet state in absorption of the near relative of retinal, dodeca-2,4,6,8,10-pentanal, using the oxygen perturbation technique and places the o-o band at 11,050 cm^{-1} (905 nm) above the ground state. Guzzo and Pool (1968), on the basis of energy transfer experiments, place the triplet of *trans*-retinal in absorption at 880 nm.

Abrahamson *et al.* (1959), Dawson and Abrahamson (1962), and Grellman *et al.* (1962) have studied the population of the triplet state of *trans*-retinal by flash photolysis. Dawson and Abrahamson (1962) observed triplet–triplet absorption with a maximum at 450 nm and a molar absorbance of approximately 80,000 liter cm^{-1} mole^{-1}. At room temperature they determined the triplet state to form with a quantum yield of 0.11 and to decay by a first-order process with a half-life of 10^{-5} second. In hydroxylic solvents they found the triplet to undergo hydrogen bonding at the carbonyl oxygen atom. Their measured formation constant of this triplet-hydrogen bonded complex was essentially the same as for ground state retinal, from which they concluded that the lowest triplet state of *trans*-retinal was $^3(\pi,\pi^*)$ rather than $^3(n,\pi^*)$.

3. Photochemistry

The principal photochemical processes associated with retinals is their photoisomerization. This has been studied recently in some detail by Kropf and Hubbard (1970). They found the quantum yield of isomerization of the *trans* to mono*cis* isomers at room temperature in hydrocarbon solvents to fall within the range 0.06–0.2, depending on assumptions as to the composition of the stereoisomers. For the 9-*cis* to *trans*, 13-*cis* to *trans*, and 11-*cis* to *trans* their reported quantum yields are 0.5, 0.4, and 0.2, respectively. The fact that the quantum yield of triplet state population in *trans* retinal was found to be 0.11 (Dawson and Abrahamson, 1962), suggests that the radiationless pathway to isomerization passes through the lowest $^3(\pi,\pi^*)$ state.

Another type of photochemistry has been observed by Balke and Becker (1967) and Becker *et al.* (1971a) in retinal solutions in rigid glasses at low temperatures. A compound believed to be either an oxycyclic form of retinal (I) or its photoenol (II) is formed reversibly.

(I)   (II)

Becker *et al.* (1971a) also report a finding earlier noted in our laboratory that irradiation of solutions of retinals at room temperature which have not been degassed results in destructive photo-oxidation to colorless products.

B.   THE SPECTRA OF VISUAL PIGMENTS

1. *Absorption Spectra*

We have previously pointed out that all known visual pigments are based on 11-*cis* retinal (retinal$_1$), the rhodopsins, or 11-*cis*-3-dehydro-retinal (retinal$_2$), the porphyropsins. Those pigments based on 11-*cis* retinal predominate both in land animals and marine species and span the spectral range 340–575 nm in their principal absorption maxima with a molar absorbance of about 40,600 (Dartnall and Lythgoe, 1965; Liebman and Entine, 1968). The known porphyropsins are much fewer in number and are largely confined to freshwater marine species. Their principal absorption maxima, furthermore, span the more restricted range, 510–543 nm in nature although a synthetic "cyanopsin" absorbing maximally at 620 nm has been synthesized from 11-*cis*-3-dehydroretinal and the opsin moiety of chicken iodopsin (Wald *et al.*, 1955).

As the spread of principal spectral maxima covers a range of nearly 6000 cm^{-1} in retinal based pigments and 3500 cm^{-1} in retinal$_2$ based pigments and their oscillator strengths are essentially the same over the entire range (Bridges, 1970), it is clear that the spectra reflect the same basic electronic transition and the broad range of maxima is not achieved by a systematic alteration in the chromophore itself but rather is effected by a very precisely controlled perturbation in its microenvironment, i.e., the opsin moiety. Moreover, the perturbation appears to have a "quantized" character as is evident from the clustering of spectral maxima about certain wavelengths. Dartnall and Lythgoe (1965) find that the principal spectral maxima of retinal-based pigments tend to cluster about the series of wavelengths, 467, 478.5, 486.4, 494, 500.5, 506, 511.5, 519, and 528 nm. For retinal$_2$ based pigments, Bridges (1964) finds the clustering maxima at 512, 524, 534, and 543 nm.

Another point of interest is the behavior of the spectral maxima of retinal$_1$- and retinal$_2$-based pigment pairs synthesized from the same opsin moiety. Dartnall and Lythgoe (1965) found that on plotting the principal λ_{max} of the two against each other a roughly linear plot is obtained which shows the difference in spectral maxima of each pair to be large in the red region of the spectrum, becoming smaller toward the blue; e.g., for the pair synthesized from the opsin moiety of chicken iodopsin the wavelengths are 562 and 620 nm whereas from the opsin of a marine species the respective maxima are 486 and 501 nm.

In addition to the principal, or α, absorption band, there is a higher energy band of much lower absorbance associated with the polyene chromophore (Fig. 13). This is the so-called β band which lies in the

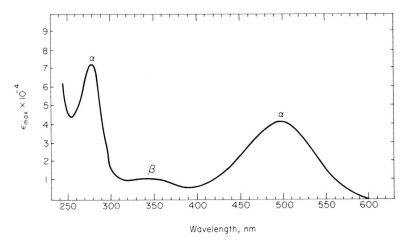

FIG. 13. Absorption spectrum of cattle rhodopsin in Emulphogene. Adapted from Shichi *et al.* (1969).

near ultraviolet with maxima ranging from 350 to 370 nm (Collins *et al.*, 1952; Wald *et al.*, 1955) and is cognate to the so-called "cis" band of 11-*cis* retinal. Both the principal, α, band and the β band of the rhodopsin chromophore have essentially the same character whether measured in the rods themselves or in aqueous digitonin micellar suspensions.

Another band even more intense than the principal absorption maximum in the visible region of the spectrum is a band at 278 nm which can be ascribed to the aromatic amino acids, tryptophan and tyrosine, of the opsin moiety (Fig. 13). Further toward the ultraviolet is a complex series of bands centered at 250 nm which can, to some extent, be ascribed to phenylalanine residues and perhaps nucleotides, but the major contribution, at least in detergent micelle preparations, appears to be partially oxidized fatty acid chains of the phospholipids (Klein, 1970).

2. Fluorescence

Fluorescence from dried bovine rod outer segments at −196°C and from glycerol-aqueous digitonin micellar suspensions of bovine rhodopsin at −3°C has been reported by Guzzo and Pool (1968). According to them, the emission from the dried rods has a maximum at 600 nm whereas that from micellar rhodopsin suspensions is centered at 570 nm at −3°C and at 575 nm at −196°C. The yield at −196°C is of the order of 0.005.

On the basis of an assumed Planck law relationship between absorption and fluorescence emission, Ross (1970) computed a hypothetical emission spectrum whose emission intensity increases exponentially at long wavelengths. To explain the maximum in the fluorescence observed by Guzzo and Pool he suggests that emission occurs from a metastable, upper vibrational level of the excited state.

3. Circular Dichroism and Optical Rotatory Dispersion Spectra

Circular dichroism (CD) and optical rotatory dispersion (ORD) spectra provide another means of characterizing visual pigments, particularly as they afford insight into the dissymmetry of the visual chromophore and its microenvironment. Such measurements are more difficult to make than are absorption spectra, and one must be careful to avoid sources of artifact such as inherent linear dichroism. For this reason reliable measurements are usually made on solutions and not on solids or organelle structures. West (1969), however, has developed a method for measuring ORD spectra which effectively eliminates this artifact and has even adapted it successfully via microspectrophotometry to the measurement of the ORD spectrum of single cells.

CD spectra generally have the appearance of absorption spectra. The curves, in fact, measure the difference in extinction, $\Delta\epsilon$, of a substance for left- and right-handed circularly polarized light. Crescitelli and Shaw (1964) and Crescitelli et al. (1966) have demonstrated in a variety of species that the principal absorption band of rhodopsin, taken in aqueous digitonin micellar suspensions, show a positive CD at its maximum in which the molar circular dichroic extinction $\Delta\epsilon_{max}$ shows unusually high values of the order of 20 cm² mmole⁻¹. Furthermore the $\Delta\epsilon_{max}$ is shifted about 10 nm to shorter wavelengths relative to the ϵ_{max} of the absorption spectrum (Fig. 14) suggesting a pronounced dissymmetry in the chromophore. Evidently the marked molecular dissymmetry found in crystals of 11-cis retinal (Gilardi et al., 1971) is also largely inherent in the rhodopsin chromophore.

The large dissymmetric factor is even more apparent in the β-band of frog rhodopsin (Fig. 14) where $\Delta\epsilon_{max}$ of the CD spectrum is much larger relative to the ϵ_{max} of the absorption spectrum than for the

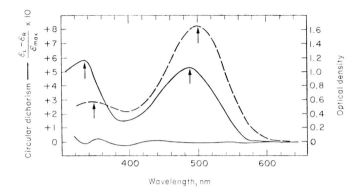

FIG. 14. Absorption spectrum (---) and circular dichroism spectrum (——) of frog rhodopsin; the upper curve showing peaks was taken before illumination, and the lower, flattened curve, after photobleaching. From Crescitelli *et al.* (1966).

principal absorption band (Azuma and Kito, 1967). But, circular dichroism in the β band does not appear to be common to all visual pigments (Crescitelli *et al.*, 1966).

ORD spectra measure the angle of rotation of plane polarized light as a function of wavelength. One can relate the ORD to the CD spectrum by means of the Kronig–Kramer theorem (Shaw, 1972) so that the two have a common theoretical background. The ORD spectra, however, have the appearance of the first derivative of the absorption spectra and are not as facile to comparison with absorption spectra as are CD spectra. On the other hand, the derivative character of ORD spectra make them, in principle, more sensitive and capable of revealing more detail than do CD spectra.

Visible ORD spectra of bovine rhodopsin have been measured in aqueous Triton X-100 and digitonin micelle suspensions (Kito and Takesaki, 1966; Williams, 1966). A large negative rotation in the region of 500 nm obscured the expected S-shaped anomaly, which was, however, manifest in the difference spectra between unilluminated and illuminated suspensions. A maximum was observed at 542 nm and a minimum at 454 nm with a rotation difference of 0.007°.

In the ultraviolet region below 250 nm, S-shaped ORD spectra are distinguishable for frog and bovine rhodopsin in digitonin suspension which are consistent with a 30% α-helical content of the lipoprotein. Both ORD and CD spectra in this region show changes on illumination (Kito and Takesaki, 1966; Crescitelli and Shaw, 1964).

CD and ORD spectra of rod suspensions and sonicated rods show a substantial and variable dichroism due to the rod or membrane structure. Difference spectra, both ORD (Kito and Takesaki, 1966) and CD (Crescitelli *et al.*, 1969) show essentially the same effects as do detergent suspensions.

In the ultraviolet region Shichi (1971a) found in the CD spectrum for bovine particles a significant negative ellipticity at 220 nm which was little affected on photolysis. However, if the particles were prepared from petroleum ether-washed rod outer segments, a treatment which removes major amounts of phospholipids, before sonication there was no change at 220 nm but subsequent photolysis resulted in a significant decrease in the negative ellipticity at this wavelength. The same qualitative effect could be produced by the addition of Emulphogene detergent to the sonicated particle suspension and, to a smaller extent, by treatment of the particles with phospholipase A. In the visible region of the spectrum the addition of Emulphogene or treatment with phospholipase decreased the positive ellipticity in the 500 nm region of the CD spectrum before illumination.

Rafferty *et al.* (1972) have also looked at the comparative CD spectra of aqueous suspensions of sonicated bovine rod outer segments and detergent micelles of rhodopsin. In the sonicated particles the relative ellipticities of the α and β brands of rhodopsin corresponded in magnitude to their molar absorbances. In micellar suspensions of rhodopsin in the aqueous detergents digitonin, Triton X-100, cetyltrimethylammonium bromide, and Emulphogene, however, the relative magnitudes of the ellipticities were opposite to those of the molar absorbances. Quite clearly this evidence along with Shichi's observations points to a considerable difference in the microenvironment of the chromophore in the two cases and emphasizes the key role of the lipid in maintaining the native conformation of visual pigments.

Cassim *et al.* (1972) have examined the far ultraviolet CD spectrum (1850–2500 Å) of sonicated bovine rod outer segment particles. Like Shichi they found no change in this region of the spectrum on illumination, which indicates that little or no change in the protein configuration of the protein moiety or rhodopsin occurs as a consequence of the light reaction. This notion is reinforced by the observations of Waggoner and Stryer (1971). They reported that sonicated rod outer segment particles and aqueous digitonin micelles of bovine rhodopsin and the early intermediates in its photolysis, metarhodopsin$_{478}$I and metarhodopsin$_{380}$II have induced rotational strengths (ORD) which do not vary appreciably one from another even though their absorption maxima are distinctly different. They interpret their results to mean that "a significant portion of the local environment of bound retinal is conserved in the transitions rhodopsin $\rightarrow$ metarhodopsin$_{478}$I $\rightarrow$ metarhodopsin$_{380}$II."

C. VISUAL PIGMENT MODELS

1. The Protonated Retinylidene Schiff Base

Morton and Pitt (1955) proposed this model shown below, for the binding of retinal to the lipoprotein opsin. Recent chemical (Hubbard, 1969) as well as spectroscopic (Rimai et al., 1970) evidence support this view. The spectroscopic evidence which is, perhaps, the most

convincing is based on the resonance enhanced-vibrational Raman spectra of bovine rod outer segments at low temperatures ($-85°C$). Laser excitation in the chromophore band at 4880 cm^{-1} yields the strongest Raman line at 1555 cm^{-1} corresponding closely with the 1560 cm^{-1} line observed in acidified ethanol and hexane solutions of retinylidene hexylamine. By contrast the unprotonated Schiff base lies at 1584 cm^{-1} in hexane. Retinal in acidified ethanol exhibits a line at 1503 cm^{-1}.

Protonated Schiff bases of simple amine complexes or retinal absorb maximally in the region 440 nm in hydroxylic solvents, and the spectral maximum is relatively independent of the anion (Erickson and Blatz, 1968). On the other hand, in solvents like CCl_4, $CHCl_3$ benzene, and chlorobenzene the spectral maximum is not only solvent dependent but also anion dependent (Irving et al., 1970; Blatz, 1972), absorbing at wavelengths as long as 480 nm in the case of the perchloric acid salt of retinylidene butylamine.

There is some question as to how the protonated retinylidene chromophore should be visualized electronically. Blatz (1972) takes the view that the retinylidenic cation at infinite separation from its anion has an intrinsic absorption maximum at about 600 nm. Strictly speaking, a protonated Schiff base model is not assumed. Instead the molecule achieves an "odd" alternate carbon configuration by rehybridization of the imine nitrogen atom from sp^2 to sp^3, removing it from the conjugated system which now supports the positive charge. The source of the promotion energy to achieve this rehybridization, however, is obscure unless the resulting electron pair on the nitrogen is tied up in a strong bonding situation. In any event, as regards the spectra of visual pigments, the function of the anion appears to be one of controlling the degree to which the positive charge is delocalized away from the nitrogen atom through regulation of its distance from the nitrogen atom. In solution this distance is governed by the solvent but in visual pigments it would be presumably governed by the conformation of the lipoportein to which the anionic group is attached. Apparently this means also that the degree of sp^2 to sp^3 promotion about the nitrogen atom is governed by the anion distance in a continuous fashion.

The difficulty with the Blatz model, theoretically, is that it seems a little too idealized. The anion nitrogen atom distance appears to have no vectorial aspect, the effect being purely coulombic, with no provision for polarization of the π electron system. There is also the question of the continuous variation of the bonding hybrid about the nitrogen atom. The principal criticism, however, is that it seems not to be in accord with the spectroscopic observations of Rimai et al. (1970). Certainly for bovine rhodopsin absorbing at 500 nm by the Blatz model the degree of sp^2 to sp^3 promotion required would leave the imine linkage with little double bond character, and one would hardly expect to obtain a Raman line for such a structure so close to that observed for the protonated imino linkage in alcohol.

The model investigated by our laboratory (Wiesenfeld and Abrahamson, 1968) is the normal protonated Schiff base. Using the notion put forth by Kropf and Hubbard (1958) that spectral control is achieved by an anionic perturbation of the π electron system, we calculated the magnitude of the effect by placing a point charge above the plane of the chromophore at various positions along the polyene chain (see Table VI and accompanying structural formula of retinylidene ammonium ion).

For this calculation, we adapted the Pariser, Parr, Pople-SCF method by correcting the coulomb integrals of each carbon and the nitrogen atom in the π electron system for the presence of the anionic charge (Wiesenfeld and Abrahamson, 1968). The data given in Table VI apply to the retinylidene configuration as found for 11-*cis* retinal by Gilardi et al. (1971). At the particular distance of 4.5 Å above the respective carbon atoms, a single point charge can perturb the spectra about 80% of the total energy range spanned by the spectral maxima. At smaller distances the full range is easily achieved. Mantione and Pullman (1971) use a somewhat more sophisticated CNDO calculation and find essentially the same effect.

It appears then that the anionic charge perturbation model can readily account for the full range of spectral maxima. A further advantage is that it predicts the pattern of differences in spectral maxima between retinal₁ and retinal₂ pigments (D. Cross, unpublished observations, 1972) as observed by Dartnall and Lythgoe (1965). Last, the model is in agreement with the Raman spectral data of Rimai.

TABLE VI

CALCULATED EFFECT OF A POINT ANIONIC CHARGE ON THE SPECTRUM
OF THE PROTONATED RETINYLIDENE AND
3-DEHYDRORETINYLIDENE AMMONIUM IONS

Location of anion charge	Retinylidene ammonium ion (nm)	3-Dehydroretinylidene ammonium ion (nm)	$\Delta\lambda$ (nm)
Infinity	438	449	11
4.5 Å above C_3	512	553	41
4.5 Å above C_5	535	561	26
4.5 Å above C_6	542	564	22
4.5 Å above C_7	540	552	12
4.5 Å above C_9	467	477	11
4.5 Å above C_{11}	458	466	8
4.5 Å above C_{13}	475	479	4
4.5 Å above C_{15}	376	396	20

A third model employing the basic protonated Schiff base theme is that proposed by the late Peter Leermakers (Irving *et al.*, 1969). It derives from the rather marked spectral perturbations afforded retinylidene quaternary ammonium by highly polarizable solvents. The model provides for a dispersive interaction between the transition dipole of the chromophore and the "microenvironment" which is envisioned as consisting of optimally positioned groups of high polarizability on the associated protein, e.g., phenylalanine, tryosine, and tryptophan. Although the model is a plausible one in principle, it is difficult to test out theoretically or experimentally.

2. The Retinylidene Schiff Base

Dartnall (1957) and Bridges (1962), primarily on the basis of the existence of pigments with $\lambda_{max} < 440$ nm, have supported the view that the chromophore is bound by an unprotonated Schiff base linkage. "Secondary bonding" of the chromophore to the opsin backbone Dartnall envisioned as occurring through interaction of the π electron system with formal charges on the lipoprotein backbone. In view of Rimai's (1971) spectroscopic evidence and the calculation of Table VI, which show that a decided *blue* shift in the spectrum can occur if an ionic charge is placed near the nitrogen atom, i.e., at C_{15}, support for this model is somewhat weakened. This calculated blue shift, however, may not be sufficient to account for the retinal$_1$ based pigment isolated from the Neuropteran *Ascalaphus* which has an absorption maximum at 345 nm (Gogala *et al.*, 1970).

V. Photolysis of Visual Pigments

A. THE QUANTUM YIELD

Measurements of the quantum yield of the photochemical bleaching of extracted visual pigments were first made by Dartnall over 35 years ago (Dartnall *et al.*, 1936, 1938). His most recent measurements (Dartnall, 1968, 1972) on a large variety of rhodopsins and porphyropsins in the principal band show the quantum yield to be essentially the same for all visual pigments, ranging between 0.65 and 0.70. From the earlier measurements of Goodeve *et al.* (1942), this same quantum yield persists for the β band.

Kropf (1969), measuring the quantum yield in the lipoprotein region of absorption, 254 and 280 nm, found the quantum yield to be one-half to three-fourths that in the principal band. He assumed that the chromophore has no absorption at the wavelengths studied and concluded that the observed bleaching must arise from intramolecular energy transfer from the protein to the polyene chromophore. It is more than likely, however, that there is absorption of the chromophore in this region in a band corresponding to the 250 nm peak of 11-*cis* retinal.

Hagins (1957) reported measurements of the photosensitivity of rhodopsin in the excised eye of an albino rabbit which, on correction for the orientation of the pigment molecules in the rod, yielded a quantum yield of 0.66. A more recent, *in situ,* measurement by Baumann (1965) on perfused frog retina yielded essentially the same result. On the other hand, Ripps and Weale (1969) reported a value of unity for the quantum yield of photobleaching in the human eye.

It is interesting to see at this stage, how well, for the most part, the quantum yield measurements in extracts and *in situ* agree. One might expect differences in view of the differences in ORD and CD spectra of membrane fragments and detergent micelle preparations of rhodopsin discussed in the previous section.

B. THE PHOTOLYSIS CYCLE IN VERTEBRATE RHODOPSIN

1. The Primary Photochemical Process

It has been well established that absorption of light induces immediate isomerization of the polyene chromophore from the 11-*cis* to the *trans* isomeric form (Hubbard and Kropf, 1958). It is not clear, however, just how such a simple isomerization can induce the observed chemical changes in the lipoprotein opsin moiety. Abrahamson and Ostroy (1967) have examined possible chemical changes, such as proton or electron transfer, that might accompany the photoisomerization and have concluded that such processes are unlikely. It would appear, therefore, that photoisomerization, alone, is the primary photochemical process, and that it must, by some molecular pathway which is still obscure, initiate the sequence of thermal (dark) reactions characterized by spectral changes in the chromophore.

The problem of the primary photochemical process is further compounded by our inexact knowledge of its product. Yoshizawa and Kito (1958) discovered a long wavelength-absorbing intermediate (λ_{max} = 543 nm) on irradiation of bovine rhodopsin in 2:1 aqueous digitonin–glycerol solutions at liquid nitrogen temperatures ($-196°C$). Later Yoshizawa and Wald (1963) found the same intermediate on irradiation of squid rhodopsin under the same conditions. This intermediate, heretofore called prelumirhodopsin (Yoshizawa and Wald, 1963), has generally been accepted as the product of the primary photochemical process. However, Yoshizawa (1972) has recently discovered a new intermediate, hypsorhodopsin (λ_{max} = 430 nm) which appears to be a precursor of prelumirhodopsin, which he has now renamed "bathorhodopsin."

Hypsorhodopsin is formed by irradiation of bovine rhodopsin at $\lambda > 540$ nm in 2:1 aqueous digitonin-glycerol solutions at liquid helium temperatures ($-269°C$). Some isorhodopsin (9-*cis*) as well as rhodopsin is formed in the mixture. Further irradiation of hypsorhodopsin at 406 nm or warming to temperatures above $-250°C$ produces bathorhodopsin. These facts suggests that hypsorhodopsin is a precursor of bathorhodopsin. However, irradiation of rhodopsin at liquid helium temperatures, but at shorter wavelengths, i.e., 437 nm, produces bathorhodopsin directly, along with some isorhodopsin. Irradiation of bathorhodopsin, on the other hand, produces only rhodopsin and isorhodopsin, but no hypsorhodopsin. The position of hypsorhodopsin *vis-à-vis* the primary process is therefore uncertain.

As to the structure of hypsorhodopsin one can only speculate. From its wavelength maximum at 430 nm and its small molar absorbance (0.9 that of rhodopsin) it probably exists as the 11-*cis* isomer of the protonated Schiff base in a relatively unperturbed environment. Photoisomerization in this case may have occurred about a formal single bond such as the C_{12}-C_{13} rather than the C_{11}-C_{12} double bond. However, as it readily reverts thermally to bathorhodopsin, some torsion in the C_{11}-C_{12} double bond seems apparent in its structure.

Bathorhodopsin, on the basis of its long wavelength maximum and a molar absorbance about 1.13 times that of rhodopsin definitely suggests a *trans* isomer but one that is "twisted" about the C_{11}-C_{12} double band since it appears capable, in the case of chicken iodopsin, of thermally reverting either to the parent chicken iodopsin or to lumi-iodopsin depending on the temperature (Yoshizawa and Wald, 1967).

Further complications are apparent in the primary process from the work of Horwitz and Heller (1971), who observe the development of an apparent biphasic CD spectrum on the illumination at 500 nm of glycerol suspensions of digitonin and CTAB micelles of bovine rhodopsin at liquid nitrogen temperatures. After full development further illumination at wavelengths longer than 560 nm produced another different biphasic CD spectrum. The CD spectra of the two states so produced were later shown to be due to photoinduced linear dichroism (Horwitz and Heller, 1972).

2. The Intermediate Sequence

The thermal decay of bathorhodopsin is the first in a sequence of thermal reactions depicted in Fig. 15. There has been some question as to whether bathorhodopsin is a true physiological intermediate (Abrahamson and Ostroy, 1967), but the most current evidence based on laser flash photolytic studies indicates that it is (Busch *et al.*, 1972).

The product of the decay of bathorhodopsin is the intermediate, lumirhodopsin, first seen by Broda and Goodeve (1941). In the form of digitonin micelles it is stable in aqueous glycerol at $-50°C$ and has its absorption maximum at 497 nm which represents a hypsochromic shift of about 5 nm relative to rhodopsin at that temperature. Its molar absorbance in bovine rhodopsin is about 10% greater than that of rhodopsin but, in bull frog rhodopsin, it is reported to be somewhat lower (Hubbard and Kropf, 1959; Hubbard *et al.*, 1959). Nevertheless the chromophore clearly appears to be in a *trans* configuration.

On warming lumirhodopsin to temperatures about $-40°C$ it undergoes a thermal conversion to an intermediate first seen by Broda and Goodeve (1941) whose λ_{max} lies near 478 nm and which was later named as metarhodopsin I by Matthews *et al.* (1963). The thermal process bathorhodopsin to lumirhodopsin and lumirhodopsin to metarhodopsin I appear to be independent of the aqueous environment. Erhardt *et al.* (1966) have shown that the latter process involves no release or consumption of hydrogen ion or exposure of sulfhydryl groups as originally postulated by Wald *et al.* (1963).

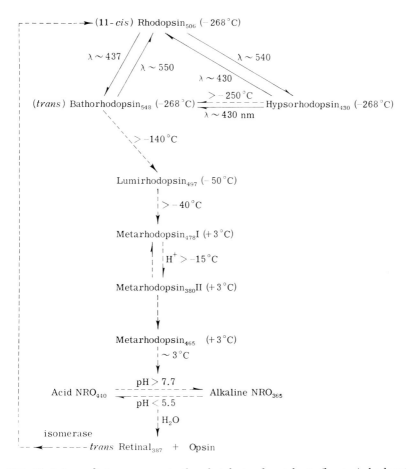

FIG. 15. Intermediate sequence in the photolysis of vertebrate (bovine) rhodopsin. Arrows with solid lines denote photoreactions; those with dotted lines denote thermal, dark reactions. Given in parentheses are temperatures at which spectra of intermediates were taken.

At temperatures near $-5°C$ metarhodopsin I undergoes a thermal conversion to an intermediate absorbing maximally at 380 nm, called metarhodopsin II by Matthews *et al.* (1963). Ostroy *et al.* (1966) prefer to add subscripts to the names to denote the wavelengths of maximum absorption. The kinetics of this process in digitonin solution was first studied by Linschitz *et al.* (1957) and Abrahamson *et al.* (1960). Its chemical character was later elucidated by Matthews *et al.* (1963) and Ostroy *et al.* (1966a). Both groups concluded that a metastable, acid sensitive, equilibrium between the two species was apparent at lower temperatures which could be described by the equilibrium constant

$$K_{\text{I}-\text{II}} = \frac{[\text{metarhodopsin}_{380}\text{II}]}{[\text{metarhodopsin}_{478}\text{I}][\text{H}_3\text{O}^+]^n} \tag{3}$$

where the exponent, n, according to Ostroy et al. (1966) had the value about 1/2. From the variation of the equilibrium constant with temperature, the thermodynamic parameters were calculated; $\Delta H = 10$ kcal/mole and $\Delta S = 34$ cal/degree mole.

As mentioned previously the calculated pK of 6.4 for the process prompted Matthews et al. (1963) to suggest that the imidazole group of histidine was being protonated in the reaction. More recently, Emrich (1971) has found, for sonicated bovine rod outer segment suspensions, two inflection points in the absorbance vs. pH curve, one at pH = 6.4 in agreeement with Matthews et al. (1963) and another one at pH = 10.5. On this basis he rejects the imidazole protonation hypothesis in favor of lipid to protein transimination suggested originally by our laboratory. However, subsequent evidence from other laboratories and particularly our most recent evidence on the cyanoborohydride reduction of these intermediates, discussed earlier, favor a lysine-protein binding site for both metarhodopsin$_{478}$I and metarhodopsin$_{380}$II.

There has been some disagreement as to the pathway by which metarhodopsin$_{380}$II decays. Matthews et al. (1963) claimed that it decays directly to trans retinal$_{387}$ and opsin while Ostroy et al. (1966a) invoked two additional intermediates in the path, metarhodopsin$_{465}$ and the acid and alkaline forms of N-retinylidene opsin (NRO). Metarhodopsin$_{465}$ has been named pararhodopsin by Wald (1968) in accordance with his view that it is a side product, outside the mainstream of physiological events (Matthews et al., 1963). N-retinylidene opsin, originally seen by Lythgoe and Quilliam (1938) and characterized by Collins (1953) as the trans retinylidene group bound to an amino site on the lipoprotein, opsin, has also been regarded by Wald as extraneous to the physiological path. Ostroy et al. (1966a), however, clearly identify it as mediating metarhodopsin$_{465}$ and the hydrolyzed products, trans retinal and opsin.

Experiments performed under near physiological conditions, i.e., the excised eye of an albino rat (Hagins, 1957) and the retina of a rat (Ebrey, 1967) suggest that parallel paths succeed metarhodopsin$_{380}$II. Donner and Reuter (1969), in fact, postulate two forms of metarhodopsin$_{380}$II in the frog retina; one decaying directly to retinal and opsin and the other equilibrating with a metarhodopsin$_{465}$-like intermediate absorbing maximally in the region 470–480 nm which they regard as regenerated metarhodopsin$_{478}$I. Whatever the true course of events in the physiological path it is unlikely that they will have any primary effect on the neural receptor potential as they occur in times of the order of minutes.

The pretreatment of micellar rhodopsin appears to affect the sequence of intermediates depicted in Fig. 15. If aqueous digitonin suspensions of bovine rhodopsin are treated with the sulfhydryl reagent Ag(Tris)$_2{}^+$, up to four thiol groups are complexed in the dark with no apparent effect on the 500 nm absorption maximum. But on illumination the first detectable product is metarhodopsin$_{380}$II, which appears to decay normally to metarhadopsin$_{465}$ with the exposure of 1-2 additional thiol groups (Ostroy et al., 1966b).

If rhodopsin is incubated with 8 M urea or with parachloromercuribenzoate (PCMB) in a 1:20 mole ratio for 2 hours near room temperature and then illuminated the first observable intermediate is metarhodopsin$_{465}$ (Ostroy et al., 1966a). Apparently the conformational changes induced in the periphery of the lipoprotein and the blocking of sulfhydryl groups affect the intermediate sequence in a major way — particularly as regards the metarhodopsin$_{478}$I to metarhodopsin$_{380}$II process, which appears to play a key role in the initiation of the neural receptor potential.

3. The Kinetics of Intermediate Processes

The study of the kinetics of intermediate processes in solution began with our earlier studies of the metarhodopsin$_{478}$I → metarhodopsin$_{380}$II process using the technique of flash photolysis (Linschitz et al., 1957). We were able to show that this process occurred in times comparable to neural impulse generation. The technique has since been applied to the earlier and later intermediate processes. Here we will focus largely on the kinetics of the early intermediate processes, those fast enough to be involved in the generation of neural activity, as one of us (Abrahamson and Wiesenfeld, 1972) has recently discussed the kinetics of all the intermediate processes in some detail.

Until quite recently the existing technology has permitted the study of processes with lifetimes of about 10 μsec or longer, but with the advent of nanosecond and picosecond pulsed laser units it has been possible to study the earliest intermediate process at room temperature.

It must be emphasized that the flash photolysis technique generally measures spectral changes in the chromophoric region and hence reflects only those changes that involve the chromophoric entity. It is gratifying, however, to find, for the most part, that the rapid measurement of other parameters, i.e., conductivity (Falk and Fatt, 1966) and pH (Emrich, 1971), appear to monitor the same processes as do spectral measurements.

In treating the kinetic data it has been useful to characterize the individual processes in terms of Absolute Reaction Rate Theory, employing the parameters: $\Delta G\ddagger$, the free energy of activation, $\Delta H\ddagger$, the enthalpy of activation, and $\Delta S\ddagger$, the entropy of activation (Abrahamson et al., 1960). The theoretical significance of these parameters in the complex processes studied may be obscure. Nevertheless they are known to have some empirical significance in protein reactions. For example, it has been shown that in the reversible denaturation of enzymes, the kinetic parameters $\Delta H\ddagger$ and $\Delta S\ddagger$ are sensible fractions of their thermodynamic counterparts (Bray and White, 1957).

a. Bathorhodopsin$_{543}$ → Lumirhodopsin$_{497}$. The thermal decay of bathorhodopsin$_{543}$ to lumirhodopsin$_{497}$ in aqueous-glycerol digitonin solutions was studied in the temperature range -50 to $-67°C$ by Livingston and co-workers (Grellman et al., 1962; Pratt et al., 1964). Their data, like those obtained for the metarhodopsin$_{478}$I → metarhodopsin$_{380}$II process (Linschitz et al., 1957; Abrahamson et al., 1960) was treated in terms of several simultaneous first-order processes. The enthalpy of activation, $\Delta H\ddagger$ for all three processes was 10 ± 2 kcal, and the entropy of activation, $\Delta S\ddagger$, varied between $+5$ and and -2 e.u. When extrapolated to $38°C$ the half-life of the fastest reaction was 1.5×10^{-7} seconds and the slowest 3.8×10^{-5} seconds. The more recent measurement of Busch et al. (1972) on LDAO solutions of bovine rhodopsin using a picosecond laser flash unit was 2.5×10^{-8} second at $25°C$ for an apparently single first-order process. For rod particle suspensions Pratt et al. (1964) found somewhat larger activation parameters, i.e., $\Delta H\ddagger = 12.5\pm3$ kcal and $\Delta S\ddagger$ between 12 and 18 e.u. The extrapolated half-life of the fastest process was 1.3×10^{-8} second.

A clue to the nature of the conversion of bathorhodopsin to lumirhodopsin is provided by the calculated $\Delta H^{\neq}$ and $\Delta S^{\neq}$. The relatively small values of these parameters suggest that little in the way of macromolecular configurational changes occur and the simple relaxation of a torsionally distorted chromophore is a picture consistent with these values.

b. Lumirhodopsin$_{497}$ → Metarhodopsin$_{478}$I. Studies of the kinetics of this process have been difficult in terms of reproducibility, and there is some question as to just how the data should be treated. Kinetic treatments of the metarhodopsin$_{478}$I → metarhodopsin$_{380}$II process clearly favor the multiform concept of intermediates, i.e., several forms of the same spectrally distinct intermediates each decaying simultaneously by a first-order process but with different rate constants. The data can clearly be fitted to this scheme, but a good fit is also obtained if a single second-order decay process is assumed in which the lumirhodopsin intermediate reacts with some other substrate.

The most recent data from our laboratory for the decay of lumirhodopsin$_{497}$ as digitonin micelles in aqueous glycerol using flash illumination (Rapp et al., 1970), when treated by the multiform first-order scheme show the several forms to decay by processes involving moderate enthalpies of activation, i.e., $\Delta H\ddagger = 17.6–18.4$ kcal, and very small entropies of activation, i.e., $\Delta S\ddagger$ 2–4.0 e.u. Although the activation parameters are somewhat different than those obtained earlier by our laboratory (Erhardt et al., 1966). The rate constants for the slowest process at $-20.0°C$ are essentially the same ($k = 2.0 \times 10^{-3}$ sec^{-1}). This contrasts with data of Matthews and Wald, as reported by Hubbard et al. (1965), who find only a single first-order rate constant at $-20°C$ of $k = 4.5 \times 10^{-4}$ sec^{-1} with a $\Delta H^{+} = 60$ kcal and a $\Delta S^{+} = +160$ e.u. Presumably the data of Matthews and Wald was taken after steady illumination for an extended period of time so that the initial decay rate was not observed. But even when the data of Rapp et al. is treated by a limiting single first-order rate scheme essentially the same rate constant at $-20°C$ is found although the activation parameters are somewhat different, i.e., $\Delta H\ddagger \sim 22.4$ kcal and $\Delta S\ddagger \sim 18$ e.u.

Suspension of rod outer segments show much enhanced rates of decay of lumirhodopsin$_{497}$ over those found in digitonin micelles. At $-40°C$ Rapp et al. (1970) find a limiting first-order rate constant of 3.4×10^{-2} sec^{-1} which increases to 4.23×10^{4} sec^{-1} at $18°C$. Furthermore the activation parameters are markedly temperature dependent. In the temperature range -40 to $-50°C$ a $\Delta H\ddagger \pm \sim 25.2$ kcal and a $\Delta S\ddagger \sim 45.0$ eV were calculated while in the range 3.0 to $18°C$ the values changed to a $\Delta H\ddagger \sim 4.5$ kcal and a $\Delta S\ddagger \sim 21.7$ eV.

Quite clearly the pronounced change in character of the decay of lumirhodopsin in going from low to high temperatures suggest a medium effect, perhaps a phase transition in the membrane milieu. This is, however, more indicative of a bimolecular rather than a monomolecular process and, indeed, when one treats the kinetic data for the decay of lumirhodopsin$_{497}$ according to Eq. (4) (Rapp et al., 1970)

$$L + E \rightarrow metarhodopsin_{478} I \qquad (4)$$

Where L is lumirhodopsin whose initial concentration is L_0 and E is some unknown substrate whose initial concentration is E_0 then a linear plot of L/E vs time can be obtained by the proper choice of E_0. L_0, of course, can be obtained from absorbance data. From the slope of such a plot the second-order rate constant K_{LE} can be obtained according to Eq. (5).

$$\text{Slope} = \frac{(L_0 - E_0)K_{LE}}{2.303} \tag{5}$$

For rod outer segment suspensions in the low temperature range, -40 to $-50°C$ and for an $L_0 : E_0$ ratio of 1.05, $\Delta H\ddagger$ and $\Delta S\ddagger$ are calculated as 25.3 kcal and 70.3 eV. At the higher temperature range, 3–36°C, the optimum L_0/E_0 ratio changes to 0.10 and the calculated $\Delta H\ddagger$ is 3.5 kcal and $\Delta S^{\pm}$ is -5.8 eV. Thus the same discontinuity in activation parameters appears in the second-order plot, but there the rather marked change in L_0/E_0 suggests that the process is taking on a first-order character at the higher temperatures.

The second-order plot is consistent with the earlier notion of lipid to protein transimination of the chromophore as postulated several years ago by this laboratory (Poincelot et al., 1969). In fact it was proposed (Rapp et al., 1970) that lumirhodopsin was a chromolipid which formed a complex with the appropriate protein, the lumi-rhodopsin$_{497}$ to metarhodopsin$_{478}$I process representing this bi-molecular complex formation. In view of our more recent findings discussed in Section III, strongly supporting a protein binding site for the chromophore in the native rhodopsin and metarhodopsin$_{478}$I, a molecularity consistent with such a second-order process is not immediately evident.

c. Metarhodopsin$_{478}$I → metarhodopsin$_{380}$II. As previously mentioned, this process was the first one studied in solution (Linschitz et al., 1957; Wulff et al., 1958; Abrahamson et al., 1960), and it is the earliest process which exhibited pronounced environmental effects (Matthews et al., 1963; Ostroy et al., 1966a). Flash kinetic data for this process occurring in aqueous suspensions of digitonin micelles and rod suspensions are given in Table VII. A typical flash oscillogram is shown in Fig. 16.

Examination of Table VII reveals several interesting points about this process. The micellar data, with the exception of data of von Sengbusch and Stieve (1971) and the Harvard Laboratory, indicate several forms of metarhodopsin$_{478}$I. Von Senbusch (von Sengbusch and Stieve, 1971) attributes these to deterioration of micellar rhodopsin preparations when stored at −70°C. Preparations stored at liquid nitrogen temperatures, as well as rod segment suspensions stored under normal conditions, according to him exhibit a single first-order decay process. This may be due to a spontaneous fractionation of the rhodopsin micelles according to their lipid content on storage at the higher temperatures or to an aging effect on the protein itself which is not apparent in the absorption spectrum.

There is a definite effect of pH on the rate of the process as is evident from the low temperature data of Ostroy et al. (1966a) which could be inferred from Eq. (3). Both Falk and Fatt (1966) and Emrich (1971) using different methods show an uptake of one proton in the process which follows the kinetics of the 478 to 380 nm spectral change. Strangely enough the spectral change is indicative of the loss of a proton at the binding site so that the overall process metarhodopsin$_{478}$I to metarhodopsin$_{380}$II should reflect changes in the periphery of the lipoprotein, a point borne out by the activation parameters which are consistent with substantial configurational changes in the lipoprotein moiety. This point, however, is not supported by the ORD and CD data discussed previously and the more recent CD data of Waggoner and Stryer (1971), which indicate only miniscule changes in the lipoprotein environment of the chromophore on photolysis.

The decay of metarhodopsin$_{478}$I in rod outer segments, whether whole or sonicated, appears to be much simpler than in micellar suspensions. Aside from the data of Pratt et al. (1964), only a single first-order decay process is apparent, which probably reflects the stabilizing character of the membrane milieu on rhodopsin molecules. We have, however, noted in our oscillograms (Fig. 16) a small deviation in the very initial stages of the decay which might indicate the presence of a small fraction of a faster decaying species, but, quite likely, this is an instrument artifact.

It is interesting to compare the multiform rate data of micellar rhodopsin with the single decay rates of metarhodopsin$_{478}$I in rod outer segments and in retina. There is no great difference in the two as shown in the decay of lumirhodopsin$_{497}$ but, in general, the rod outer segment decay rates tend more toward the slower of the multiform processes of micellar rhodopsin. It is also of interest to note how well the data on sonicated bovine rod outer segments agree with the much less precise data on the intact excised eyes of the rabbit and rat.

As the metarhodopsin$_{478}$I → metarhodopsin$_{380}$II process is the

TABLE VII

RATE DATA FOR MICELLAR BOVINE METARHODOPSIN$_{478}$I → METARHODOPSIN$_{380}$II
TREATED AS SIMULTANEOUS FIRST-ORDER PROCESSES

		Rate constants (sec^{-1})		$\Delta G\ddagger$ (kcal/mole)	$\Delta H\ddagger$ (kcal/mole)	$\Delta S\ddagger$ (cal/deg·mole)
Wulff et al. (1958)		28°C	36.7°C			
Aqueous digitonin pH=7	k_1	3300	22,000	12.5	36.2	78
	k_2	120	2,700	14.5	50.2	119
	k_3	21.0	200	15.8	43.0	90
Abrahamson et al. (1960)		6.7°C	15.8°C			
Aqueous digitonin pH=7	k_1	577				
	k_2	45.5	303.0	15.0	37.1	76.5
	k_3	0.88	9.9	15.6	43.1	95.2
Ostroy et al. (1966)		−9.2°C	−13.7°C			
33% Glycerol–aqueous digitonin	k_2	0.0353	0.0051		59.9	162
pH=5.85, pH=4.5	k_2	0.0836	0.0121		58.7	159
Pratt et al. (1964)		5°C	25°C			
33% Glycerol–aqueous digitonin	k_1					
pH=7	k_2	0.45	126		43	97
	k_3	0.09	17		41	83

Study						19	60	160
Matthews and Wald as quoted by Hubbard et al. (1965)			Rate constants not reported					
von Sengbusch and Stieve (1971) Digitonin centrifuged 4000 g	k	37°C	1150±110			$E_A = 33.0 \pm 1.5$ kcal/mole		
Pratt et al. (1964) Bovine ROS[a]	k_1	10°C	6.0	20°C	50	35	28	70
	k_2		1.3		12	37	29	74
Rapp (1970) Sonicated bovine ROS	k	18°C	41.4	39.4°C	1480	14–15	30.7	54.8
Hagins (1957) Excised rabbit eye	k	12°C	30.0	26°C	600	13.0	37.6	80.0
Ebrey (1967) Rat retina measured as decay of ERP	k	60°C	~3.5	13.0°C	~28	~15	41±8	91+20
von Sengbusch and Stieve (1971) Bovine ROS suspension	k	37°C	1180±90			$E_A = 33.7 \pm 1.0$ kcal/mole		

[a]ROS = rod outer segments.

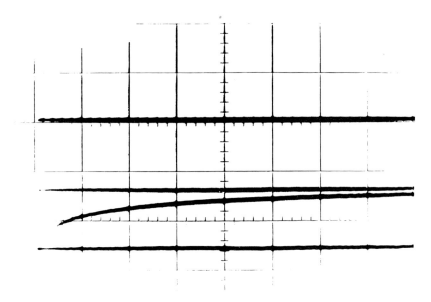

FIG. 16. Flash oscillogram of sonicated bovine rod outer segments, pH = 6.2, temperature = 21.5°C, transmission changes monitored at 380 nm, 2 msec per division; curved trace shows growth of metarhodopsin$_{380}$II approaching asymptotically, its final absorbance denoted by linear trace.

earliest one in the sequence to show chemical involvement of the environment, i.e., pH effects, and significant macromolecular configurational changes according to its kinetics, it appears to be the most likely candidate reaction of the early intermediate processes for initiating of neural activity, particularly since it appears to correlate temporally with the early receptor potential (ERP) of the mammalian electroretinogram (Ebrey, 1967).

C.   INTERMEDIATES IN THE PHOTOLYSIS OF CEPHALOPOD (SQUID) RHODOPSIN

1. The Intermediate Sequence

The intermediate picture in squid rhodopsin is decidedly different than in vertebrates although there are striking similarities in the spectra of the native pigment and its earliest (bathorhodopsin) intermediate. It is generally assumed that the sequence established by the Harvard Laboratory (Hubbard and St. George, 1958; Kropf et al., 1959; Yoshizawa and Wald, 1964) and shown in Fig. 17 is common to all invertebrates.

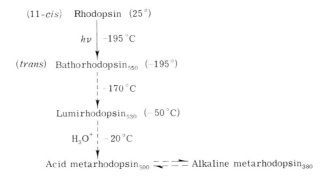

FIG. 17. Intermediate sequence in the photolysis of squid rhodopsin.

The primary photochemical process in the photolysis of squid appears to be identical to the vertebrate case. No substance analogous to hypsorhodopsin, however, has yet been identified. Beyond the bathorhodopsin stage, events clearly differ from the vertebrate case. Nothing is known, to date, as to the character of the bathorhodopsin → lumirhodopsin conversion, but the conversion of lumirhodopsin → metarhodopsin has a character more in keeping with the metarhodopsin$_{478}$I → metarhodopsin$_{380}$II process of bovine rhodopsin. Abrahamson and Ehrhart (1964) have found that the lumirhodopsin → metarhodopsin process is acid catalyzed and thiol groups become titratable. The terminal intermediate, metarhodopsin, is an acid base indicator like N-retinylidene opsin although its acid form very closely resembles the spectra of native squid (*Loligo pealii*) rhodopsin save for its enhanced molar absorbance.

2. Kinetic Studies of the Lumirhodopsin to Metarhodopsin

The early studies of Abrahamson and Erhardt (1964) showed the process to proceed at classically measurable rates at low temperatures exhibiting a single first-order decay rate, with activation parameters consistent with the notion that substantial lipoprotein configurational changes were occurring. This has been borne out by the recent studies in our laboratory (Brauner, 1973) using flash photolysis. These later studies show more clearly the pronounced effect of pH on the reaction (Table VIII). Conversion to acid metarhodopsin (pH = 6.65) is faster by two orders of magnitude near room temperature than conversion to alkaline metarhodopsin (pH = 9.7) but the $\Delta H\ddagger$ for the latter process is almost 15 kcal lower. This would imply a considerable configurational change in the peripheral lipoprotein in the conversion.

TABLE VIII

Rate Data for the Lumirhodopsin to Metarhodopsin Conversion in Aqueous Digitonin Micellar Preparation of Squid Rhodopsin

Process	Rate constant (sec^{-1})			$\Delta G^{\ddagger}$ (kcal/mole)	$\Delta H^{\ddagger}$ (kcal/mole)	$\Delta S^{\ddagger}$ (cal/mole degree)
Abrahamson and Erhardt (1964) pH = 6.6 in 2:1 glycerol:H$_2$O	-40°C				40	90
Brauner (1973)	3.9°C	20.3°C	31.8°C			
flash photolysis of aqueous digitonin suspension pH = 9.7	8.8 0°C	86.9 10.8°C	332.4 16.5°C		20.5±1	20±1
pH = 7.5	2.89 0°C	7.66 12.3°C	59.0 19.3°C		26.5±1	
pH = 6.65	135.9	2303	8366		34.5	78

VI. Other Retinal-Based Pigments

We have been concerned up to this point with the visual pigments of vertebrate rod cells and the invertebrate squid rhabdomes, i.e., rhodopsins. There are, however, several other retinal-based photosensitive pigments, similar in some respect to rhodopsin but unique in others. Among these are the cone pigments associated with color vision, cephalopod retinochrome, and the purple membrane protein from the halophilic bacterium *Halobacterium halobium*.

1. Cone Pigments

The quantities of cone pigments present in the visual vertebrate retina is markedly less than the rod pigment rhodopsin. Furthermore cone pigments are considerably less stable. These two facts have largely prevented their study by methods which have proved convenient for rhodopsins. To date the most thoroughly biochemically characterized cone pigment is chicken iodopsin (Wald *et al.*, 1955). However, the methods used here still produce a pigment considerably less pure than rhodopsin. Perhaps the most effective tool in the study of cone pigments has been microspectrophotometry (Liebman, 1972). The method involves the focusing of a compensated monochromatic microbeam of light on the outer segment and scanning the visible spectrum at a light level low enough to prevent excessive bleaching but high enough for measurement at a satisfactory signal to noise ratio. By this method it has been demonstrated that primates and gold fish have three cone pigments, each sensitive to a different spectral region, blue, green, and red (Marks *et al.*, 1964; Wald and Brown, 1963; Liebman and Entine, 1964).

Generally in the study of cone pigments their long wavelength sensitivity requires the use of an infrared image converter for viewing them under the microscope or in ordinary laboratory procedures.

The fact that cone pigments regenerate an order of magnitude faster than rhodopsin and are stabler over a much narrower pH range suggest that the chromophore binding site is much more accessible to the aqueous environment. This is further borne out by the ready reactivity of unilluminated cone pigments with hydroxylamine and sodium borohydride (Fager *et al.*, 1973c) in contrast to the inertness of unilluminated rhodopsin to these reagents. The much more enhanced reactivity of cone pigment no doubt is related to physiological function, i.e., chemical stability is sacrificed for more rapid regenerability.

2. Retinochrome

A second pigment, which is of great interest is retinochrome, a minority photopigment in cephalopod eyes (Hara and Hara, 1965, 1967, 1968, 1972), which appears to be located in pigmented tissue beneath the rhodopsin-containing rhabdomes. The chromophore is retinal, but in its native form it is the *trans* form and after illumination becomes 11-*cis*. In detergent solution this pigment exchanges readily with free retinal but, so far, this exchange has not been demonstrated *in vivo*. It therefore appears to act like a photoisomerase rather than a visual pigment, but, its exact function remains to be established.

3. Microbial Pigment

A microbial, retinal-based, photopigment of the purple membrane of the halophilic bacterium *Halobacterium halobium* has been studied by Stoeckenius and Oesterhelt (1971). It has a molecular weight about 30,000 and is embedded in a membrane of rather peculiar composition. There are no amino phospholipids and cardiolipin-type lipids constitute an appreciable fraction of the membrane. There are no unsaturated side chains, and branched chains are present in large quantity. Finally the hydrophobic side chains are attached by ether rather than ester linkages.

The pigment molecules appear to have a high degree of order in the membrane plane and unlike rhodopsin, they exhibit an interesting photoreversibility between two states of differing absorption spectra. The purple membrane only appears under certain conditions of growth, but accounts for as much as 20% of the total membrane surface. It is far from clear, however, for what function the membrane is specialized.

VII.   A Summing Up

We may sum up our current knowledge of visual photoreceptors by first recognizing that such cells are but a very small part of the visual system. The primate retina which we think of largely in terms of the photoreceptor cells contains in addition some four layers of nerve cells which perform a complicated integrating function of the receptor signals. Conceptually, however, we can view the photoreceptor cell as an isolated unit feeding essentially a unidirectional signal to a "neural net" constituting the rest of the visual system, although the possibility of feedback cannot be discounted.

It is convenient to classify our knowledge of photoreceptors into structural, neurophysiological and molecular categories. Structurally the photoreceptor cell in both vertebrates and invertebrates consists of an outer and inner segment, the inner segment containing the nucleus and mitochondria and other metabolic machinery while the' outer segment is the locus of the visual pigment.

In vertebrates the outer segment is generally ensheathed by the plasma membrane whose apparent function, in addition to mediating ion flow, is to support a stack of approximately 500 unitary disc membranes. Each disc membrane encloses an aqueous region and on the internal surfaces interfacing with this aqueous region are located the visual pigment molecules, arranged in a short-term ordered pattern, but appearing to have some mobility in the surface while maintaining a fixed orientation of the chromophore coplanar with it. Our most recent work supports the notion that light at high levels of illumination initiates a structural change in the disc membrane, the visual pigment molecules undergoing a translocation from the inner hydrophilic surface to the median hydrophobic (lipid) region of the membrane which is the main permeability barrier.

From a neurophysiological viewpoint, we associate with the photoreceptor cell an electric receptor potential of several milliseconds latency which clearly has the properties of a membrane potential. Preceding this in time and with an amplitude normally several orders of magnitude smaller is an early receptor potential (ERP) which appears to be associated with the photobleaching of the pigment molecules themselves (Brown and Murakami, 1964; Pak and Cone, 1964) rather than ion flow across membranes. Whether it is in the mainstream of physiological events or an indirectly related phenomena is not known.

The inner segment of the vertebrate cell appears to contain an ion pump whose energy arises in the mitochondria. It is fully in action in the dark, sending a cyclic sodium ion current proceeding out from the inner segment membrane externally through the extracellular solution and entering the inner segment through the plasma membrane. On exposure to light, electrophysiological experiments (Tomita, 1970) and the recent osmotic studies of Korenbrot and Cone (1971) point to a rapid reduction in sodium ion permeability of the outer segment on illumination, i.e., a hyperpolarization. In the vertebrate rod cell this sodium ion permeability change is associated with the ensheathing plasma membrane. The apparent role of the rhodopsin-containing disc membranes is one of releasing some small messenger molecule(s) as a consequence of light absorption which directly or indirectly changes the plasma membrane permeability. Hagins (1972) has suggested that calcium ion is the messenger molecule. The apparent light-controlled adenyl cyclase (Bitensky *et al.*, 1971) and the protein kinases (Frank *et al.*, 1972; R. C. Pannbacker, personal communication, 1972) of the rod outer segment may also mediate this process.

In the invertebrate squid the membrane structure is not known in any detail. However, its behavior is in contrast to the vertebrate case in that a depolarizing, i.e., an increase in the sodium ion current, rather than a hyperpolarization is apparent on illumination (Hagins, 1965).

From a molecular point of view our knowledge of visual pigments and their membranes is quite substantial but by no means complete. We know the pigment to be a chromolipoprotein whose chromophore by chemical and spectroscopic evidence is the protonated Schiff base derived from 11-*cis*-retinal or, in a few cases, its 3-dehydro derivative. Its binding site in the native pigment is now known with reasonable certainty in both vertebrates and invertebrates to be the epsilon amino group of a lysine unit of the protein rather than an amino group of the lipid phosphatidylethanolamine. The shape, molecular weight, and amino acid composition of the pigment protein of the vertebrates differs markedly from invertebrates as does the lipid composition and degree of rigidity of their membranes.

The molecular events following illumination of visual pigment molecules have been characterized in some degree both in vertebrates and in the invertebrate squid. The primary photochemical process, the photoismerization of the 11-*cis*-retinylidene group to a *trans* conformation, initiates a chain of thermal processes which, although differing in vertebrates, has certain features common to both.

In vertebrates the key thermal process appears to be the conversion of metarhodopsin$_{478}$I $\rightarrow$ metarhodopsin$_{380}$II, the earliest reaction in the chain involving not only chemical reactions with its environment but also, by kinetic evidence, distinct conformational changes. It is this reaction that correlates temporally with the early receptor potential and apparently, from our recent studies, with the translocation of the pigment molecule in the disc membrane.

In the invertebrate squid the reaction closest in analogy to the metarhodopsin$_{478}$I $\rightarrow$ metarhodopsin$_{380}$II process is the conversion of squid lumirhodopsin to metarhodopsin.

A number of problems remain to be solved at the molecular level.

There is the amino acid sequence and three-dimensional structure of rhodopsin; the latter problem particularly will be difficult as the lipid composition is not precisely known aside from the fact that no one has yet succeeded in crystallizing a membrane lipoprotein.

From the dynamic point of view we have a rather incomplete knowledge of the molecular changes that take place in the sequence of intermediate reactions. Of prime interest is the mechanism by which a simple photoisomerization of the chromophore initiates the chain of events resulting in what may be a translocation of the pigment molecules in the membrane and the still larger problem of just what function, if any, this apparent translocation serves. In this regard the conflicting evidence of kinetics and chemistry on the one hand, and ORD and CD spectral measurements, on the other, as to configurational changes in the protein, needs to be resolved. This poses the question of the driving force behind the apparent translocation of pigment molecules. Is it simply a question of the relative thermodynamic stabilities of native rhodopsin molecules as ordered monodispersed charged entities in the hydrophilic surface of the membrane as opposed to an agglomerate of uncharged lipoprotein molecules in the photobleached form in a hydrophobic environment, or is some other factor involved?

Finally there is the problem of minor constituents such as enzyme systems. In particular the role of adenyl cyclase and related enzyme systems found in copious quantities in the rod outer segment needs to be clarified.

ACKNOWLEDGMENTS

The authors gratefully acknowledge support of their own work reported in this article by the National Eye Institute of the National Institutes of Health, through Grants EY-00209 and EY-00471. We wish to thank Dr. Richard Eakin for aid in preparation of this review and Dr. W. T. Mason for careful reading of the manuscript.

REFERENCES

Abrahamson, E. W., and Erhardt, F. (1964). *Fed. Proc. Fed. Amer. Soc. Exp. Biol.* 23, 384.
Abrahamson, E. W., and Ostroy, S. E. (1967). *Prog. Biophys. Mol. Biol.* 17, 181–213.
Abrahamson, E. W., and Wiesenfeld, J. R. (1972). *In* "Handbook of Sensory Physiology" (H. J. A. Dartnell, ed.), Chapter 3. Springer-Verlag, Berlin and New York.
Abrahamson, E. W., Adams, R. G., and Wulff, V. J. (1959). *J. Phys. Chem.* 63, 441.
Abrahamson, E. W., Marquisee, J., Gavuzzi, P., and Roubie, J. (1960). *Z. Elektrochem.* 64, 177.
Adams, R. G. (1967). *J. Lipid Res.* 8, 245.

Akhtar, M., and Hirtenstein, M. D. (1969). *Biochem. J.* **115**, 607.
Akhtar, M., Blosse, P. T., and Dewhurst, P. B. (1967). *Chem. Commun.* p. 631.
Anderson, R. E. (1970). *Exp. Eye Res.* **10**, 339.
Anderson, R. E. (1972). *Biochemistry* **11**, 1224.
Anderson, R. E., and Maude, M. B. (1970). *Biochemistry* **9**, 3624.
Anderson, R. E., Feldman, L. S., and Feldman, G. L. (1970). *Biochim. Biophys. Acta* **202**, 367.
Azuma, M., and Kito, Y. (1967). *Annu. Rep. Biol. Works, Fac. Sci., Osaka Univ.* **15**, 59.
Balke, D. E., and Becker, R. S. (1967). *J. Amer. Chem. Soc.* **89**, 5061.
Baumann, C. (1965). *Vision Res.* **5**, 425.
Becker, R. S., Inuzuka, K., and Balke, D. (1971a). *J. Amer. Chem. Soc.* **93**, 38–42.
Becker, R. S., Inuzuka, K., King, J., and Balke, D. (1971b). *J. Amer. Chem. Soc.* **93**, 43–50.
Bitensky, M. W., Gorman, R. E., and Miller, W. H. (1971). *Proc. Nat. Acad. Sci. U.S.* **68**, 561.
Bitensky, M. W., Gorman, R. E., and Miller, W. H. (1972). *Science* **175**, 1363.
Blasie, J. K. (1972). *Biophys. J.* **12**, 191.
Blasie, J. K., and Worthington, C. R.·(1969). *J. Mol. Biol.* **39**, 417.
Blasie, J. K., Dewey, M. M., Blaurock, A. E., and Worthington, C. R. (1965). *J. Mol. Biol.* **14**, 143.
Blasie, J. K., Worthington, C. R., and Dewey, M. M. (1969). *J. Mol. Biol.* **39**, 407.
Blatz, P. H. (1972). *Photochem. Photobiol.* **5**, 1–6.
Blaurock, A. E., and Wilkins, M. H. F. (1969). *Nature (London)* **223**, 906.
Blout, E. R., and Fields, M. (1948). *J. Amer. Chem. Soc.* **70**, 189.
Borggreven, J. M. P. M., Daemen, F. J. M., and Bonting, S. L. (1970). *Biochim. Biophys. Acta* **202**, 374.
Borggreven, J. M., Rotmans, J. P., Bonting, S. L., and Daemen, F. J. (1971). *Arch. Biochem. Biophys.* **145**, 290.
Bownds, D. (1967). *Nature (London)* **216**, 1178.
Bownds, D., and Wald, G. (1965). *Nature* **205**, 254.
Brauner, A. J. (1973). Ph.D. Thesis, Case Western Reserve University, Cleveland, Ohio.
Bray, H. G., and White, K. (1957). "Kinetics and Thermodynamics in Biochemistry." Academic Press, New York.
Bridges, C. D. B. (1957). *Biochem. J.* **66**, 375.
Bridges, C. D. B. (1962). *Vision Res.* **2**, 201.
Bridges, C. D. B. (1970). *In* "Biochemistry of the Eye," (C. N. Graymore, ed.), pp. 563–644. Academic Press, London and New York.
Broda, E. E. (1941). *Biochem. J.* **35**, 960.
Broda, E. E., and Goodeve, C. F. (1941). *Proc. Roy. Soc. Ser. A.* **179A**, 151.
Brown, K. T., and Murakami, M. (1964). *Nature* **204**, 739.
Brown, P. K. (1972). *Nature (London) New Biol.* **236**, 35.
Busch, G. E., Appelbury, M. L., Lamola, A. A., and Rentzepis, P. (1972). *Proc. Nat. Acad. Sci. U.S.* in press.
Cassim, J., Rafferty, C. N., and McConnell, D. (1972). *Biophys. Soc. Abstr., 16th Annu. Meet., 1972* p. 205a.
Cavanagh, H. D., and Wald, G. (1969). *Fed. Proc., Fed. Amer. Soc. Exp. Biol.* **28**, 344.
Clark, A. W., and Branton, D. (1968). *Z. Zellforsch. Mikrosk. Anat.* **91**, 586.
Collins, F. D. (1953). *Nature* **171**, 469.
Collins, F. D., Love, R. M., and Morton, R. A. (1952). *Biochem. J.* **51**, 292–298.
Cone, R. A. (1972). *Nature (London), New Biol.* **236**, 37.
Cone, R. A., and Cobbs, W. H. (1969). *Nature* **221**, 820.

Crescitelli, F., and Shaw, T. I. (1964). *J. Physiol. (London)* 175, 43P–45P.

Crescitelli, F., Mommaerts, W. F., and Shaw, T. I. (1966). *Proc. Nat. Acad. Sci. U.S.* 56, 1729–1734.

Crescitelli, F., Foster, R. F., and Shaw, T. I. (1969). *J. Physiol.* 202, 189.

Dartnall, H. J. A. (1957). "The Visual Pigments," Methuen, London, New York, John Wiley.

Dartnall, H. J. A. (1968). *Vision Res.* 8, 339–358.

Dartnall, H. J. A. ed. (1972). "Handbook of Sensory Physiology," Vol. VII. Springer-Verlag, Berlin and New York.

Dartnall, H. J. A., and Lythgoe, J. N. (1965). *Vision Res.* 5, 81–100.

Dartnall, H. J. A., Goodeve, C. F., and Lythgoe, R. J. (1936). *Proc. Roy. Soc., Ser. A* 156, 158–170.

Dartnall, H. J. A., Goodeve, C. F., and Lythgoe, R. J. (1938). *Proc. Roy. Soc., Ser. A* 164, 216–230.

Dawson, W. R. (1962). Ph.D. Thesis, Case Institute of Technology, Cleveland, Ohio.

Dawson, W. R., and Abrahamson, E. W. (1962). *J. Phys. Chem.* 66, 2542.

Donner, K. P., and Reuter, T. (1969). *Vision Res.* 9, 815.

Downer, N. W., and Englander, S. W. (1972). *Biophys. Soc. Abstr.* 103a.

Dratz, E. A., Gaw, J. E., Schwartz, S., and Ching, W. M. (1972). *Nature (New Biol.)* 237, 99.

Eakin, R. M. (1965). *Cold Spring Harbor Symp. Quant. Biol.* 30, 363.

Eakin, R. M. (1968). *In* "Evolutionary Biology" (Dobzhansky, T., Hecht, M. K., Steele, W. C., eds.), Vol. II. Appleton, New York.

Eakin, R. M. (1972). *In* "Handbook of Sensory Physiology, Vol. VII/1 (H. J. A. Dartnall, ed.). Springer-Verlag, Berlin, New York.

Ebrey, T. (1967). Ph.D. Thesis, University of Chicago, Illinois.

Eichberg, J., and Hess, H. H. (1967). *Experimentation* 23, 993.

Emrich, H. M. (1971). *Z. Naturforsch. B* 26, 352.

Erhardt, F., Ostroy, S. E., and Abrahamson, E. W. (1966). *Biochim. Biophys. Acta* 112, 256.

Erickson, J. O., and Blatz, P. E. (1968). *Vison Res.* 8, 1367.

Evans, D. F. (1960). *J. Chem. Soc.* 1735.

Fager, R. S., Kimbel, R. L., and Abrahamson, E. W. (1971). *Biophys. Soc. Abstr.* TPME-11.

Fager, R. S., Sejnowski, P., and Abrahamson, E. W. (1972). *Biochem. Biophys. Res. Commun.* 47, 1244.

Fager, R. S., Heppner, T., Kandel, M., and Abrahamson, E. W. (1973a). In preparation.

Fager, R. S., Gentilcore, P., and Abrahamson, E. W. (1973b). In preparation.

Fager, R. S., Schanzlin, D., Heppner, T., Ricart, P., and Abrahamson, E. W. (1973c). In preparation.

Fager, R. S., Kimbel, R. L., and Abrahamson, E. W. (1973d). In preparation.

Fager, R. S., Mason, W. T., and Abrahamson, E. W. (1973e). In preparation.

Falk, G., and Fatt, P. (1966). *J. Physiol. (London)* 183, 211.

Fernández-Morán, H. (1961). *In* "The Structure of the Eye" (G. K. Smelser, ed.). Academic Press, New York.

Frank, R. N., Cavanagh, H. D., and Kenyon, K. R. (1972). *Biophys. Soc. Abstr., 16th Annu. Meet., 1972* SaAM B-12.

Gilardi, R., Karle, I. L., and Karle, J., and Sperling, W. (1971). *Nature (London)* 232, 187–189.

Girsch, S., and Rabinovitch, B. (1972). *Biochem. Biophys. Res. Commun.* 44, 550.

Gogala, M., Hamdorf, K., and Schwemer, J. (1970). *Z. Vergl. Physiol.* 70, 410.

Goldsmith, T. H. (1962). *J. Cell Biol.* **14**, 489.

Goodeve, C. F., Lythgoe, R. J., and Schneider, E. E. (1942). *Proc. Roy. Soc., Ser. B* **130**, 380–395.

Gras, W. J., and Worthington, C. R. (1967). *Proc. Nat. Acad. Sci. U.S.* **63**, 233.

Grellman, K. H., Livingston, R., and Pratt, D. C. (1962). *Nature (London)* **193**, 1258.

Guzzo, A. V., and Pool, G. L. (1968). *Science* **159**, 312.

Hagins, W. A. (1957). Ph.D. Thesis, Cambridge University.

Hagins, W. A. (1965). *Cold Spring Harbor Symp. Quant. Biol.* **30**, 403.

Hagins, W. A. (1972). *Annu. Rev. Biophys. Eng.* **1**, 131.

Hall, M., and Bachrach, A. (1970). *Nature (London)* **225**, 637.

Hamanaka, T., Mitsui, T., Ashida, T., and Kakudo, M. (1972). *Acta Crystallogr. Sect. B* **28**, 214.

Hara, T. (1958). *J. Gen. Physiol.* **41**, 857.

Hara, R. (1963). *J. Gen. Physiol.* **47**, 241.

Hara, T., and Hara, R. (1965). *Nature (London)* **206**, 331.

Hara, T., and Hara, R. (1967). *Nature (London)* **214**, 573.

Hara, T., and Hara, R. (1968). *Nature (London)* **219**, 450.

Hara, T., and Hara, R. (1972). *In* "Handbook of Sensory Physiology" (H. J. A. Dartnall, ed.), Vol. VII, Part 1. Springer-Verlag, Berlin and New York.

Hays, D., and Goldsmith, T. H. (1969). *Z. Vergl. Physiol.* **65**, 218.

Hecht, S., Shlaer, S., and Pirene, M. (1942). *J. Gen. Physiol.* **25**, 819.

Hedrick, J. L., and Smith, A. J. (1968). *Arch. Biochem. Biophys.* **126**, 155.

Heitzmann, H. (1972). *Nature (London), New Biol.* **235**, 114.

Heller, J. (1968a). *Biochemistry* **7**, 2906.

Heller, J. (1968b). *Biochemistry* **7**, 2914.

Heller, J. (1969). *Biochemistry* **8**, 675.

Heller, J., and Lawrence, M. A. (1970). *Biochemistry* **9**, 864.

Hirtenstein, M. D., and Akhtar, M. (1970). *Biochem. J.* **119**, 359.

Honig, B., and Karplus, M. (1971). *Nature (London)* **229**, 558.

Horwitz, J., and Heller, J. (1971). *Biochemistry* **10**, 1402.

Horwitz, J., and Heller, J. (1972). *Biophys. Soc. Abstr.* 205a.

Hubbard, R. (1953). *J. Gen. Physiol.* **37**, 381.

Hubbard, R. (1956). *J. Amer. Chem. Soc.* **78**, 4662.

Hubbard, R. (1969). *Nature* **221**, 432.

Hubbard, R., and Kropf, A. (1958). *Proc. Nat. Acad. Sci. U.S.* **44**, 130.

Hubbard, R., and Kropf, A. (1959). *Ann. N.Y. Acad. Sci.* **81**, 388.

Hubbard, R., and St. George, C. C. (1958). *J. Gen. Physiol.* **41**, 502.

Hubbard, R., Brown, P. K., and Kropf, A. (1959). *Nature* **183**, 442.

Hubbard, R., Bownds, D., and Yoshizawa, T. (1965). *Cold Spring Harbor Symp. Quant. Biol.* **30**, 301.

Inuzuka, R., and Becker, R. (1968). *Nature* **219**, 383.

Irving, C. S., Byers, G. W., and Leermakers, P. A. (1969). *Biochemistry* **9**, 858.

Ishimoto, M., and Wald, G. (1946). *Fed. Proc., Fed. Amer. Soc. Exp. Biol.* **5**, 50.

Kimbel, R. L., Poincelot, R. P., and Abrahamson, E. W. (1970). *Biochemistry* **9**, 1817.

Kimbel, R. L., Fager, R. S., and Abrahamson, E. W. (1973). In preparation.

Kito, Y., and Takesaki, M. (1966). *Nature* **211**, 197.

Klein, R. A. (1970). *Biochim. Biophys. Acta* **210**, 486.

Korenbrot, J. I., and Cone, R. A. (1972). *J. Gen. Physiol.* **60**, 20.

Krinsky, N. I. (1958). *Annu. Med. Ass. Ophthalmol.* **60**, 688.

Kropf, A. (1967). *Vision Res.* **7**, 811–818.

Kropf, A. (1969). *Vision Res.* **7**, 811.

Kropf, A., and Hubbard, R. (1958). *Ann. N.Y. Acad. Sci.* **74**, 226.

Kropf, A., and Hubbard, R. (1970). *Photochem. Photobiol.* **12**, 249–260.

Kropf, A., Brown, P. K., and Hubbard, R. (1959). *Nature* **183**, 446.

Langlet, J., Berthod, H., and Pullman, B. (1969). *J. Chim. Phys.* **66**, 566.

Leeson, T. S. (1970). *Can. J. Ophthal.* **5**, 91.

Liebman, P. A. (1972). *In* "Handbook of Sensory Physiology" (H. J. A. Dartnall, ed.), Vol. VII. Springer-Verlag, Berlin and New York.

Liebman, P. A., and Entine, G. (1964). *J. Opt. Soc. Amer.* **54**, 1951.

Liebman, P. A., and Entine, G. (1968). *Vision Res.* **8**, 761–775.

Linschitz, H., Wulff, V. J., Adams, R. G., and Abrahamson, E. W. (1957). **68**, 233.

Lythgoe, R. J., and Quilliam, J. P. (1938). *J. Physiol. (London)* **93**, 24.

McConnell, D. G., and Scarpelli, D. G. (1963). *Science* **139**, 848.

McConnell, D. G., Rafferty, C. N., and Dilley, R. A. (1968). *J. Biol. Chem.* **243**, 5820.

Mantione, M. J., and Pullman, B. (1971). *Int. J. Quant. Chem.* **5**, 349.

Marks, W. B., Dobelle, W. H., and MacNickol, E. F. (1964). *Science* **143**, 1181.

Mason, W. T., Fager, R. S., and Abrahamson, E. W. (1973a). *Biochim. Biophys. Acta,* in press.

Mason, W. T., Fager, R. S., and Abrahamson, E. W. (1973b). *Biochim. Biophys. Acta.* In press.

Mason, W. T., Fager, R. S., and Abrahamson, E. W. (1973c). In preparation.

Mason, W. T., Fager, R. S., and Abrahamson, E. W. (1973d). In preparation.

Mason, W. T., Fager, R. S., and Abrahamson, E. W. (1973e). In preparation.

Mason, W. T., Fager, R. S., and Abrahamson, E. W. (1973f). In preparation.

Matthews, R. G., Hubbard, R., Brown, P. K., and Wald, G. (1963). *J. Gen. Physiol.* **47**, 215.

Millar, P. G., Shields, J. E., Hendriksen, R. A., and Kimbel, R. L. (1969). *Biochim. Biophys. Acta* **175**, 345.

Miller, W. H., Gorman, R. E., and Bitensky, M. W. (1971). *Science* **174**, 295.

Morton, R. A., and Pitt, G. A. J. (1955). *Biochem. J.* **59**, 128.

Morton, R. A., and Pitt, G. A. (1957). *Fortschr. Chem. Org. Naturst.* **XIV**, 244.

Nash, H. A. (1969). *J. Theor. Biol.* **22**, 314.

Nielsen, M. C., Fleisher, S., and McConnell, D. G. (1970). *Biochim. Biophys. Acta* **211**, 10.

Nilsson, S. E. G. (1965). *J. Ultrastruct. Res.* **12**, 207.

Oroshnik, W., Brown, P. K., Hubbard, R., and Wald, G. (1956). *Proc. Nat. Acad. Sci. U.S.* **42**, 578.

Ostroy, S. E. (1971). *Photochem. Photobiol.* **14**, 747.

Ostroy, S. E., Erhardt, F., and Abrahamson, E. W. (1966a). *Biochim. Biophys. Acta* **112**, 265.

Ostroy, S. E., Rudney, H., and Abrahamson, E. W. (1966b). *Biochim. Biophys. Acta* **126**, 409.

Pak, W. L., and Cone, R. A. (1964). *Nature* **204**, 836.

Patel, D. J. (1969). *Nature (London)* **221**, 825.

Poincelot, R. P., and Abrahamson, E. W. (1970a). *Biochemistry* **9**, 1920.

Poincelot, R. P., and Abrahamson, E. W. (1970b). *Biochim. Biophys. Acta* **202**, 382.

Poincelot, R. P., and Zull, J. E. (1969). *Vision Res.* **9**, 647.

Poincelot, R. P., Millar, P. G., Kimbel, R. L., and Abrahamson, E. W. (1969). *Nature (London)* **221**, 256.

Poincelot, R. P., Millar, P. G., Kimbel, R. L., and Abrahamson, E. W. (1970). *Biochemistry* **9**, 1809.

Pratt, O., Livingston, R., and Grellman, K. H. (1964). *Photochem. Photobiol.* **3**, 121.

Pullman, B., Langlet, J., and Berthod, H. (1969). *J. Theor. Biol.* **23**, 482.

Radding, C., and Wald, G. (1955). *J. Gen. Physiol.* **39**, 909.

Rafferty, C. W., Cassim, J. Y., and McConnell, D. (1972). *Biophys. Soc. Abstr., 16th Annu. Meet., 1972,* p. 206a.

200   EDWIN W. ABRAHAMSON AND ROGER S. FAGER

Rapp, J. (1970). Ph.D. Thesis, Case Western Reserve University, Cleveland, Ohio.

Rapp, J., Wiesenfeld, J. R., and Abrahamson, E. W. (1970). *Biochim. Biophys. Acta* **201**, 119.

Reporter, M., and Reed, D. W. (1972). *Biophys. Soc. Abstr., 16th Annu. Meet.,* 1972 SaPM-HI.

Rimai, L., Kilponen, R. G., and Gill, D. (1970). *Biochem. Biophys. Res. Commun.* **41**, 492–497.

Ripps, H., and Weale, R. A. (1969). *J. Physiol. (London)* **200**, 151.

Robinson, W. E., Gordon-Walker, A., and Bownds, D. (1972). *Nature (London) New Biol.* **235**, 112.

Ross, R. T. (1970). *Photochem. Photobiol.* **12**, 261.

Schmidt, W. J. (1938). *Kolloid-Z.* **85**, 137.

Shaw, T. I. (1972). *In* "Handbook of Sensory Physiology" (H. J. A. Dartnall, ed.), Vol. VII, Part 1, pp. 180–198. Springer-Verlag, Berlin and New York.

Shichi, H. (1971a). *J. Biol. Chem.* **246**, 6178.

Shichi, H. (1971b). *Photochem. Photobiol.* **13**, 499.

Shichi, H., Lewis, M. S., Irreverre, F., and Stone, A. L. (1969). *J. Biol. Chem.* **244**, 529.

Shields, J. E., Dinovo, E. C., Hendricksen, R. A., Kimbel, R. L., and Millar, P. G. (1967). *Biochim. Biophys. Acta* **147**, 238.

Sjöstrand, F. S. (1959). *Ergeb. Biol.* **21**, 128.

Stoeckenius, W., and Oesterhelt, D. (1971). *Biophys. Soc. Abstr., 15th Annu. Meet.,* 1971. WPAM-A8.

Tomita, T. (1970). *Quart. Rev. Biophys.* **3**, 179.

von Planta, C., Schweiter, V., Chopard-Dit-Jean, L., Ruegg, R., Kofler, M., and Isler, O. (1962). *Helv. Chim. Acta* **45**, 548–561.

von Sengbusch, G., and Stieve, H. (1971). *Z. Naturforsch. B,* **26**, 488.

Waggoner, A. S., and Stryer, L. (1971). *Biochemistry* **10**, 3250–3253.

Wald, G. (1953). *Annu. Rev. Biochem.* **22**, 492–526.

Wald, G., and Brown, P. K. (1950). *Proc. Nat. Acad. Sci. U.S.* **36**, 84.

Wald, G., and Brown, P. K. (1952). *J. Gen. Physiol.* **35**, 797.

Wald, G., and Brown, P. K. (1963). *Nature (London)* **200**, 37.

Wald, G., Brown, P. K., and Smith, P. H. (1950). *Science* **111**, 179–181.

Wald, G., Brown, P. K., and Smith, P. H. (1955). *J. Gen. Physiol.* **38**, 623.

Wald, G., Brown, P. K., and Gibbons, I. R. (1963). *J. Opt. Soc. Amer.* **53**, 20.

Waterman, T. H., Fernandez, H. R., and Goldsmith, T. H. (1969). *Z. Vergl. Physiol.* **68**, 154.

West, S. S. (1970). *Introd. Quant. Cytochem.* **2**, 451.

Wiesenfeld, J., and Abrahamson, E. W. (1968). *Photochem. Photobiol.* **8**, 487.

Williams, T. P. (1966). *Vision Res.* **6**, 293–300.

Worthington, C. R. (1971). *Fed. Proc., Fed. Amer. Soc. Exp. Biol.* **30**, 57.

Wu, S. W., and Stryer, L. (1972). *Biophys. Soc. Abstr., 16th Annu. Meet.,* 1972 Sa-AM-B10.

Wulff, V. J., Adams, R. G., Linschitz, H., and Abrahamson, E. W. (1958). *Ann. N.Y. Acad. Sci.* **74**, 281.

Yoshizawa, T. (1972). *In* "Handbook of Sensory Physiology" (H. J. A. Dartnell, ed.), Vol. VII, Part 1, pp. 146–177. Springer-Verlag, Berlin and New York.

Yoshizawa, T., and Kito, Y. (1958). *Nature* **182**, 1604.

Yoshizawa, T., and Wald, G. (1963). *Nature* **197**, 1279.

Yoshizawa, T., and Wald, G. (1964). *Nature* **201**, 340.

Yoshizawa, T., and Wald, G. (1967). *Nature* **214**, 566.

Zonana, H. (1961). *Bull. Johns Hopkins Hosp.* **109**, 185.

Zorn, M. (1971). *Biochim. Biophys. Acta* **245**, 216.

Zorn, M., and Futterman, S. (1971). *J. Biol. Chem.* **246**, 881.

Mechanism of Actomyosin ATPase and the Problem of Muscle Contraction

EDWIN W. TAYLOR

MRC Muscle Biophysics Unit,
Kings College,
London, England

I. Introduction

In 1939 Engelhardt and Ljubimova reported that the fibrous protein actomyosin was an enzyme capable of the hydrolyses of ATP and thereby initiated the study of the molecular basis of muscle contraction. During the past thirty years the physical and chemical properties of the actomyosin system have been studied intensively. (The term "system" appears appropriate since it consists of five or six proteins.) As progress was made in elucidating the properties of actomyosin as a structural protein and as an enzyme, models of contraction were proposed and discarded. In this article recent work on the mechanism of the actomyosin system will be reviewed and current models of contraction will be critically evaluated. Undoubtedly, today's models will be superseded and discarded in their turn, but we appear to be entering a phase in which structural, physiological, and chemical studies are beginning to converge. Although the properties of actomyosin as an enzyme is the primary subject of this review, it is important to relate the kinetic studies to the properties of the system in which the enzyme must function.

Actomyosin, like any other enzyme, brings about the hydrolysis of its substrate by a series of intermediate steps. The purpose of kinetic studies is to determine the sequence of intermediate steps in the mechanism and to measure the respective rate constants. In a mechanism of any complexity there will be multiple reaction pathways, and it is particularly important in this system to determine their relative rates since one pathway must be coupled to an external load.

The problem to be solved can be stated with reasonable clarity. The mechanism of the enzyme reaction determined in solution has to be fitted together with the properties of the contraction cycle in muscle determined from structural and physiological studies. Two kinds of difficulties stand in the way of carrying out this program. In muscle, the reaction occurs subject to the restrictions imposed by a highly ordered lattice structure. It could be argued that the dominant reaction pathway in muscle is quite different than in solution. There is no simple way to get around this objection, other than the careful application of common sense. Properties of the homogeneous system in solution cannot be immediately translated into the properties of muscle. Conclusions based on enzyme studies have to be validated whenever possible by a study of ordered structures of increasing complexity, namely, thick filaments, myofibrils, and glycerinated muscles. A second problem is the coupling of the reaction to the performance of work. Again, it can be argued that coupling will alter the rate of the reaction in such a way as to favor an alternative reaction pathway in muscle. This is a serious difficulty, and perhaps the hardest property to explain is not that muscle contracts, but that it does so with an efficiency as high as 50%. Studies of the enzyme mechanism cannot directly determine which is the mechanochemically coupled step. However, introducing a coupled step does not present a conceptual problem, and it may be hoped that eventually the enzyme mechanism and the contraction cycle will fit together in a "natural" way so that there is only one logical choice for the coupled step.

II. Some General Properties of Muscle

A. Ultrastructure and Localization

Striated muscles of rabbit and frog have provided the main sources of material for study. Although the structure of muscle shows interesting variations among invertebrates, the general features of contraction are likely to be similar, and we will refer mainly to work on these two animals. A striated muscle consists of contractile units (sarcomeres) arranged in series. The composition of a sarcomere and the approximate locations of the various proteins is shown in Fig. 1.

The thin filaments appear to be linked to projections arising from an interwoven lattice which makes up the Z line (Knappeis and Carlson,

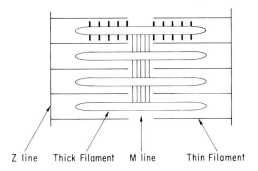

FIG. 1. Structure and composition of sarcomere.

Protein	Location	Mass per cent of myofibril	Molecular weight	Molar composition relative to myosin
Myosin	Thick filament	55–60	4.6×10^5	1
Actin	Thin filament	20	4.7×10^4	3.5
Tropomyosin	Thin filament Z line?	4–5	6.8×10^4	0.5
Troponins	Thin filament	3–5	$\sim 8 \times 10^4$	0.5
α-actinin	Z line region	2	1.8×10^5	0.1
M protein	M line	~ 0.5	1.1×10^5	0.04
C protein	Thick filament	2–3	1.5×10^5	0.10–0.15

1962). Tropomyosin (Huxley, 1963) and α-actinin have variously been assigned to the Z line region (Masaki et al., 1967), but the evidence is not entirely convincing and the connecting links have not been identified. The thin filament proper appears to bind α-actinin, but the precise localization of this protein in muscle is not clear although it is near the Z line (Robson et al., 1970). The chief constituent of the thin filament itself is actin, which forms a two-stranded helix of globular subunits, each having a diameter of about 5.5 nm, with a half-period repeat of about 35.5 nm. Tropomyosin molecules, which are completely helical of length 39.5–40.0 nm (Caspar et al., 1969), appear to lie in the two grooves formed by the actin helices (Moore et al., 1970). The third component, troponin, binds to tropomyosin and is spaced along the thin filament with the tropomyosin periodicity, circa 40 nm (Ohtsuki et al., 1967). Troponin has been resolved into at least two and possibly four components, one of which possesses Ca binding sites of high affinity (Schaub et al., 1967; Schaub and Perry, 1969; Ebashi et al., 1971; Greaser and Gergely, 1971).

The thick filament consists mainly of myosin, although recently the presence of a second component, C protein, has been reported (Starr and Offer, 1971). Myosin is arranged on a 6/2 helix, i.e., a helix with six projections per turn, occurring in pairs with a spacing of 14.3 nm (Huxley and Brown, 1967). The projections from the thick filament contain the globular portion of the myosin molecule. In solution myosin has a length of 150–160 nm, of which 13.5–14.0 nm is a helical-coiled coil. The exact packing structure in the thick filament is still a matter of debate. To accommodate the distance between thick and thin filaments, part of the rod portion is probably extended from the thick filament surface. Thick filaments are joined to each other by a set of projections at the center called M bridges, which together make up the M line (Knappeis and Carlson, 1968).

B. Contractile Mechanism

The well known sliding filament model of Hanson and Huxley attributes the shortening of a sarcomere to the relative motion of the thin filaments with respect to the thick filaments. Experiments have failed to detect any change in thick and thin filament lengths with sarcomere length. A decrease in thick filament length has been reported, particularly when the muscle has been allowed to shorten extensively. These reports are difficult to evaluate because of artifacts arising in the orienting and sectioning of very short sarcomeres. In addition, a muscle is often damaged when allowed to shorten past the physiological range. Constancy of filament lengths has been established over most of the range of sarcomere lengths occurring in the normal working cycle of a muscle and this finding must be the starting point for any contraction mechanism.

The force which produces sliding or the development of tension at fixed length must be attributed either to the direct action, and consequently the movement of the cross bridges, or to electrostatic and van der Waals forces possibly mediated by the cross bridge projections but not requiring to and fro movements of the bridges. Although the former explanation is the more generally accepted, it is difficult to prove. X-Ray evidence indicates that in relaxed muscle the bridges are not in contact with actin, whereas in rigor (the relatively rigid state of the muscle when depleted of ATP) mass has moved outward to the position of the actin filaments. In excited muscle, the pattern is consistent with attachment of a fraction of the bridges to the thin filaments and a disordering or movement of the bridges (Huxley and Brown, 1967). This is still short of a direct proof of attachment and motion, and the majority of the bridges are apparently not attached on the average in the isometric state. Granting the indirect nature of part of the evidence, a reasonable and generally accepted explanation is shown diagrammatically in Fig. 2. The bridges are presumed to execute a cycle of detachment, motion of the free bridge, reattachment in an altered configuration and movement to the first configuration with

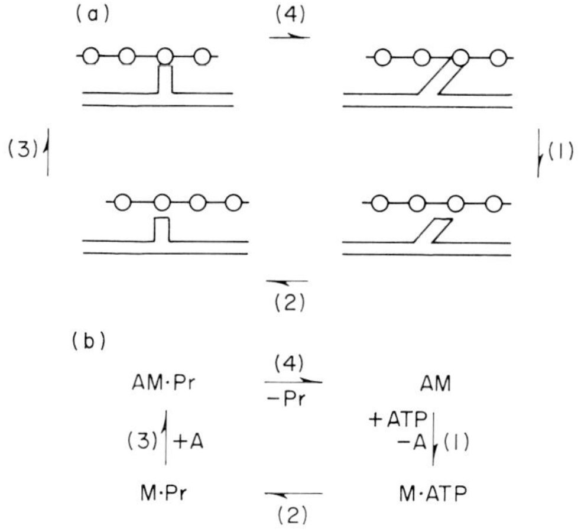

FIG. 2. (a) Contractile cycle for a single cross bridge. Actin sites which are suitably oriented to interact with a cross bridge are indicated by circles. (b) Steps in chemical mechanism for ATP hydrolysis by actomyosin. Binding of ATP and dissociation of actin is shown as a single step because actin dissociation is very fast after substrate binding. M · Pr stands for the intermediate complex.

relative displacement of the lattices by 80–100 Å. This distance is the extent of shortening per half sarcomere which will reduce the isometric tension to zero and should provide a measure of the range over which a bridge can move while developing tension (Huxley and Simmons, 1971). It is suggested, though not deduced, from X-ray data that the globular portion of myosin may rotate and that the rod region of about 40 nm (the S-2 portion) may hinge outward from the thick filament.

This general picture of the contractile system suggests questions for the chemist. The contractile cycle presumably is accompanied by hydrolysis of one or more ATP molecules, and the cycle requires at least four steps. What are the corresponding steps in the mechanism of ATP hydrolysis by actomyosin? A satisfactory explanation of the enzyme mechanism should allow us to identify the steps in ATP hydrolysis with the steps in the contractile cycle.

The activation of muscle involves the release of Ca ion from the sarcoplasmic reticulum. The only protein in the system possessing exchangeable Ca binding sites is troponin. Ca binding then must be supposed to relieve an inhibition of enzyme activity and in some way favor actin–myosin interaction. Relaxation requires removal of Ca ions by the sarcoplasmic reticulum pump. One of the questions to be asked of the enzyme scheme is what step or steps in the ATP hydrolysis cycle are blocked by removal of Ca ion.

Physiological studies have established a number of facts which must bear on the enzyme mechanism as it occurs in the muscle. The efficiency of muscle contraction is relatively high, certainly 50% of the available energy can be converted into work at optimal load (Gilbert *et al.*, 1971). The rate of energy release as heat plus work should be proportional to the rate of substrate hydrolysis, at least if the muscle attains a steady state (Gilbert *et al.*, 1971). The rate of energy output increases as the load is decreased and may pass through a maximum at low value of the load (Woledge, 1971). Unless there is a relatively large contribution to the energy output from some source other than the hydrolysis of ATP by actomyosin, the rate of one or more steps in the enzyme reaction must depend on the load or the velocity of shortening.

III. Enzymatic Properties

We now consider the properties of the muscle proteins myosin and actomyosin as enzymes. Although the contraction mechanism includes the action of a number of proteins, actomyosin free of other components can hydrolyze ATP at a rate that could account for energy liberation in muscle. As a first approximation, one can consider the mechanism of hydrolysis by myosin or actomyosin alone and later consider the effects of other proteins as regulators.

A. MYOSIN ATPASE

Myosin has a molecular weight of 4.6×10^5 (Godfrey and Harrington, 1970); the molecule contains two heavy chains of molecular weight 2.0×10^5 (Woods *et al.*, 1963), and probably four light chains of molecular weights in the range 1.6 to 2.5×10^4 (Weeds and Lowey, 1971). The question of the light-chain constitution is still under study. Recent evidence for striated muscle myosin favors four light chains. Two chains (MW 1.7×10^4) can be removed by treatment with 1-fluoro-2,4-dinitrobenzene (FDNB) without loss of enzyme activity (we shall refer to these chains as C_2). Two other light chains of molecular weights 2.1 and 2.5×10^4 are present, which closely resemble each other, with the exception of one peptide, and which are necessary for enzyme activity (denoted C_1 and C_3) (Weeds and Lowey, 1971; Sarkar *et al.*, 1971). A myosin preparation may contain roughly one each of C_1 and C_3, but the stoichiometry is not firmly established. It is possible that a myosin preparation may contain molecules with either two C_1 or two C_3.

Little is known about the details of the function of light chains. The steady-state ATPase activity of myosin or actomyosin from different muscles is distinctly different; a fast muscle has a faster actomyosin. Cross innervation studies have shown that the activity of the myosin can be changed in correspondence with changes in the speed of the muscles (Bárany and Close, 1971). It is suspected, but not yet proved, that the difference lies in the light chains. Reconstitution of light and heavy chains with regeneration of ATPase activity has been reported in one laboratory (Dreizen and Gershman, 1970) although this result has not been successfully duplicated by other workers.

Myosin can be partly digested with proteolytic enzymes to yield active fragments. Brief tryptic digestion splits myosin into light meromyosin (LMM), a helical fragment approximately 80 nm in length, and heavy meromyosin (HMM) (MW 3.5×10^5) consisting of the globular region and a helical tail. The enzymatic and actin combining sites are retained in HMM which has the advantage of being soluble at physiological ionic strength and is extensively used in enzyme studies. Further tryptic digestion of HMM or digestion of myosin by papain yields two globular fragments, subfragment 1 (MW 110,000), which again retains the catalytic and actin combining activities. Each subfragment 1 has a single catalytic site, while HMM and myosin appear to have two catalytic sites (Lowey et al., 1969). Two binding sites for ADP and pyrophosphate are present in HMM and myosin and one site in subfragment 1 (Lowey and Luck, 1969; Nauss et al., 1969).

From these studies it is generally concluded that myosin has two substrate and two actin combining sites and that one of each type of site is located in each subfragment 1. It is important to determine whether the two substrate and/or actin sites are identical and, if identical, whether they are independent. This question has not been answered. Small differences in sequence have been reported for the heavy chains and the light chains, C_1 and C_3 are also not identical. Consequently, the question has to be answered by physical and enzymatic studies, yet for almost every type of experimental evidence, discordant results have been presented by at least one laboratory (not the same one in each case). Identical and independent sites are favored by several workers while the opposite extreme that there is only one catalytic site per myosin and two populations of subfragment 1 molecules is supported by Tonomura et al. (1969) and Shimidzu and Morita (1969). At best it can be stated that effects arising from non-identical or nonindependent sites are small enough to make detection and agreement difficult; as a beginning, kinetic data will be discussed on the assumption of indistinguishable sites.

Myosin is a very poor enzyme under physiological conditions (i.e., pH 7, 0.1 M KCl, 10^{-3} to 10^{-2} $MgCl_2$). We will, throughout this article, express rates in standard chemical units, sec^{-1} for a first-order process and $M^{-1}sec^{-1}$ for a second-order process. Per site, the rate at 20°C is roughly 0.025 sec^{-1}, which corresponds to a half-life of the rate-limiting intermediate of 20–30 seconds.

A peculiar feature of actomyosin or myosin ATPase is the more rapid hydrolysis of ATP at the beginning of the reaction than during the steady state. The effect, at least for myosin, is not due to product inhibition. The phenomenon was termed the early burst and was extensively studied by Tonomura and collaborators (1969; Kanazawa and Tonomura, 1965; Kokiwa and Tonomura, 1965; Imamura *et al.*, 1965, 1966; Nakamura and Tonomura, 1968; Onishi *et al.*, 1968a,b; Kinoshita *et al.*, 1969a,b; Inoue *et al.*, 1972), who reported that the size of the extra phosphate burst was 1 mole per myosin (although numbers larger than 1 were sometimes obtained). A burst of 1 mole per mole was also found for subfragment 1, which poses a difficulty; other laboratories obtain values closer to 2 moles per mole. These results suggested that a phosphorylated intermediate may be formed whose slow breakdown could account for the slow steady-state rate, i.e.,

$$\text{M} + \text{ATP} \underset{(1)}{\rightleftharpoons} \text{M} \cdot \text{ATP} \underset{(2)}{\rightleftharpoons} \text{M} \sim \text{P} + \text{ADP} \underset{(3)}{\overset{\text{slow}}{\rightleftharpoons}} \text{M} + \text{P}_i + \text{ADP}$$

When the reaction is stopped in acid, M ~ P could liberate phosphate and the assay would thus show the rapid formation of 1 mole of phosphate followed by a much slower hydrolysis in the steady state. These ideas were further elaborated by Tonomura, but the interpretation has been difficult to substantiate. Whatever conditions have been used to stop the reaction, a phosphorylated myosin has never been isolated. Studies of ^{18}O exchange by Sartorelli *et al.* (1966) also failed to show any identifiable phosphorylated intermediate in the steady state. In this work the reaction was stopped at various pH's and $\text{H}_2{}^{18}\text{O}$ was added at the moment of stopping the reaction. Hydrolysis of the intermediate should lead to ^{18}O incorporation into the enzyme or the products, but none was found. Nevertheless, when the reaction is carried out in $\text{H}_2{}^{18}\text{O}$ there is excess ^{18}O exchange into phosphate (up to 4 atoms per mole). This finding requires that a phosphate intermediate of some kind be formed, but it need not be covalently bound. Other enzymes that have a stable phosphorylated intermediate often show a reversal of steps leading to incorporation of phosphate into added ADP or of ^{18}O into unhydrolyzed ATP. No such effects have been found for myosin, but so-called "medium exchange" does occur, namely added ^{18}O-phosphate undergoes oxygen exchange with $\text{H}_2{}^{16}\text{O}$ if ATP or ADP is present (Dempsey and Boyer, 1961).

The conclusions to be drawn from ^{18}O studies appear to be that (1) there is no evidence for a phosphorylated intermediate in the steady state, (2) the phosphate produced by hydrolysis gives excess ^{18}O exchange which requires some form of bound phosphate. The intermediate is probably not phosphate itself, but the state can be reached by binding phosphate if nucleotide is present. As suggested by Sartorelli *et al.*, a possible state is a bound metaphosphate which undergoes reversible hydration–dehydration

$$M \cdot PO_3^- \xrightleftharpoons{\pm H_2O} M \cdot H_2PO_4^-$$

Considering the limit of detection in ^{18}O studies, a phosphorylated intermediate present in the steady state to the extent of 5 or 10% of total intermediates might have gone undetected. Furthermore, since studies were done in the steady state, they do not rule out the possibility that the reaction passes through a phosphorylated intermediate, but if so it is not the main intermediate present in the steady state. The extent of excess ^{18}O exchange into phosphate is reduced when the rate of hydrolysis is increased, but exchange is not simply related to the rate. It has been argued that exchange is not occurring into the rate-limiting complex, but because of complications to be discussed below, this conclusion need not follow.

The kinetic parameters of the early phase were determined by Lymn and Taylor (1970) employing a rapid-quenching apparatus to measure phosphate formation. As the nature of the intermediate formed from ATP has not been established, it will be written as (M,ADP,P), including parentheses, and referred to as the intermediate complex. It need not be identical to the complex formed by adding ADP and P_i to myosin. The reaction can be written

$$M + ATP \underset{(1)}{\rightleftharpoons} M \cdot ATP \underset{(2)}{\rightleftharpoons} (M,ADP,P)$$

For each step i, there are rate constants $k_{\pm i}$. With MgATP as substrate, the steady state rate is very small compared to the early phase; it can be subtracted from the experimental data and ignored in the analysis of the rate equations. As long as substrate concentration is constant, the mechanism, however complex, reduces to a series of steps of the form

$$x_1 \rightleftharpoons x_2 \rightleftharpoons \cdots \rightleftharpoons x_n$$

and, in general, transitions between any pair of states x_i, x_j are allowed. The solution of the kinetic equations is a sum of exponential terms, and the number of such terms is one less than the number of states. In the simple mechanism under consideration, two exponential terms are expected. One term corresponds to an early lag for the buildup of M ·ATP since the quantity measured is the second intermediate (M,ADP,P). A lag was not clearly detected in the experiments, possibly because of the uncertainty introduced by subtraction of a zero time blank. Except at the earliest times, the data fitted a single exponential of apparent rate constant λ. λ was found to increase linearly with substrate concentration at low substrate concentrations and appeared to reach a plateau at high concentrations. The rate equations can be solved to give λ as a function of the rate constants (k_i). There are two limiting cases. If $k_{-1} << k_2$, the dominant exponential term is $\lambda = k_1 S$ at low S such that $k_1 S << k_2$ and $\lambda = k_2$ at high S such that $k_1 S \geq k_2$. If $k_{-1} >> k_2$, then at low S, $\lambda = (k_1/k_{-1})k_2 S = K_1 k_2 S$ and at high S we again have $\lambda = k_2$. These considerations are presented in detail since the method of analysis is repeated in all transient state studies. A distinction between the two interpretations of the dependence of the rate on substrate concentration can be made in some cases by detecting the early lag or from the shape of the λ versus S plot. We will refer to the quantity determined in the experiment as an apparent rate constant for substrate binding since the interpretation has not been settled conclusively. In 0.1 M KCl at pH 8 and 20°C, approximate values are $k_1 = 2 \times 10^6 \ M^{-1}sec^{-1}$ and $k_2 = 100$–$150 \ sec^{-1}$. Both rate constants decrease with increasing ionic strength.

Any other conveniently measurable parameter, such as difference spectrum, change in fluorescence, or proton liberation, could be used to measure k_1, and reasonable agreement has been obtained. Measurement of phosphate formation is the most direct method of following the reaction; the result of primary importance is the high rate of the actual hydrolysis step, which is 2000–4000 times faster than the steady-state rate. The value of k_2 has not been accurately determined, and a criticism of the results arises from the restricted range of substrate concentration (up to $2.5 \times 10^{-4} \ M$) used to establish the plateau.

For later reference, this rate is at least equal to the rate of fully activated actomyosin ATPase and fast enough to account for the rate of energy liberation by muscle. The fast hydrolysis step and slow steady-state rate are sufficient to account for a stoichiometric early burst; consequently there is no compelling reason to invoke a phosphorylated intermediate.

In 0.5 M KCl the half-life of the rate-limiting step is 30 seconds. Consequently, if this step is the decay of the intermediate complex (M,ADP,P), it should be measurable. A rapid column separation procedure using Sephadex G-25 allowed myosin to be separated from unreacted substrate in less than 30 seconds. The myosin peak and the tail of radioactivity following it consisted of both ADP and P_i, and the rate of decay was equal to the steady-state rate, at least to within a factor of 2 (Taylor et al., 1970).

These results indicate that it is the breakdown of the intermediate complex which determines the steady-state rate. This possibility was first suggested by Blum and Felauer (1959) based on a comparison of K_M and maximum steady state rates for various substrates and further developed by Kiely and Martonosi (1969), who compared the binding of ADP and pyrophosphate to the rate of hydrolysis under varying conditions.

In the original work of Taylor et al., the complex was regarded as a product complex equivalent to the complex formed by binding ADP to the enzyme. This interpretation appears to be incorrect, or at best only approximately correct under some conditions. Various lines of evidence require that a distinction be made between the intermediate complex formed during hydrolysis, (M,ADP,P), and $M \cdot ADP$ or $M \cdot ADP \cdot P_i$. The shape of the difference spectrum (Morita, 1967), the shape of the electron spin resonance spectrum of spin-labeled myosin (Seidel and Gergely, 1971), and the change in intrinsic fluorescence (Werber et al., 1972) in the presence of ATP are different than in the presence of ADP.

The rate of the dissociation step for the reaction

$$M + ADP \underset{k_{-1}}{\overset{k_1}{\rightleftharpoons}} M \cdot ADP$$

has been measured by determination of the equilibrium constant and k_1 (Malik and Martonosi, 1972) or by a chase experiment in which a chromophoric substrate reacts with free M (Trentham et al., 1972). In each instance k_{-1} was found to be much larger than the steady-state rate by a factor of 20- to 50-fold. Furthermore, it is well known that titration of a specific sulfhydryl group activates the steady-state rate by a factor of 5 to 10, yet myosin modified in this way shows a similar or even larger binding constant for ADP and a smaller value of k_{-1} (Malik and Martonosi, 1972). However, for the modified enzyme, k_{-1} is approximately equal to the steady-state rate. On the other hand, studies of the effect of modifiers on the decay rate of the (M,ADP,P) complex showed that it was increased by modifiers in proportion to the increase in the steady-state rate (McEntee and Taylor, 1973).

As suggested by Trentham et al., 1972, the scheme could be expanded to

$$M \longleftrightarrow M \cdot ATP \longleftrightarrow (M,ADP,P) \overset{slow}{\longleftrightarrow} M \cdot ADP \cdot P_i \overset{fast}{\longrightarrow} M \cdot ADP \overset{fast}{\longrightarrow} M$$

The rate-limiting step is the conversion of the intermediate complex to the product complex. As the product complex will be present in very small amounts, this scheme is consistent with the direct measurements of the rate of decay of the intermediate complex as determined by column chromatography.

Alternatively, one might consider an ordered dissociation mechanism

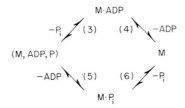

If there are no configuration changes or interactions between bound products $k_3 = k_6$ and $k_4 = k_5$, but in general the rates of all four steps could be different. In the original studies of Taylor *et al.* the apparent rates of dissociation of ADP and P_i were indistinguishable at 20° in 0.5 M KCl, but at lower ionic strengths and temperatures P_i dissociation was faster than ADP dissociation. In an ordered mechanism, at the higher temperature the rate-limiting step could be P_i dissociation followed by rapid ADP dissociation, whereas at the low temperature P_i dissociation is the faster step and ADP dissociation becomes rate limiting. At low temperatures Malik and Martonosi (1972), in fact, found that dissociation of M · ADP formed by adding ADP to myosin proceeds at the same rate as the enzyme reaction.

Myosin does show a complex temperature dependence of the steady-state rate and of the difference spectrum, and modifiers usually inhibit at low temperatures and activate at high temperatures. These phenomena could be accounted for by an ordered dissociation mechanism with a change in the rate-limiting step at some intermediate temperature. Thus, at 20°C the (M,ADP,P) intermediate does not appear to be equivalent to M · ADP · P_i whereas at low temperatures and low ionic strength a clear distinction cannot be made. The environment of ADP in the (M,ADP,P) state is different than that of the M · ADP complex. Whether this is due to a different configuration of myosin or to the direct influence of the bound phosphate or both has not been clearly settled.

A more complex scheme has been proposed by Tonomura and collaborators (1969) in which there are at least two pathways leading to release of products, primarily because agreement was not obtained between rate of decay of the product complex and the steady-state rate. If both sites participate in the hydrolysis reaction, the discrepancy is only a factor of 2; considering the errors involved in such experiments, it appears dangerous to postulate a second type of intermediate on this basis. [The Tonomura scheme is reviewed in more detail by Taylor (1972).]

The scheme as discussed up to this point is derived from relatively direct measurements of phosphate production, decay of intermediates, and rate of nucleotide binding and dissociation determined spectrophotometrically. Since at pH 8 one H^+ is released in the hydrolysis of ATP, the transient kinetics could be studied by stop-flow methods employing a pH indicator. The original study by Tonomura failed to find net H^+ liberation during the burst phase, and in fact a H^+ absorption of 1 mole per mole of myosin was obtained, followed by a slower proton release. Finlayson and Taylor (1969) reported an H^+ burst with a time course similar to the phosphate burst (the H^+ studies were actually performed before the phosphate work). The reason for this discrepancy is difficult to understand unless it can be attributed to artifacts produced by the instrument. Results of Finlayson and Taylor were obtained with an instrument of their own design. However, an H^+ burst has recently been reported by Pembrick and Walz (1972) using a Durrum stop-flow instrument. The problem has been reinvestigated by Koretz et al. (1972) using a modified Aminco–Morrow stop-flow apparatus, and again a rapid proton burst was obtained. There seems little cause to question the reality of a fast H^+ release, but the significance of the result is still unclear.

The obvious explanation is that a proton was liberated accompanying the hydrolytic step $MS \longleftrightarrow (M,ADP,P) + H^+$, and although this interpretation may be correct, there are quantitative discrepancies with the rate constants determined from phosphate data. In the original studies, it appeared that H^+ release could be better fitted by two rate processes. Furthermore, the magnitude of H^+ release and its dependence on substrate concentration did not agree with the phosphate burst. Recent studies by Koretz, Hunt, and Taylor on myosin, HMM and subfragment 1 gave approximately the same value for k_2 as was obtained for phosphate experiments, but it was doubtful whether two rate processes were present. Pembrick and Walz (1972) obtained a single rate process for subfragment 1, but two rate processes were required to fit data for myosin. Since such an effect would indicate substrate or product interaction, the result is of considerable interest. It is felt by the reviewer that statistical analysis of data by a computer program is necessary to determine whether a second rate process is really present.

A further problem is that the maximum rate for the H^+ step at very high substrate concentrations is at least twice the value reported for phosphate measurements (which for technical reasons were restricted to a ten times smaller concentration range). Further studies are clearly required to prove that the H^+ is actually liberated in the bond hydrolysis step although at present this appears to be the most reasonable interpretation.

In summary, the hydrolysis scheme [reaction Equation scheme (1)], to a first approximation, is

$$
M + S \underset{(1)}{\rightleftharpoons} MS \underset{(2)}{\overset{\text{fast}}{\rightleftharpoons}} (M,ADP,P) \underset{(3)}{\overset{\text{slow}}{\rightleftharpoons}} ? \underset{(4)}{\overset{\text{fast}}{\rightleftharpoons}} M + ADP + P_i \tag{1}
$$

with H^+ entering and leaving at step (2).

Steps (3) and (4) involve either the formation of $M \cdot ADP \cdot P_i$ as an intermediate step or an ordered decay from the (M,ADP,P) state. All in all, this scheme may seem to provide a rather small gain for the investment of effort. However, there are two important and well established results: the hydrolysis step is very fast and a long-lived intermediate state is produced which may represent a different configuration of myosin and which is stabilized by the binding of the products.

The question of distinguishable sites within one myosin molecule still remains unanswered, but it is worth listing the conflicting evidence in the hope that further studies will be directed at this question. Data on H^+ and phosphate formation by subfragment 1 fit a single identical site mechanism, whereas two sets of rate constants for steps (1) and (2) have been reported for myosin although recent studies in the author's laboratory have not confirmed the earlier report. The size of the phosphate early burst for myosin does not fit a simple Scatchard plot is expected from Eq. 1, and extrapolated data give close to two hydrolytic sites. One site and a simple concentration dependence was found by Tonomura (Inoue *et al.*, 1972). Accurate data are not yet available for subfragment 1. The steady-state rate does not fit a simple Schatchard plot, as it should for indistinguishable sites according to one laboratory (Lymn and Taylor, 1970), but linear plots have been obtained by other laboratories (most recently by L. Schliselfeld, personal communication). The maximum difference spectral change is given by binding of one ATP at 20°C, but two ATP's or ADP's are required at 6°C (Morita, 1971). The binding of ADP fits a single type of site according to Lowey and Luck (1969) and shows cooperativity according to Morita (1971).

The interaction with actin is equally puzzling. Rate of dissociation is proportional to ATP concentration, which requires that the binding of one ATP dissociates both heads (Finlayson *et al.*, 1969). Also, under relaxing conditions, recombination of (M,ADP,P) with actin is blocked by 1 mole of "products" per HMM (Koretz *et al.*, 1972). If both heads are capable of binding simultaneously then the occupancy of one site by substrate or products appears to block the interaction of the other head with actin. But as yet no experiment, including measurement of the stoichiometry of HMM binding, has conclusively proven that both heads are simultaneously bound. In the face of consistent disagreement for almost every parameter that has been measured one can only reserve judgment.

B. ACTOMYOSIN ATPASE

The ATPase activity of an actomyosin suspension at low ionic strength has long been known to exceed that of myosin by 10–50 times. At a high ionic strength, such that myosin and actomysin are soluble, the ATPase activities are very similar and the two proteins are largely dissociated as judged by physical measurements, i.e., viscosity, light scattering, flow birefringence, ultracentrifugation.

In spite of considerable work, attempts to understand the activation mechanism were largely unsuccessful. Addition of ATP to a turbid actomyosin suspension generally causes a decrease in turbidity termed "clearing." During the clearing the ATPase activity differs but little from myosin alone. This phase is followed by regain of turbidity and superprecipitation together with an increase in ATPase activity (Maruyama and Gergely, 1967). Rapid superprecipitation and increased enzyme activity require low concentrations of Ca. Although this system mimics some of the properties of muscle, namely activation by Ca, increase in ATPase activity, and a form of contraction, it remains a poor model system since the activation is quite small compared to an intact muscle, the dependence on ATP concentration is complex, and the effects of the changing physical state of the system cannot be sorted out from the chemical changes. In addition, much of the earlier work was done before the discovery of the relaxing protein system by Ebashi. Removal of troponin from crude actomyosin, or reconstitution of actomyosin from myosin and actin free of troponin, yields a system which shows activation of myosin ATPase without the requirement of Ca ions. The two main problems can now be dealt with individually—the mechanism of actin activation and the control of activity by Ca.

The first problem was clarified by the studies of Eisenberg and

Moos (1967, 1968, 1970; Eisenberg *et al.*, 1968), who worked with the homogeneous system acto-HMM. They recognized that ATP brings about dissociation of the system which competes with activation. The rate of hydrolysis continued to increase with actin concentration at constant HMM concentration over a range which exceeds the actin to myosin ratio of natural actomyosin. The true activation was assumed to be given by extrapolating to an infinite actin concentration, and corresponded to a 200-fold activation, i.e., $V_{max} \sim 10$ sec^{-1}.

The following mechanism was proposed to account for these results:

$$
\begin{array}{ccccc}
\text{AM+S} & \underset{(1)}{\rightleftharpoons} & \text{AMS} & \xrightarrow{(2)} & \text{AM+Pr} \\
& & \updownarrow (3) & & \\
\text{M+S} & \underset{(4)}{\rightleftharpoons} & \text{MS} & \xrightarrow{(5)} & \text{M+Pr}
\end{array}
\tag{2}
$$

where $k_5 << k_2$. From the slope and intercept of a double reciprocal plot one obtains $\overline{K} = k_3/(k_{-3} + k_2)$ which the authors take as a measure of the association constant for the formation of AMS from MS

$$
\text{MS} + \text{A} \underset{k_{-3}}{\overset{k_3}{\rightleftharpoons}} \text{AMS}
$$

Since $\overline{K}$ is much smaller than the association constant for the AM complex, the scheme accounts for dissociation of actomyosin by ATP with activation of the enzyme activity. This scheme provided the first reasonable explanation of the behavior of actomyosin.

A somewhat more complex scheme was proposed by Lymn and Taylor (1971) to account for the transient as well as the steady state behavior and differs in one important aspect from the Eisenberg-Moos scheme. Since the magnitude and maximum rate of the phosphate early burst was very similar to that of HMM alone and since the rate of the hydrolysis step is faster than V_{max} determined by Eisenberg and Moos, the activation need not be of the hydrolysis step itself. Furthermore, dissociation of acto-HMM as measured by turbidity change appeared to be faster than the maximum rate of hydrolysis. The following scheme was proposed to account for these facts:

$$
\begin{array}{ccccccc}
\text{AM+S} & \underset{(1)}{\rightleftharpoons} & \text{AMS} & & (\text{AM,Pr}) & \xrightarrow[(2)]{\text{fast}} & \text{AM+Pr} \\
& & \updownarrow (3) & & \updownarrow (7) & & \\
\text{M+S} & \underset{(4)}{\rightleftharpoons} & \text{MS} & \underset{(5)}{\rightleftharpoons} & (\text{M,Pr}) & \xrightarrow[(6)]{\text{slow}} & \text{M+Pr}
\end{array}
\tag{3}
$$

The major hydrolysis pathway is presumed to proceed via dissociation into A plus MS, hydrolysis on the free MS complex, and recombination of the (M,Pr) complex with actin. It was further shown by turbidity experiments that (M,Pr) will complex with actin at a reasonable rate and by rapid column separation experiments it was also shown that binding actin displaces the reaction products. In this case $\bar{K} = k_7/(k_{-7} + k_2)$. This scheme differs from previous mechanisms in that dissociation is not a competing reaction, but a step in the cycle; consequently binding and splitting of ATP brings about a dissociation and recombination of actomyosin. Since the general ideas of a contraction cycle require bridges to dissociate and recombine once per cycle, the kinetic scheme fits the contraction cycle in a natural way. The main feature of the mechanism, namely that dissociation precedes ATP hydrolysis must stand or fall on the accuracy of the rate constants for dissociation (step 3) and hydrolysis (step 5). An improvement in the accuracy of these measurements and the use of a method other than turbidity to monitor actomyosin dissociation would be desirable. Essentially the opposite sequence, i.e., the formation of an intermediate complex prior to dissociation has been proposed by Takeuchi and Tonomura (1971).

IV. Problem of Relaxation

Removal of Ca ion inhibits the activation of the complete actin–tropomyosin–troponin–myosin system but does not in itself cause dissociation of myosin from the actin-relaxing protein complex. ATP is still required for dissociation. Referring back to either of the kinetic schemes, the "relaxed" state in solution should be characterized by a reduction in $\bar{K}$ or k_2 or both. Studies by Eisenberg and Kielley (1970) and by Parker *et al.* (1970) supported this general expectation, but a more direct approach would be to attempt to measure the various rate constants in the transient state in the presence and in the absence of Ca. Preliminary studies (Koretz *et al.*, 1972) have been made of the rates of the reactions $A + M \rightleftharpoons AM$, $AM + ATP \rightleftharpoons A + M \cdot ATP$, and $A + (M,Pr) \rightleftharpoons AM,Pr$ using turbidity to follow the various association and dissociation reactions. Removal of Ca^{2+} reduces the rate of formation of AM by a factor of two or three, has little effect on dissociation of AM by ATP and essentially blocks the formation of the (AM,Pr) complex. These results support the notion that Ca^{2+} removal affects the site(s) on actin to which M or M,Pr is bound, and the primary step which is inhibited is the combination of actin with the myosin intermediate complex.

V. Enzyme Schemes and Contraction Models

The essential goal of studies of the kinetics and mechanism of the actomyosin system is to provide a quantitative model of the contraction cycle which will fit in a natural way with the structural and physiological evidence and which will also account for activation and relaxation. The word quantitative has to be emphasized, since qualitative models in which various intermediate states are postulated cannot be properly tested.

Recent studies have led to a clearer understanding of the actomyosin mechanism and its control by Ca^{2+}. In Fig. 2 the simplified contraction cycle is compared with the enzyme model of Lymn and Taylor. The contraction cycle occurs in at least four steps; dissociation of the bridge, movement of the free bridge, reattachment of the bridge, and the power stroke translating the thick–thin filament lattices with respect to each other.

It is evident that the kinetic scheme appears to fit in a reasonable way with the contraction cycle. As a working hypothesis, we identify the dissociation and recombination of a bridge with the dissociation of AM by ATP and the recombination of actin with the (M,Pr) intermediate complex. The chemical studies tell us nothing about configuration changes, but only the order of identifiable steps in the cycle. Nevertheless, these are features of the kinetic scheme which are suggestive when interpreted in relation to the contraction cycle. ATP is hydrolyzed on the free myosin or bridge to produce a long-lived intermediate complex which can combine with an actin site. In some sense, discussed more fully below, energy has been made available for the mechanochemical step. In relaxed muscle recombination of actin and myosin is somehow prevented. The kinetic evidence suggests that one step which is altered by the absence of Ca is the recombination of actin with the (M,Pr) intermediate (although other steps may also be affected). In relaxed muscle the bridges might be present as the intermediate complex (M,Pr) and consequently an amount of ADP equal to the number of enzyme sites should be bound. Marston and Tregear (1971) have shown that in the presence of ATP and in the absence of Ca^{2+} the required amount of ADP is bound by preparations of myofibrils. However, Bárany (1973) has reported that there is not sufficient ADP present in a relaxed muscle to complex with myosin.

The scheme is no more than a working hypothesis which does not deal with the complexities of the actual cycle, and kinetic evidence for the steps proposed is still incomplete. The rate and order of dissociation of products from the (AM,Pr) complex is still uncertain. Eisenberg and Moos obtained a value of 20 sec^{-1} at 20° for the maximum rate of ATP hydrolysis at infinite actin concentration, and it was suggested by Lymn & Taylor that this rate corresponds to the rate of product dissociation from the (AM,Pr) state. However, recent studies by A. Weber (personal communication) have yielded a value of at least 100 sec^{-1} for the maximum rate. The kinetic scheme (Eq. 3) contains two first-order processes—the bond hydrolysis step (k_5) and the product dissociation step (k_2). The maximum rate at infinite actin concentration would be determined by whichever of these steps is slower. Since the hydrolysis step is the order of 100 sec^{-1} it may determine the maximum rate, in which case k_2 is 100 sec^{-1} or larger and the value is unknown. This is a crucial question since at the maximum velocity of shortening the attached bridge executes its movement with a rate constant of the order of 1000 sec^{-1}. The state of bound products on the attached bridge and the sequence of product dissociation versus bridge movement are important questions that have to be answered before a detailed contraction scheme can be formulated.

We have made no attempt to deal with the two heads of myosin since, as was discussed above, the evidence on site interactions is too contradictory to allow reasonable conclusions to be drawn. It is possible that models which ignore interaction are wrong in principle, but at present we have no basis for introducing this complication into contraction schemes.

A general objection to kinetic schemes is that they must contain only those steps which one has been able to measure. Another first-order step can be inserted as long as it is faster than the step that follows it. For example, substrate binding could bring about a change in configuration which causes the attached bridge to rotate.

$$AM + S \rightleftharpoons AM \cdot S \underset{}{\overset{\text{rotation}}{\rightleftharpoons}} AM'S \rightarrow \text{dissociation}$$

If the rate for bridge movement is faster than for dissociation and if we have no experiment that detects this movement, then this reaction sequence can not be ruled out. But one does not construct models using negative evidence and it should be clear that an attempt to relate the enzyme mechanism to the contractile cycle must be based on the measurable steps. The model has to be regarded as highly provisional and the glaring weakness of contraction models is the lack of any evidence on the rates of configurational changes.

Detailed kinetic models of contraction have been proposed, as well as a variety of abstract models. We shall not consider the latter class since models derived from irreversible thermodynamics, statistical mechanics or long range forces are relatively independent of kinetic schemes.

The models proposed by Huxley (1957) and Huxley and Simmons (1971) are in essence kinetic schemes modified to include a mechano-chemical step. The models are based largely on physiological data, namely, the dependence of heat, work, and velocity of shortening on load and the response to rapid stretch or release of the muscle. It is appropriate to ask whether kinetic studies of the enzyme mechanism have any bearing on physiological models and whether there are sufficient data available to formulate a model based on solution studies.

Before the question can be answered, it is necessary to consider the general problem of a cyclic mechanochemical reaction. The schemes proposed so far have oversimplified the problem in order to concentrate on one aspect of the cycle. Although simplifying assumptions are necessary to make the problem tractable, such assumptions are potentially dangerous when dealing with a cyclic process. Questions such as, What is the immediate source of energy? What is the relation between work done by the coupled step and the chemical free energy change? Can ATP be synthesized by stretching a muscle? cannot be properly formulated unless the cyclic nature of the process is taken into account. As to the source of energy, the original Huxley model postulated that the bridge was equivalent to a spring in thermal motion. The Huxley–Simmons scheme postulates an angular dependence of the interaction energy between the actin–myosin bridge. Physical chemists prefer a direct coupling between ATP hydrolysis and myosin configuration which somehow stores the free energy of hydrolysis in a special myosin state, a so-called high energy state.

In order to make clear the energetics of the process we will give an elementary treatment of a cyclic-mechanochemically coupled process. We first present a formulation for a cyclic process without coupling. Let x_i be the relative concentration of the myosin or actomyosin intermediates, $\Sigma\, x_i = 1$.

For the simple enzyme scheme which will serve as a concrete example, the states are:

$$(AM, Pr) \xleftarrow{\;-Pr\;} AM \xrightarrow{\;+S\;} AMS$$
$$\downarrow \qquad\qquad\qquad\qquad \downarrow -A$$
$$(M, Pr) \longleftarrow\!\!\!\longrightarrow MS$$

Thus there are five myosin intermediates. To represent reaction cycles it is convenient to use a grid, the points denote the x_i, and lines connecting the points are possible elementary steps. Thus a possible scheme could be represented by

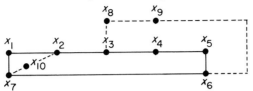

The grid illustrates an important feature of the cyclic process. There is a loop x_1 through x_7 which, under some conditions, is the dominant reaction pathway. However, there will always be alternative loops, along which the reaction can proceed at a slower rate. These are drawn by completing a loop with a dashed line. Thus the loop x_2 to x_7, via x_3, etc., to x_{10} to x_2 bypasses the steps x_7 to x_1 to x_2. If x_1 to x_2 is the mechanochemical step, it can be short-circuited by the alternate pathway. A major problem is to show that there is a main pathway and to provide evidence that the alternate paths are kinetically forbidden. To begin with we consider a system in which ATP is hydrolyzed in a reaction cycle with no branching pathways. The simple enzyme scheme will again serve as an example. For each step in the cycle $x_i \longleftrightarrow x_j$ the rate constants are k_{ji} and k_{ij} and the equilibrium constant is $K_{ji} = k_{ji}/k_{ij}$. It is assumed that all of the k_{ji} have been measured by suitable kinetic experiments. When the system reaches a steady state, φ, the flux around cycle, which is the rate of ATP hydrolysis per myosin site is given by

$$\varphi = k_{j+1,j}\, x_j - k_{j,j+1}\, x_{j+1} \tag{4}$$

For simplicity we take the substrate and product concentrations to be constant and the actin concentration to be sufficiently larger than the myosin concentration so that the free actin can also be treated as a known constant. The x_j can then be readily calculated from the set of simultaneous linear equations, $dx_j/dt = 0$ and $\Sigma\, x_j = 1$. Reactions involving substrate, product, or actin are second-order but can be treated as first-order by including the concentration of the second reactant in the rate constant. For example,

$$AM + S \underset{k_{-1}}{\overset{k'_1}{\rightleftharpoons}} AM \cdot S$$

can be expressed as

$$AM \underset{k_{-1}}{\overset{k_1}{\rightleftharpoons}} AM \cdot S$$

where $k_1 = k_{1'}(S)$. Similarly, equilibrium constants for second-order reactions can be treated as effective first-order constants by setting

$K^e = K(S)$ as in the above reaction. In this manner the reaction cycle can be treated as a set of first-order reactions between successive x_j described by the effective first-order rate and equilibrium constants.

We now ask what is the free energy difference for each step in the cycle? If the reaction is allowed to come to equilibrium it is easily verified by writing out the definition of equilibrium constants taken clockwise around the cycle, that

$$\Pi K_{ji} = K_{\text{ATP}} \qquad (5)$$

where Π signifies the product of equilibrium constants and K_{ATP} is the equilibrium constant for ATP hydrolysis, a number of the order of 10^6. The numerical condition on the equilibrium constants still holds when the system is not in equilibrium. Furthermore if the reaction comes to a steady state and gradients of concentration and temperature are small, the free energy of the system is determined by the concentrations of the components. This condition is likely to be satisfied for actomyosin in solution or for an intact muscle.

The change in free energy for the step $x_i \rightarrow x_j$ is

$$\Delta F_{ji} = \Delta F^\circ_{ji} + RT \ln(x_i/x_j) \qquad (6)$$

$$-\Delta F^\circ_{ji} = RT \ln K_{ji} \approx 1.3 \log K_{ji} \qquad (7)$$

The equation as written applies to a first-order reaction. For second-order reactions the concentration of the second reactant must be included in the logarithm. However the same transformation used in treating the rate equations can be applied to second-order reactions. Using the same example, the binding of substrate to actomyosin gives $\Delta F = \Delta F^\circ + RT \ln [(AM \cdot S)/(AM)(S)]$ which can be expressed as $\Delta F = -RT \ln K(S) + RT \ln [(AM \cdot S)/AM]$.

Replacing $K(S)$ by K^e and noting that AM and AMS are two successive states in the cycle gives $\Delta F_{ji} = (\Delta F^\circ_{ji})_e + RT \ln (x_j/x_i)$ where $(\Delta F^\circ_{ji})_e = -RT \ln K^e$. This transformation simply defines a new set of standard states and standard free energies referred to the concentration of substrate, product, or actin present in the system. Substitution of equation (7) into (5) gives

$$\Sigma \Delta F^\circ_{ji} = \Delta F^\circ_{\text{ATP}} \qquad (8)$$

Substitution for second-order equilibrium constants in Eq. (5) in terms of effective equilibrium constants, and noting that the actin concentration cancels out since it appears both as a product and a reactant, gives

$$\Pi K_{ji}^e = \Pi K_{ji} \frac{(\text{ATP})}{(\text{ADP})(\text{P}_i)} = K_{\text{ATP}} \frac{(\text{ATP})}{(\text{ADP})(\text{P}_i)}$$

Using Equations (6) and (7) to convert this result into a free-energy relationship gives

$$\Sigma(\Delta F^\circ_{ji})_e = \Delta F_{\text{ATP}} \tag{9}$$

For convenience the quantity $[K_{\text{ATP}}(\text{ATP})/(\text{ADP})(\text{P}_i)]$ is denoted by K^e_{ATP}. Since the reaction is a closed cycle for the states x_j, $\Sigma(\Delta F^\circ_{ji})_e = \Sigma \Delta F_{ji}$. These equations lead to a simple description of the free-energy changes for a single reaction cycle. For each step in the cycle, taken clockwise, there is an effective standard free energy change $(\Delta F^\circ_{ji})_e$. The algebraic sum of these changes is equal to ΔF_{ATP}. The free-energy change is calculated for each step from Eq. (6) using the values of x_i and x_j obtained by solution of the steady-state rate equations. The effective standard free-energy change at each step is increased or decreased by the contribution RT ln (x_j/x_i) but the sum is constant. Whereas the effective standard free-energy differences could be positive or negative, the actual free-energy differences are all negative. The flux around the cycle is positive by definition and from Equation (4) it is easily shown that $\Delta F_{ji} < 0$. Thus for each intermediate step in the cycle there is a drop in free energy, the total drop being equal to ΔF_{ATP}.

The treatment can be extended to include alternate reaction pathways in addition to the main cycle. The concentration ratios for successive states of the main cycle will be perturbed by the side reactions but $\Sigma \Delta F_{ji}$ is still equal to ΔF_{ATP} for each closed reaction pathway.

The treatment can be easily generalized to include mechanochemical coupling. For simplicity we assume that only one step in the pathway is coupled to the external load, namely,

$$x_1 \underset{k_{12}}{\overset{k_{21}}{\rightleftharpoons}} x_2$$

Within the context of a moving bridge model, the conversion from x_1 to x_2 is accompanied by a movement of the bridge and a relative translation of the lattices by a distance h. If internal mechanical dissipation is negligible and the load per bridge is P, an amount of work $W = hP$ will be done on the external load. The external work W is equal to a change in free energy which is related to an equilibrium constant by the equation $K_L = \exp(-W/RT)$ or $W = +\Delta F_L = -RT \ln K_L$. Thus the coupling of the reaction to an external load can be introduced by means of an equilibrium constant K_L. Since equilibrium constants are multiplied and free energies are added, we have for the coupled step

$$K = K_L K_{21} \quad \text{and} \quad \Delta F = \Delta F_L + \Delta F^\circ_{21} + RT \ln \frac{x_2}{x_1} \tag{10}$$

The relations for the chemical system $\Pi K_{ji} = K_{ATP}$ and $\Sigma \Delta F_{ji} = \Delta F_{ATP}$ are replaced by $\Pi K_{ji} K_L = K_{ATP} K_L$ and $\Sigma \Delta F_{ji} + \Delta F_L = \Delta F_{ATP} + \Delta F_L = \Delta F_{ATP} + W$. Since K_L is less than one, ΔF_L is positive while ΔF_{ATP} is negative. The chemical driving force is $-\Delta F_{ATP}$, and it is reduced by the external work W. The condition for equilibrium is simply $\Delta F_{ATP} + W = 0$.

The problem can be solved in the same manner as before from known values of the k_{ji}. However, there is an ambiguity in the introduction of $K_L K_{21} = K$ since

$$K = \frac{k_{21}}{k_{12}} e^{-W/RT} = \frac{k'_{21}}{k'_{12}}$$

Only the ratio is specified and the manner in which the individual rate constants change will depend on the properties of the system. The simplest assumption is a decrease in k_{21} by the factor $e^{-W/2RT}$ and an increase in k_{12} by $e^{W/2RT}$. This partitioning of the effects would occur if the maximum of the activation energy barrier between the chemical states is at $h/2$ and the external energy profile is proportional to distance. If the external force is regarded as equivalent to a linear spring the energy is proportional to the square of the displacement and the simple assumption is incorrect. Fortunately, the calculations are not very dependent on how the effect is distributed.

Since the reaction proceeds at a finite velocity, ΔF_L for the mechanochemical step cannot in general be equal to external work as this condition is true only for a reversible process. The energetics of the process can still be treated by a kinetic model because the dissipation of energy could be calculated in principle from the rate constants. We previously assumed that concentration and temperature gradients were small and the fluxes around alternative pathways were to be taken into account in calculating the concentration ratio x_1/x_2 which determines the chemical part of the ΔF of the coupled step. The remaining source of energy dissipation is the internal viscous forces generated by the movement of the lattices. If these are not negligible, ΔF_L is determined both by the external work and the free energy dissipated by viscous forces.

The importance of viscous forces is not easily determined, although rough calculations on the dissipation of energy due to parallel translation of the lattice through a fluid of low viscosity (that of water) indicates that such effects may be small.

The discussion is intended as a prologue to the formulation of contraction models. The main purpose was to show that a cyclic mechanochemical reaction could be treated by elementary methods if certain reasonable assumptions are made. With the evidence currently available on rate constants and intermediate states we are in no position to formulate a kinetic model of contraction, but it is still of interest to investigate the properties of a realistic kinetic scheme in order to clarify some points of energetics. As an illustration, we have calculated the effect of load on the rate of ATP hydrolysis and the free-energy drop between successive states for a model in which there is a single reaction cycle. It should be emphasized that the model is not intended as yet another theory of contraction since it makes predictions which are clearly wrong.

Some assumption must be made regarding the effective actin concentration since the rate of combination of a myosin or myosin intermediate state with an actin site in muscle can not be determined from measurements of the second-order rate constant in solution. The effective actin concentration is assumed to be constant, as any other choice would require a detailed treatment of the geometry of the lattice and the flexibility of the bridges.

The model is based on the following considerations: (a) Binding of substrate or products to myosin appears to reduce the affinity for actin. (b) Binding of actin to myosin appears to reduce the affinity for products and possibly for substrate although the latter effect has not been measured. (c) Actin and substrate or products do not appear to occupy the same site. (d) Myosin may bind to actin in two orientations, perpendicular and at a 45° angle to the actin filaments.

Combining (a), (b), and (c) suggests that actin and substrate or products either interact directly or induce changes in the configuration of myosin. In the latter case the configuration change need not be, and probably is not, the step in which the bridge moves. Consideration of (d) suggests that myosin is bound to at least two sites on actin. Rotation of the bridge is a transition from binding at one site to binding at two sites, or to binding at a much stronger second site. [This hypothesis has been developed by Huxley and Simmons (1971).]

These "facts" can be combined into a kinetic scheme by postulating that myosin exists in two states M_1 and M_2. In state 1, substrate and products are strongly bound and actin is weakly bound. In state 2 the converse is true. In the AM_1 complex, myosin is bound at a single site; in the AM_2 complex, it is bound at both sites and the transition requires a rotation of myosin. The rotated state is denoted by $*$ since we will not distinguish between orientations of the free myosin, and subscripts 1 and 2 refer to the myosin state; thus $AM_1 \longleftrightarrow A^*M_2$. The system is described by the equilibrium constants for the binding processes

$$
\begin{array}{ll}
A + M_1 \longleftrightarrow AM_1 & K = 10^3 \ M^{-1} \\
A + M_2 \longleftrightarrow A^\circ M_2 & K = 10^7 \ M^{-1} \\
S + M_1 \longleftrightarrow M_1 S & K = 10^7 \ M^{-1} \\
S + M_2 \longleftrightarrow M_2 S & K = 10^3 \ M^{-1} \\
Pr + M_1 \longleftrightarrow M_1 Pr & K = 10^7 \ M^{-2} \\
Pr + M_2 \longleftrightarrow M_2 Pr & K = 10^5 \ M^{-2}
\end{array}
$$

The affinity is determined by the state of myosin, and consequently binding constants are not affected by the presence of another ligand; i.e., $S + AM_2 \longleftrightarrow AM_2 S$, $K = 10^3 \ M^{-1}$. The states of the free myosin are assumed to be equally probable. $M_1 \longleftrightarrow M_2$, $K = 1$. The equilibrium constants for all the other transitions can be calculated from the appropriate cyclic reactions and the condition $\pi K = 1$. For example,

$$
\begin{array}{ccc}
AM_1 & \longleftarrow & A^*M_2 \\
10^3 \big\uparrow & \bigcirc & \big\downarrow 10^{-7} \\
M_1 & \longrightarrow & M_2 \\
& (1) &
\end{array}
$$

gives

$$
AM_1 \xleftarrow{\ 10^4\ } A^\circ M_2
$$

The choice of the K's is in reasonable accord with the available evidence. If one wishes to think in terms of a concrete model, the behavior would arise if the transition from state 1 to state 2 was the movement of a segment of the polypeptide chain from a position in which it participates in the binding of S or Pr to a position in which it participates in the binding of actin. The contractile cycle based on this scheme, ignoring side reactions, is as follows:

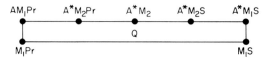

(a) Mechanochemical cycle

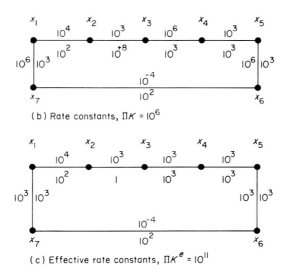

(b) Rate constants, $\Pi K = 10^6$

(c) Effective rate constants, $\Pi K^e = 10^{11}$

Rate constants in the forward direction are written outside the loop. Values for the rate constants are shown in (b) based on experimental data where available and reasonable guesses otherwise. The concentrations of actin, ATP, ADP, and P_i are taken to be 10^{-3} M, 10^{-3} M, 10^{-5} M, and 10^{-3} M, respectively, and the effective rate constants are then given in (c). There are three steps which have large standard free energy changes: the mechanochemical step $x_1 \rightarrow x_2$ $K = 10^2$ and $-\Delta F = 2.6$ kcal, the dissociation of products from A^*M_2Pr, $(-\Delta F°)_e = 3.9$ kcal, and for the hydrolysis step, $-\Delta F = 7.8$ kcal. The concentrations can be calculated by solving the steady-state rate equations. The relevant parameters are given in Table I.

TABLE I
CONCENTRATIONS AND ENERGY LEVELS OF INTERMEDIATES

	Unloaded			$K_L = 10^{-4}$, $W = 5.2$ kcal		
	Rate, $\varphi =$ 20.3 sec^{-1}	$(-\Delta F_{ji})_e^0$ (kcal)	$(-\Delta F_{ji})$ (kcal)	Rate, $\varphi =$ 3.7 sec^{-1}	$(-\Delta F_{ji})_e^0$ (kcal)	$(-\Delta F_{ji})$ (kcal)
"Dissociation" $(x_6 + x_7)$	0.225			0.448		
x_1 (AM$_1$Pr)	0.002	2.6	1.3	0.407	-2.6	$+0.05$
x_2 (A°M$_2$Pr)	0.020	3.9	2.4	0.0037	3.9	2.6
x_3 (A°M$_2$)	0.263	0	0.043	0.0481	0	0.043
x_4 (A°M$_2$S)	0.243	0	0.048	0.0444	0	0.048
x_5 (A°M$_1$S)	0.223	0	0.053	0.0407	0	0.053
x_6 (M$_1$S)	0.203	7.8	9.0	0.037	7.8	6.34
x_7 (M$_1$Pr)	0.022	0	1.36	0.411	0	0.005
			14.3			9.1

The rate of the cycle is 20.3 sec^{-1} although the slowest step in the forward direction is 100 sec^{-1}. The system is largely "associated" in that myosin is present largely in combination with actin, although the bridges are almost entirely in the rotated states and the bound nucleotide is present mainly as ATP. The effect of a "heavy" load of 5.2 kcal is also shown in Table I. The rate is reduced to 3.7 sec^{-1} and the system is present largely as AM_1Pr and M_1Pr. Thus the attached bridges are mainly present in the perpendicular state, and the bound nucleotide is present as products. The total bound nucleotide was actually increased from 0.74 to 0.95 by loading the system.

Two important points can now be clarified. The standard free energy change for the mechanochemical step in the absence of load is assumed to be 2.6 kcal. The main free energy drop occurs in the $MS \longleftrightarrow (M,Pr)$ reaction. For the reaction of myosin alone $M \longleftrightarrow MS \longleftrightarrow (M,Pr) \longleftrightarrow M + Pr$, the kinetic evidence indicates that the substrate binding constant is the order of $10^7 M^{-1}$. Product binding constant is not known accurately, but the constant for ADP binding is $10^5 M^{-1}$; if phosphate is weakly bound ($K = 10^2$), the composite binding constant is $10^7 M^{-2}$. Since the hydrolysis process is a cycle $\Pi K = 10^6$, consequently the $MS \longleftrightarrow M,Pr$ step has $K \sim 10^6$. The product dissociation step must also have a moderate free energy drop, so the low energy change for the mechanochemical step is not unreasonable. With a different set of assumptions the free energy drop for this step could be made much larger.

Although the source of the idea is not known to me, it is often assumed that the standard free energy drop for the mechanochemical step must be equal to the maximum work that can be done per cycle. The suggestion is clearly wrong and may arise from the failure to recognize the implications of a cyclic process. The actual free energy change is 1.3 kcal in the absence of load, which is smaller than the standard free energy because the concentrations must adjust to the ratio of rate constants; the concentration of x_1 must be much less than x_2 since $\varphi = k_{21}x_1 - k_{12}x_2$ and $k_{21} >> k_{12}$. The system will still shorten against a load of 5.2 kcal, and it can be seen from the table that the actual chemical free energy change is close to zero in this case. The reason is simply that the load reduces the standard free-energy change by 5.2 kcal since it changes the equilibrium constant by a factor of 10^4. The unfavorable equilibrium, corresponding to a $\Delta F°$ of $+2.6$ kcal, is compensated by the adjustment in the concentration ratio which brings ΔF almost to zero. Consequently there is no relationship between the standard chemical free energy change for the coupled step and the work done. The work done is simply determined by whatever load the system is lifting, the effect of the load being to reduce the rate of the cycle. Although the isometric case cannot be treated since it does not correspond to equilibrium it is evident that there is no justification for the assumption that the ratio of x_1 to x_2 will be unity in this case.

Finally, it can be asked whether a "high energy state" is required as the direct source of energy for contraction. The only meaning that can be given to the statement is the requirement of a large free energy drop for the coupled reaction in the absence of load. However, as noted above, the actual energy drop is not a property of the states alone but depends on the concentration ratio. In the example shown in Table I, the contribution of the concentration ratio to the free energy was changed by 4 kcal as a result of loading. In fact, the system would shorten and do work if the standard chemical free energy change were zero for the coupled step. However, the system would show a very sharp dependence of the rate on the load. Calculation of the rate for this case gave a value of only 0.05 sec^{-1} for a load of 5.2 kcal. Thus a high energy state is not necessary but it is an advantage to have a moderate standard free energy drop at the coupled step to buffer the effect of load on the rate of reaction. The macroscopic parameters, velocity of shortening, work and energy output can be calculated from this kinetic model which also shows the effect of load on the free-energy differences of the successive states of the system. The model is not intended as a theory of contraction since it clearly leads to a number of wrong predictions. Since $v = h\varphi$, the rate of ATP hydrolysis would be zero in the isometric state and would show the same functional dependence on load as the velocity of shortening. Both predictions are known to be wrong (Woledge, 1971). The most obvious shortcoming is the omission of alternate reaction pathways which bypass the mechanochemically coupled step. As the load is increased the flux rate around the cycle is reduced and alternate pathways become important.

A more complex model which includes alternate pathways could probably be made to agree with the macroscopic properties of muscle. There is little use in carrying out such an exercise since one does not have the experimental results to support even the relatively simple scheme used here. There is no direct evidence for the binding of myosin in two possible orientations. The large standard free energy drop for the $M_1S \longleftrightarrow M_1Pr$ step was necessitated by the requirement that the product of the equilibrium constant be equal to the equilibrium constant for ATP hydrolysis. As there are other steps in this reaction part of the free energy might be conserved by a change in configuration of myosin. A number of different kinetic schemes could be formulated which would be consistent with the available data, but each involves configurational changes at different steps. Kinetic models of contraction will continue to be based on arbitrary assumptions until clear evidence is obtained regarding the configurational states of the system.

REFERENCES

Bárany, M. (1973). *Cold Spring Harbor Symp. Quant. Biol.* In press.
Bárany, M., and Close, R. I. (1971). *J. Physiol. (London)* **213**, 455.
Blum, J. J., and Felauer, E. (1959). *Arch. Biochem. Biophys.* **81**, 285.
Caspar, D. L. D., Cohen, C., and Longley, W. (1969). *J. Mol. Biol.* **41**, 87.
Dempsey, M. E., and Boyer, P. D. (1961). *J. Biol. Chem.* **236**, PC-6.
Dreizen, P., and Gershman, L. C. (1970). *Biochemistry* **9**, 1688.
Ebashi, S., Wakabayashi, T., and Ebashi, F. (1971). *J. Biochem. (Tokyo)* **69**, 441.
Eisenberg, E., and Kielley, W. W. (1970). *Biochem. Biophys. Res. Commun.* **40**, 50.
Eisenberg, E., and Moos, C. (1967). *J. Biol. Chem.* **242**, 2945.
Eisenberg, E., and Moos, C. (1968). *Biochemistry* **7**, 1486.
Eisenberg, E., and Moos, C. (1970). *Biochemistry* **9**, 4106.
Eisenberg, E., Zobel, C. R., and Moos, C. (1968). *Biochemistry* **7**, 3186.
Engelhardt, W. A., and Ljubimova, M. N. (1939). *Nature (London)* **144**, 668.
Finlayson, B., and Taylor, E. W. (1969). *Biochemistry* **8**, 802.
Finlayson, B., Lymn, R. W., and Taylor, E. W. (1969). *Biochemistry* **8**, 811.
Gilbert, C., Kretzschmar, K. M., Wilkie, D. R., and Woledge, R. C. (1971). *J. Physiol. (London)* **218**, 163.
Godfrey, J. E., and Harrington, W. F. (1970). *Biochemistry* **9**, 894.
Greaser, M. L., and Gergely, J. (1971). *J. Biol. Chem.* **246**, 4226.
Huxley, A. F. (1957). *Progr. Biophys.* **1**, 225.
Huxley, A. F., and Simmons, R. M. (1971). *Nature (London)* **233**, 533.
Huxley, H. E. (1963). *J. Mol. Biol.* **7**, 281.
Huxley, H. E., and Brown, W. (1967). *J. Mol. Biol.* **30**, 383.
Imamura, K., Kanazawa, T., Tada, M., and Tonomura, Y. (1965). *J. Biochem. (Tokyo)* **57**, 627.
Imamura, K., Tada, M., and Tonomura, Y. (1966). *J. Biochem. (Tokyo)* **59**, 280.
Inoue, A., Shibato-Sekiya, K., and Tonomura, Y. (1972). *J. Biochem. (Tokyo)* **71**, 115.
Kanazawa, T., and Tonomura, Y. (1965). *J. Biochem. (Tokyo)* **57**, 604.
Kiely, B., and Martonosi, A. (1969). *Biochim. Biophys. Acta* **172**, 158.
Kinoshita, N., Kubo, S., Onishi, H., and Tonomura, Y. (1969a). *J. Biochem. (Tokyo)* **65**, 285.
Kinoshita, N., Kubo, S., Onishi, H., and Tonomura, Y. (1969b). *J. Biochem. (Tokyo)* **65**, 567.
Knappeis, G. G., and Carlson, F. (1962). *J. Cell Biol.* **13**, 323.
Knappeis, G. G., and Carlson, F. (1968). *J. Cell Biol.* **38**, 202.
Kokiwa, T., and Tonomura, Y. (1965). *J. Biochem. (Tokyo)* **57**, 616.
Koretz, J., Hunt, T., and Taylor, E. W. (1973). *Cold Spring Harbor Symp. Quant. Biol.* In press.
Lowey, S., and Luck, S. M. (1969). *Biochemistry* **8**, 3195.
Lowey, S., Slayter, H. S., Weeds, A. G., and Baker, H. (1969). *J. Mol. Biol.* **42**, 1.

Lymn, R. W., and Taylor, E. W. (1970). *Biochemistry* **9**, 2975.

Lymn, R. W., and Taylor, E. W. (1971). *Biochemistry* **10**, 4617.

McEntee, K., and Taylor, E. W. (1973). In preparation.

Malik, M. N., and Martonosi, A. (1972). *Arch. Biochem. Biophys.* **152**, 243.

Marston, S. B., and Tregear, R. T. (1971). *Nature (London)* **235**, 23.

Maruyama, K., and Gergely, J. (1967). *J. Biol. Chem.* **237**, 1085.

Maruyama, K., and Weber, A. (1972). *Biochemistry* **11**, 2990.

Masaki, T., Endo, M., and Ebashi, S. (1967). *J. Biochem. (Tokyo)* **62**, 630.

Moore, P. B., Huxley, H. E., and DeRosier, D. J. (1970). *J. Mol. Biol.* **50**, 279.

Morita, J. (1967). *J. Biol. Chem.* **242**, 4501.

Morita, J. (1971). *J. Biochem. (Tokyo)* **69**, 517.

Nakamura, K., and Tonomura, Y. (1968). *J. Biochem. (Tokyo)* **63**, 279.

Nauss, R. M., Kitagawa, S., and Gergely, J. (1969). *J. Biol. Chem.* **244**, 755.

Ohtsuki, I., Masaki, T., Tonomura, Y., and Ebashi, S. (1967). *J. Biochem. (Tokyo)* **61**, 817.

Onishi, H., Nakamura, K., and Tonomura, Y. (1968a). *J. Biochem. (Tokyo)* **63**, 739.

Onishi, H., Nakamura, K., and Tonomura, Y. (1968b). *J. Biochem. (Tokyo)* **64**, 769.

Page, S., and Huxley, H. E. (1963). *J. Cell Biol.* **19**, 369.

Parker, L., Pyun, M. Y., and Hartshorne, J. (1970). *Biochim. Biophys. Acta* **223**, 453.

Pembrick, S. M., and Walz, F. G. (1972). *J. Biol. Chem.* **247**, 2959.

Robson, R. M., Goll, D. E., Arakawa, N., and Stromer, M. H. (1970). *Biochim. Biophys. Acta* **250**, 296.

Sarker, S., Streter, F. A., and Gergely, J. (1971). *Proc. Nat. Acad. Sci. U.S.* **68**, 946.

Sartorelli, L., Fromm, H. S., Benson, R. W., and Boyer, P. D. (1966). *Biochemistry* **5**, 2877.

Schaub, M. C., and Perry, S. V. (1969). *Biochem. J.* **115**, 993.

Schaub, M. C., Hartshorne, D. J., and Perry, S. V. (1967). *Biochem. J.* **105**, 1235.

Seidel, J. C., and Gergely, J. (1971). *Biochem. Biophys. Res. Commun.* **44**, 826.

Shimidzu, T., and Morita, J. (1969). *Biochim. Biophys. Acta* **180**, 545.

Starr, R., and Offer, G. (1971). *FEBS Lett.* **15**, 40.

Takeuchi, K., and Tonomura, Y. (1971). *J. Biochem. (Tokyo)* **70**, 1011.

Taylor, E. W. (1972). *Annu. Rev. Biochem.* **41**, 577.

Taylor, E. W., Lymn, R. W., and Moll, G. (1970). *Biochemistry* **9**, 2984.

Tonomura, Y., Nakamura, H., Kinoshita, N., Onishi, H., and Shigekawa, M. (1969). *J. Biochem. (Tokyo)* **66**, 599.

Trentham, D. R., Badsley, R. G., Eccleston, J. F., and Weeds, A. G. (1972). *Biochem. J.* **126**, 635.

Werber, M. M., Szent-Györgyi, A. G., and Fasman, G. D. (1972). *Biochemistry* **11**, 2872.

Weeds, A. G., and Lowey, S. (1971). *J. Mol. Biol.* **61**, 701.

Woledge, R. C. (1971). *Progr. Biophys. Mol. Biol.* **22**, 37.

Woods, E. F., Himmelfarb, S., and Harrington, W. F. (1963). *J. Biol. Chem.* **238**, 2374.

Energy-Transducing Components
in Mitochondrial Respiration[1]

DAVID F. WILSON, P. LESLIE DUTTON, and MICHAL WAGNER
Department of Biophysics and Physical Biochemistry,
Johnson Research Foundation,
University of Pennsylvania Medical School,
Philadelphia, Pennsylvania

[1]Supported by National Science Foundation grant GB-28125 and National Institute of Health grant GM-12202. DFW is the recipient of U.S. Public Health Service Career Development Award 1-KO4-GM 18154.

I.   Introduction

The understanding of energy conservation in mitochondria and of the dark reactions of photosynthesis has been delayed by a failure to obtain information on the mechanism of energy transduction or even the identity of the energy-transducing components. A large volume of literature exists which discusses current hypotheses on energy conservation, including excellent reviews by Greville (1969), Skulachev (1971), and Slater (1971). We feel that little would be gained by presenting another review of existing literature. Instead we will confine our attention to experimental contributions toward a thermodynamic picture of the mitochondrial respiratory chain. We will then discuss the application of the thermodynamic approach to the energy transduction processes and the design of experimental procedures which can be used to identify energy-transducing components. These procedures have been applied to two energy conservation sites in the mitochondrial respiratory chain and are applicable to the third energy conservation site as well as the respiratory chains of bacteria and those of photosynthetic systems.

II.   The Thermodynamic Behavior of Oxidation-Reduction Reactions

The behavior of oxidation-reduction components is best analyzed according to their oxidation-reduction potentials (see Clark, 1960). Each component may be regarded as one-half of an electrical cell (Eq. 1) with its electron-donating tendency or potentiality described by Eq. (2).

$$Ox + ne^- \rightleftharpoons Red \tag{1}$$

$$E_h = E_m + \frac{RT}{nF} \ln \frac{[ox]}{[red]} \tag{2}$$

In Eq. (2), E_h expresses the tendency of the oxidation-reduction couple to donate electrons to a standard hydrogen electrode; E_m is the characteristic half-reduction potential for the couple; R, T and F are the gas constant, absolute temperature, and the Faraday constant, respectively, and n is the number of electrons transferred when the component is oxidized or reduced. The charge balance is not directly expressed in order to simplify the notation. The thermodynamic properties of electron transfer in the general reaction:

$$\text{A red} + \text{B ox} \rightleftharpoons \text{A ox} + \text{B red} \tag{3}$$

is described in Eq. (4):

$$\Delta E_{(A-B)} = \Delta E_{m(A-B)} + \frac{RT}{nF} \ln \frac{[\text{A ox}][\text{B red}]}{[\text{A red}][\text{B ox}]} \tag{4}$$

In Eq. (4), $\Delta E_{(A-B)}$ is the potential of the electrical cell formed by the oxidation-reduction couples of A and B, $\Delta E_{m(A-B)}$ is the difference between the characteristic half-cell potentials of the two couples. It should be noted that the activity coefficients for the oxidized and reduced forms of a given compound may be assumed to be equal (Clark, 1960), and thus they divide out when the ratios are calculated.

A knowledge of the characteristic half-reduction potential for the oxidation-reduction components of the respiratory chain is essential to any thermodynamic discussion of the reactions involved because of the relationship that Gibbs free energy change $(\Delta G) = -nF\ \Delta E$. Experimentally, a number of techniques have been used to measure the half-reduction potentials of oxidation-reduction components (Clark, 1960). These include polarographic techniques, the method of mixtures, and the potentiometric technique. The last has a much broader applicability and generally greater precision than the other techniques when applied to biological systems. The appropriate instrumentation has been developed to permit the use of the potentiometric technique to measure the oxidation-reduction midpoint potentials of components in suspensions of biological materials. The methodology has been published in detail (Dutton, 1971; Wilson and Dutton, 1970a). It is sufficient here to note that the method is designed to electrometrically measure the oxidation-reduction potential of an anaerobic sample and to either simultaneously measure by optical techniques the reduction of the component or to anaerobically transfer aliquots of the suspension to electron paramagnetic resonance (EPR) sample tubes. The EPR sample tubes are then immersed in liquid nitrogen in order to trap the oxidation-reduction state and to permit EPR measurements at down to helium temperature.

III. The Oxidation-Reduction Potentials of the Components of Intact Mitochondria

We have set out to systematically determine the half-reduction potentials and n values of the oxidation-reduction components of the respiratory chain of intact mitochondria. These values are essential to a discussion of energy transduction; a complete tabulation of the measured values for the components of pigeon heart mitochondria are presented in Fig. 1.

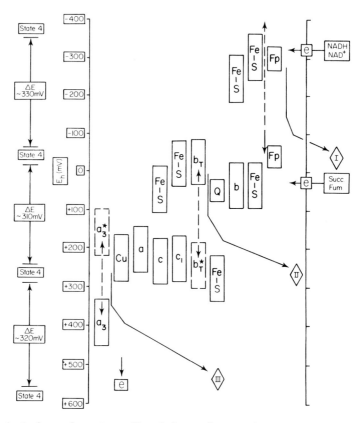

FIG. 1. A thermodynamic profile of the oxidation–reduction components of the respiratory chain of pigeon heart mitochondria. Each component is represented by a rectangle which is centered on its half-reduction potential at pH 7.2 and extends from the potential at which the component is 9% reduced to the potential at which it is 91% reduced. The positions of the rectangles are not intended to indicate the sequence of electron transfer. On the left side of the figure are indicated the E_h values of the iso-potential groups in pigeon heart mitochondria under state 4 conditions with succinate and glutamate as substrate. Two values are indicated for cytochromes b_T and a_3, one measured for uncoupled mitochondria and the other measured for coupled mito-chondria in the presence of excess ATP (see text for details).

The cytochromes of the respiratory chain are called cytochromes a_3, a, c, c_1, b_K, and b_T. All have n values of 1.0, and the measured half-reduction potentials at pH 7.2 are +385 mV, +210 mV, +235 mV, +225 mV, +30 mV, and −30 mV, respectively. For a more complete reference list and discussion of the literature for the cytochromes $a + a_3$, see Tsudzuki and Wilson (1971); for cytochromes c and c_1, see Dutton *et al.* (1970); and for cytochromes b_K and b_T, see Wilson and Dutton (1971).

Iron–sulfur proteins identified as associated with the respiratory chain have rapidly increased in number in recent years, primarily owing to the work of Ohnishi *et al.* (1970, 1971, 1972) and Orme-Johnson *et al.* (1973). Ohnishi and co-workers (1972) have combined the technique of oxidation-reduction potential measurements with temperature control down to near liquid helium temperatures to characterize the different iron–sulfur proteins. At liquid N_2 temperatures EPR spectra of pigeon heart or beef heart mitochondria at pH 7.2 reveal only two distinguishable signals; one with a half-reduction potential of +30 mV and an *n* value of 1.0 and the other with a half-reduction potential of −305 mV and an *n* value slightly less than 1 (Wilson *et al.*, 1970). At lower temperatures, additional signals are seen. For instance, Rieske's iron–sulfur protein (Rieske *et al.*, 1964a,b) has a measured E_m 7.2 of 280 mV, $n = 1$ (Wilson *et al.*, 1971; but, see also, Rieske *et al.*, 1964a) and additional components (all $n = 1$) are seen which have other half-reduction potentials. Ohnishi and co-workers, using temperatures lower than liquid N_2, have measured several different iron-sulfur components; they are schematically presented in Fig. 2 in terms of their position in the respiratory chain of pigeon heart mitochondria. What has been designated as center 1 actually represents two components with very similar half-reduction potentials and EPR spectral properties. The total number of iron–sulfur proteins which have been clearly identified by EPR and their half-reduction potentials measured is now 8, but it is conceivable that this number will eventually be even larger.

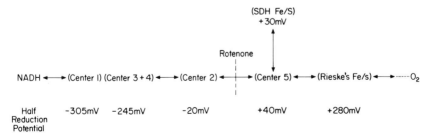

FIG. 2. The iron–sulfur proteins associated with the respiratory chain of pigeon heart mitochondria. This schematic representation is that presented by Ohnishi *et al.* (1972).

The mitochondrial respiratory chain also contains two copper atoms (in cytochrome oxidase), one of which is measurable by its absorbance at 830 nm and its EPR absorbance. The other is not yet measurable. The measurable copper has an n value of 1.0 and a half-reduction potential of +245 mV in intact mitochondria (Erecińska et al., 1971). Coenzyme Q has been measured in beef heart submitochondria particles (Urban and Klingenberg, 1969), and this is the value presented in Fig. 1.

A report that a new molybdenum containing component is associated with NADH dehydrogenase (Albracht and Slater, 1970) is unconfirmed and appears to directly contradict the studies of Orme-Johnson et al. (1973) and Ohnishi et al. (1970, 1971, 1972).

IV. The Dependence of the Half-Reduction Potentials of the Components on the Phosphate Potential

The experimental technique developed by Dutton and co-workers (Dutton, 1971; Wilson and Dutton, 1970a) can be used to measure the half-reduction potentials of components in a "potential clamped" system (see Appendix I) not only in the "low energy" state (uncoupled) mitochondria, but also in coupled mitochondria in the "high energy" state (under the influence of a high phosphate potential). It has been reported that in the presence of excess ATP, the measured values for cytochromes a, c_1, and b_K and copper are essentially the same as in uncoupled mitochondria with cytochrome a changing by 30 mV and the other components by less than 10 mV. By contrast, ATP induces the cytochrome b_T (resting E_m −30 mV) to assume an E_m of +245 mV (+ATP) while cytochrome a_3 changes from +385 mV (uncoupled to +155 mV (+ATP) (Wilson and Dutton, 1970a,b; Dutton et al., 1971; Wilson et al., 1972a; Lindsay et al., 1972).

Although the existence of two chemically distinct b cytochromes in intact mitochondria (Wilson and Dutton, 1970b) has been accepted (Slater et al., 1970b; Wegdam et al., 1970), the properties of these two cytochromes are in very active discussion. Thus in a series of papers (Wilson and Dutton, 1970b; Chance et al., 1970; Sato et al., 1971a,b; Dutton et al., 1970, 1972; Wilson et al., 1972a) the concept has been developed of two b cytochromes having different half-reduction potentials and absorption spectra, one of which (cytochrome b_T) has a phosphate potential dependent half-reduction potential. By contrast, Slater and co-workers have developed the concept of two b cytochromes with similar absorption spectra but one of which (b_i) has an ATP and antimycin A induced spectral shift to longer wavelengths (Slater et al., 1970a,b; Wegdam et al., 1970; Slater, 1971). The concept of Slater and co-workers is difficult to reconcile with the observation that uncoupled mitochondria (Sato *et al.*, 1971a,b; Wikström, 1971; Dutton *et al.*, 1972) and purified succinate: cytochrome *c* reductase (Wilson *et al.*, 1971, 1972c) contain two distinct *b* cytochromes: cytochrome b_K (E_m 7.2 = +30 mV; alpha maximum 561 nm) and cytochrome b_T (E_m 7.2 = −30 mV; alpha maximum 565 nm). These latter workers reported that in coupled systems the addition of ATP causes oxidation or reduction of the cytochromes (depending on the experimental conditions) but no spectral shift. They further reported that the antimycin effect is 2-fold; a small spectral shift in the alpha maximum of cytochrome b_K as described by Pumphrey (1962) and a respiration dependent shift in the half-reduction potential of cytochrome b_T to a more positive value (see Rieske, 1971; Wilson *et al.*, 1971, 1972c).

Berden *et al.* (1972) have presented a short communication reporting (in contrast to Wilson and Dutton, 1970a,b; Dutton *et al.*, 1971) that the addition of ATP to beef heart mitochondria changes the measured half-reduction potentials of cytochromes *c*, c_1, $b_{561}(b_K)$ and $b_{565}(b_T)$, with the cytochromes *c* and c_1 becoming more negative and part of the b_{561} and b_{565} becoming more positive. This experimental difference cannot be attributed to the mitochondria used (rat liver, beef heart and pigeon heart mitochondria were used in the previous study, as were beef heart and pigeon heart phosphorylating submitochondrial particles, all with the same result; while Berden *et al.* used beef heart mitochondria) or to the technique per se, as Berden *et al.* reported using the technique of Wilson and Dutton. The difference in experimental results must arise from the use of the technique. Berden *et al.* (1972) have not reported the essential control experiments showing that their results are independent of mediator concentration or the reversibility of their measurements. In our experience, the presented data are consistent with a poorly mediated system in which the electron flux from endogenous donors is greater than can be accommodated by the mediators used. This could arise for two reasons: (1) the beef heart mitochondria normally have large amounts of endogenous donor relative to pigeon heart mitochondria and (2) two of the key mediators (phenazine ethosulfate and diaminodurene — they omitted phenazine methosulfate) are unstable and could become depleted during the experiment. Phenazine ethosulfate is continuously degraded by the measuring light. Diaminodurene is unstable in the oxidized form (half-time of a few minutes in the presence of ferricyanide) and may be accidentally destroyed before the titration is started or during the titration.

V.   A Thermodynamic Profile of the Respiratory Chain Components and the Energy Conservation Sites

An examination of Fig. 1 shows that the midpoint potentials of the components of the respiratory chain form four groups: one at -300 mV, the second at 0 mV, the third at 220 mV, and the fourth at 400 mV. These divisions roughly correlate with the potential spans utilized for ATP synthesis. The actual oxidation-reduction potential of each component can be estimated from its steady-state percent reduction, midpoint potential, and n value.

In mitochondria in state 4 the estimated oxidation-reduction potentials of each of the components in a group is very close to that for all other members of the group, and the components may thus be regarded as being essentially in equilibrium. For example, under the experimental conditions utilized, cytochromes a, c, and c_1 all have oxidation–reduction potentials near 260 mV. The respiratory chain may be thought of as a series of isopotential groups of components with energy conservation associated with electron transfer between these groups. The oxidation-reduction potential for each of the four isopotential groups for mitochondria in state 4 with glutamate + succinate as substrate have been estimated (Wilson et $al.$, 1972a), and the values are designated in the rectangles on the left side of Fig. 1. The approximate potential span available at the first, second and third phosphorylation sites (I, II, and III) are 330 mV, 310 mV, and 320 mV, respectively. The values for the first and second sites are readily estimated from direct measurements, but the value for site III makes use of the measured second-order rate constant for the reaction of O_2 with reduced cytochrome a_3 of 1×10^8 M^{-1} sec^{-1} (Chance et $al.$, 1971; McCray and Anderson, 1972), an assumed oxygen concentration of 200 μM, and a measured half-time for the oxidation of cytochrome a by cytochrome a_3 of 6 msec. These values permit us to estimate that in state 4 the cytochrome a_3 is only 0.1% reduced.

This interpretation of the mitochondrial respiratory chain as functioning near equilibrium is in agreement with Klingenberg and coworkers (Klingenberg, 1961, 1969; Klingenberg and Schollmeyer, 1961, 1969), who have pioneered in applying thermodynamic (equilibrium) concepts to mitochondrial behavior. Prior to the availability of precise data on the half-reduction potentials of the oxidation–reduction components in intact mitochondria, they were able to present strong evidence in support of an equilibrium between the phosphate potential and the ΔE of the respiratory chain carriers (see Klingenberg and Schollmeyer, 1961; Klingenberg, 1969; Muraoka and Slater, 1969). Wohlrab (1970) measured the effect of CO on the rate of oxidation of cytochromes c and a in cytochrome c-depleted mitochondria and concluded that cytochrome c permitted a very rapid interchain equilibration of cytochrome a. Boveris *et al.* (1972) have reported that during rapid reduction of the respiratory chain by durohydroquinone the coenzyme Q, cytochrome b_{561}, and cytochrome b_{565} remain in equilibrium.

When electrons are transferred from the pyridine nucleotide linked substrate to cytochrome a_3 the potential change (ΔE) is approximately 1 V (960 mV). The Gibbs free energy available for ATP synthesis on transfer of 2 electrons through this potential span may be calculated to be approximately −45 kcal. When this available energy is distributed to three phosphorylation sites, each individual site can sustain approximately −15 kcal. Cockrell and associates (1966) have measured the maximum phosphate potential which could be formed by mitochondria under state 4 conditions and found it to be approximately 15.6 kcal/mole. Slater (1970) has repeated these experiments and obtained similar experimental values. He chose to use a more negative ΔG for ATP hydrolysis than was used by Cockrell *et al.* (1966), (~ −10.5 kcal/mole vs −8.4 kcal/mole) and thus reported a larger ΔG for ATP synthesis. A reevaluation of the ΔG for ATP hydrolysis has been carried out by Rosing and Slater (1972), and the reported new value is approximately −7.5 kcal/mole at pH 7.0. Our data are consistent with the value being between −7.5 and −8 kcal/mole in usual mitochondrial media. The work of Rosing and Slater (1972) represents a very important contribution to the study of cellular energetics. When the ΔG determined by Cockrell *et al.* (1966) is used, it is within the limits of the available data equal to that calculated from the ΔG available at each phosphorylation site. This would be expected from the reversibility of the reactions. The free energy change which accompanies a reaction is a function of the ratio of the forward and reverse fluxes. The observation that the overall ΔG from NADH to cytochrome a_3 is approximately zero requires an equality of the forward and reverse fluxes of all of the intermediate reactions within the respiratory chain.

VI. Oxidation-Reduction Potentials in "Open" and "Potential Clamped" Systems

As has been discussed in the previous section, the mitochondrial respiratory chain has been shown to consist of four groups of components in series. Each group consists of components with similar midpoint potentials. Rapid electron exchange among the members of each individual group sustains the components in an isopotential state (same E_h) even under conditions in which the net electron flux is high (such as in the presence of ADP and P_i). The energy transduction system which is responsible for transferring the electrochemical potential into a form suitable for ATP synthesis (group transfer potential) operates from one isopotential group to another. For the most thermodynamically efficient energy conservation, the transducer system must be involved in the transfer of all the electrons from one isopotential group to another. This is equivalent to an electrical circuit which is open at each end (to the more negative isopotential group on one end and to the more positive isopotential group on the other end), but which is insulated between the two isopotential groups. Situated on the only electrical connection between the two electron pools is a reversible energy transducer which maintains a stoichiometry of two electrons transferred per ATP molecule. This system is referred to in the present paper as an "open" system and has the property that it is fully capable of synthesizing ATP by electron transport, and that the relative oxidation–reduction potentials of the isopotential groups are dependent on the phosphate potential.

Experimentally the behavior of the respiratory chain components may also be examined under conditions in which the oxidation–reduction potential is clamped to an externally controlled value. This is attained by adding oxidation–reduction mediators which are in excess of and can readily interact with respiratory components of both the low potential pool and high potential pool as well as each other. This is equivalent to opening a large number of electrical connections which do not contain energy transducers, resulting in an equilibration of the isopotential pools to the point at which the ΔE_h is equal to zero. This experimental system ("potential clamped") has the property that it cannot support net ATP synthesis driven by electron transport or, in the more general sense, cannot support any reaction requiring the existence of a ΔE_h. The "potential clamped" system is useful for examining the oxidation-reduction components for evidence that the phosphate potential is directly coupled to chemical transformations of the oxidation–reduction component (transformations not involving electron transfer).

A. THE RELATIONSHIP OF THE PHOSPHATE POTENTIAL TO THE OXIDATION–REDUCTION POTENTIAL IN "OPEN" SYSTEMS

In a respiratory chain which is operating very near equilibrium, it follows that the electron flow and ATP synthesis reactions are reversible. Since the ΔG for this situation is zero, the ΔG for ATP hydrolysis (reaction 5)

$$\text{ATP} \rightleftharpoons \text{ADP} + \text{P}_i \tag{5}$$

must be equal but opposite in sign to the ΔG for the electron transfer reaction:

$$b_K^{+2} + c^{+3} \rightleftharpoons b_K^{+3} + c^{+2} \tag{6}$$

where cytochrome b_K [$E_m = +30$ mV] and cytochrome c [$E_m = +235$] form the low potential and high potential extremes of site II, respectively. When the reacting species are expressed in the appropriate stoichiometry of 2 electrons per ATP the overall reaction is

$$2b_K^{+2} + 2c^{+3} + \text{ADP} + \text{P}_i \rightleftharpoons 2b_K^{+3} + 2c^{+2} + \text{ATP} \tag{7}$$

At equilibrium (ΔG overall $= 0$)

$$K = \frac{[\text{ATP}]}{[\text{ADP}][\text{P}_i]} \frac{[b_K^{+3}]^2 [c^{+2}]^2}{[b_K^{+2}] [c^{+3}]^2} \tag{8}$$

This equilibrium constant can be readily manipulated to give the expression

$$\log \frac{[\text{ATP}]}{[\text{ADP}][\text{P}_i]} = \frac{(E_h b_K - E_h c) - (E_m b_K - E_m c)}{0.030} + \log K \tag{9}$$

where $E_h b_K$ and $E_h c$ are the oxidation–reduction potentials of cytochromes b_K and c respectively, $E_m b_K$ and $E_m c$ are the respective half-reduction potentials and 0.03 is the ΔE required for two electrons to provide 1.36 kcal, equivalent to a change in the [ATP]/([ADP][P$_i$]) ratio of 10.

Although the equation is derived for cytochromes b_K and c, it is completely general and applies to all the oxidation-reduction components *except* those that undergo a phosphate potential dependent chemical modification. Thus components from the low potential pool such as coenzyme Q or iron–sulfur proteins can be substituted for cytochrome b_K while components from the high potential pool such as cytochrome c_1 or copper can be substituted for cytochrome c. The only change required in the equation is that the appropriate half-reduction potentials and n values be used. Analogous equations can be written for individual energy conservation sites or even to include all three sites.

Experimentally, the applicability of the equations to the mito-chondrial respiratory chain is readily measurable. Both Klingenberg and Chance have measured certain aspects of this relationship. Chance and Hollunger (1961) observed that the addition of ATP to sulfide-inhibited mitochondria causes an oxidation of cytochrome c and a concomitant reduction of NAD. Both effects were dependent on the phosphate potential — ratio of [ATP]/([ADP][Pi]), and not on just the concentration of ATP. At phosphate potential of approximately $10^4\ M^{-1}$ the cytochrome c and NAD were each 50% reduced. Assuming a $\Delta G'_0$ for ATP hydrolysis of -8.4 kcal/mole and E_m values of 235 mV and -320 mV, respectively, the ΔG for the difference in oxidation-reduction potentials (ΔE) is approximately 90% of that for ATP hydrolysis. The 10% was presumably lost as a result of mitochondrial ATPase activity and of kinetic restrictions; relatively low concentra-tions of ADP (44 μM) phosphate (440 μM) and ATP (70–700 μM) were used. Klingenberg and Schollmeyer (1961) presented evidence that equilibrium is approached in mitochondria respiring in the presence of substrate (no added ADP, ATP, or P_i) when substrates were used which increased the reduction of NAD, the cytochrome c also became more reduced such that these redox couples appeared to have nearly the same midpoint potentials.

Klingenberg (1969) reported that in mitochondria under both aero-bic and anaerobic conditions the state of reduction of cytochrome c was dependent on the phosphate potential according to the relation-ship:

$$\frac{[c^{+2}]}{[c^{+3}]} = \frac{k[\text{ADP}][P_i]}{[\text{ATP}]} + \beta \tag{10}$$

where k and β are constants. This relationship was interpreted as evidence for the existence of an energy rich reduced form of cyto-chrome c. It should be considered, however, that in a closed system, this behavior is expected from the phosphate potential dependent equilibration of electrons from the cytochrome c-containing pool to the NAD-containing pool (two phosphorylation sites). The equation relevent to this redistribution of electrons across two phosphorylation sites is

$$\log \frac{[\text{ATP}]}{[\text{ADP}][P_i]} = \frac{(E_h\text{NAD}-E_h c) - (E_m\text{NAD}-E_m c)}{0.060} + \log K \tag{11}$$

Thus if the NAD pool were clamped to a constant potential (this would result if the substrate equilibrating with NAD and the NAD itself were a large pool relative to the cytochrome c pool), then the experimental result described by Klingenberg (1969) would be observed.

The results of Chance and Hollunger (1961) appear to be inconsistent with those of Klingenberg (1969), and in the original papers different interpretations are given. The former authors obtained an n value approximately 2 cytochrome c per ATP while the latter obtained an apparent n value of 1 (60 mV per 10-fold change in the phosphate potential). The data are completely consistent, however, because in the experiment of Chance and Hollunger (1961) the electron equilibrium is from cytochrome c (reduced by sulfide) to NAD such that the NAD became 30 mV more negative and the cytochrome c 30 mV more positive per 10-fold change in the phosphate potential ($\Delta E = 60$ mV/10 x change in phosphate potential). In the experiment reported by Klingenberg, the NADH potential remained unchanged while the cytochrome c changed by 60 mV more positive per 10-fold change in the phosphate potential ($\Delta E = 60$ mV/10 x change in phosphate potential). Thus these two experiments should be considered to represent two methods for demonstrating an approach to equilibrium across energy conservation sites I and II. Unfortunately in each set of experiments the requisite quantitative relationships of the ΔE (between the NAD and cytochrome c couples) and the phosphate potential were not measured or the theoretical relationships recognized and described.

Caswell (1968) utilized potentiometric methods to measure the oxidation-reduction potential of cytochromes b and c under conditions of extreme oxidation or reduction, conditions normally difficult to measure by optical techniques. In principle the technique used by Caswell requires that an oxidation-reduction mediator be used which interacts specifically with the desired region of the respiratory chain and which readily reacts with a platinum electrode. If this interaction is sufficiently specific and rapid, the mediator will stay in equilibrium with the selected electron pool and the potentiometric reading will accurately reflect the oxidation-reduction potential of that pool ("open" system). It is evident that an ideal mediator for this purpose has no effect on the "insulation" of the respiratory chain and the system remains "open." Thus Eqs. (7) through (9) accurately reflect the interaction of the phosphate potential with the oxidation-reduction components. It is unlikely that any of the presently known mediators have the specificity required to maintain an "open" system under low flux conditions. This can, however, be readily tested by the addition of mediator to a mitochondrial suspension which is anaerobic and in the presence of moderate phosphate potentials. If the ΔE:phosphate potential relationship between components in pools on either side of the phosphorylation site are not changed, this would be good evidence that is is adequately specific.

B. THE BEHAVIOR OF "OPEN" SYSTEMS WITH A DIRECT INTERACTION BETWEEN THE PHOSPHATE POTENTIAL AND THE COMPONENT BEING MEASURED

A number of possible mechanisms for energy conservation exist in which an oxidative reaction is coupled to ATP synthesis. Such a reaction in an open system should be treated as a special case if the measurements are made directly of the energy-transducing component. A suitable example of this type is the combined reactions catalysed by glyceraldehyde-3-phosphate dehydrogenase and phosphoglycerate kinase (for details, see Bucher, 1947; Velick and Furfine, 1963; Boyer, 1968).

$$\text{NAD} + \text{G-3-P} + \text{P}_i \rightleftharpoons \text{NADH} + \text{1,3-d P G} \tag{12}$$

$$\text{1,3-d P G} + \text{ADP} \rightleftharpoons \text{3-P-G} + \text{ATP} \tag{13}$$

where G-3-P, 1,3-d P G, and 3-P-G represent glyceraldehyde 3-phosphate, 1,3-diphosphoglycerate, and 3-phosphoglycerate, respectively. The apparent half-reduction potential (E_m^*) as measured by the NAD couple and using G-3-P as the reduced form and the sum of 1,3-d P G and 3-P-G as the oxidized form is

$$-\frac{E_m^* - E_m\text{NAD}}{0.030} = \log\left[K_{12}K_{13}\frac{[\text{ADP}][\text{P}_i]}{[\text{ATP}]} + K_{12}[\text{P}_i]\right] \tag{14}$$

where K_{12} and K_{13} are the equilibrium constants for Eqs. (12) and (13), respectively. The half-reduction potential of the glyceraldehyde 3-phosphate is limited at high phosphate potential to a single value. As the phosphate potential is lowered the half-reduction potential becomes more negative at approximately 30 mV per 10-fold decrease in the phosphate potential.

The difference between an "open" system without interaction described earlier and an "open" system with interaction lies in the component being measured. In all "open" systems which have a coupling between the oxidation–reduction system and the phosphate potential, there is an energy-transducing oxidation-reduction component. Equations (7) through (9) describe measurements of the components, not the energy-transducing element, whereas Eqs. (12)–(14) extend the "open" system measurements to include the energy-transducing component. The exact behavior of the energy-transducing element in an "open" system with interaction is dependent on the mechanism involved, but a complete analysis of a number of mechanisms is possible. The "open" system with interactions is directly applicable to respiratory chains and can in principle be used to identify the components responsible for energy transduction. The appropriate use of the technique requires the assumption that equilibrium exists among the oxidation-reduction components of the equipotential groups ($\Delta E = 0$) and that the ΔE between isopotential groups is equivalent to the ΔG for hydrolysis of ATP. With these assumptions it is only necessary to measure simultaneously the reduction of two components at various points of the respiratory chain in the presence of varying phosphate potentials. Equations (7) through (9) will accurately describe the relative behavior of any two components *unless* one or more of two components is interacting with the phosphate potential. This method of analysis requires neither special apparatus nor a difficult theoretical treatment. It would be necessary to measure a series of different pairs of components, and some special techniques would be required to obtain the measurements for components such as iron–sulfur proteins. Care should be exercised to measure only components that are either part of the respiratory chain or in rapid equilibrium with it.

The preferred method for presenting the comparative data would be a plot of the ΔE_h against the logarithm of the phosphate potential. The result of such a treatment will be linear for two components which do not interact with the phosphate potential and the slope will reflect the number of phosphorylation sites. A slope other than the theoretical value, particularly accompanied by a biphasic curve, is diagnostic of an interaction of the phosphate potential with one of the components.

Unfortunately, although this type of analysis can strongly implicate a component in energy transduction, very precise analytical data will be required to gain much information about the mechanism itself. De Vault (1971) has mathematically analyzed a number of hypothetical mechanisms for energy transduction assuming a mediator interacting only at one side (high or low potential) of the energy transducer. The analysis was applied to the data of Wilson and Dutton (1970a,b) for a "potential clamped" system, but these data were obtained using mediators that react on both the high and low potential sides, and the analysis is not applicable.

The "open" system with interaction is essentially that assumed by DeVault (except that no mediators are used). Even mechanisms which have a stoichiometry of 1 electron per "high energy" intermediate can give many different behavior patterns (DeVault, 1971). It is apparent that mechanisms which account for the stoichiometry of 2 electrons per "high energy" intermediate will present an even larger number of possibilities. An appropriate use of the "open" system with interaction is to obtain the experimental data and then use these data to exclude some of the possible mechanisms suggested by other experimental approaches.

C.   The Relationship between Phosphate Potential and Oxidation-Reduction Potential in "Potential Clamped" Systems

The "potential clamped" system differs greatly from the previously described "open" systems. Oxidation-reduction mediators are added to the mitochondrial suspension which are readily oxidized and reduced by the components of the respiratory chain. They form an electrical "short circuit" and prevent the formation of a ΔE between the isopotential groups. The kinetic requirements of the mediators are dependent on the behavior of the respiratory chain and the type of particles used. Some of the requirements of the mediators and experimental tests for a "potential clamped" system are discussed in Appendix I.

The "potential clamped" system is useful for measuring the effect of the phosphate potential on the chemical properties of the oxidation–reduction components. In a "potential clamped" system the half-reduction potential of those components which function only as electron transfer agents should be unaffected by the addition of ATP. Components which are involved in energy transduction would be expected to respond in some way to the applied phosphate potential. The change induced by the phosphate potential can be either a direct change in the component itself or a change in its chemical environment (such as a pH difference across membrane with the components localized only on one side of the membrane).

It is convenient initially to consider a general mechanism of energy transduction which requires two coupled one electron carriers (a mechanism suitable for cytochrome involvement).

The mechanism itself should not be considered to be more than an expression of the formal logic required to fit the available data. Where possible, the symbols are referred to chemical species, primarily to give a chemical perspective to the arguments.

$$A^{2+}L_1 + I \rightleftharpoons A^{3+}L_2 - I + 2e^- \tag{15}$$

$$A^{3+}L_2 - I \rightleftharpoons A^{3+}L_2 + I\sim \tag{16}$$

$$A^{3+}L_2 - I + e^- \rightleftharpoons A^{2+}L_2 - I \tag{17}$$

$$A^{2+}L_2 - I \rightleftharpoons A^{2+}L_2 + I \sim \tag{18}$$

$$A^{3+}L_2 + e^- \rightleftharpoons A^{3+}L_1 \tag{19}$$

$$A^{3+}L_1 + e^- \rightleftharpoons A^{2+}L_1 \tag{20}$$

$$I \sim + ADP + P_i \rightleftharpoons I + ATP \tag{21}$$

The equations represent the energy-transducing component as A L, where both A (cytochrome b_T or a_3 [?] and L (cytochrome ligand?) can be oxidized and reduced in a mechanism which includes a specific modifier I (protein-bound phosphate?). Once the modifier has been added in a two-electron process it is a "high energy" bond which is stable when A is either oxidized or reduced. The ΔG for its hydrolysis may be dependent on the state of reduction of A, and thus either reactions 16 or 18 may be the preferred energy-transfer reaction, although both are capable under certain conditions of driving the ATP synthesis. The measured dependence of the half-reduction potential of two cytochromes (b_T and a_3) on the phosphate potential indicates that one of the two (16 or 18) is kinetically very slow relative to the other. When the data for cytochrome b_T is fitted to these equations, Eq. (18) must be the slower; whereas if the data for cytochrome a_3 are fitted, Eq. (16) must be the slower. Only one of these reactions is required. The other being slow does not affect the existence of an equilibrium between the phosphate potential and the other reactions.

In the absence of added mediators the presented equations are formally capable of net ATP synthesis. This would occur if the oxidant in Eq. (15) is a member of the high potential pool and the reductant in Eqs. (19) and (20) is a member of the low potential pool. In the presence of mediators, the low- and high-potential pools equilibrate to $\Delta E = 0$, and all the oxidation-reduction reactions not directly part of the transduction mechanism are "clamped" to the same external oxidation-reduction potential.

The transduction reactions are written in a cyclic form and, as such, represent an ATPase when the phosphate potential is high and the ΔE_h approaches zero [the sum: (15) + (16) + (19) + (20) is I $\longrightarrow$ I $\sim$]. If, however, under "potential clamped" conditions one of the reactions is much slower than the rest, a "local equilibrium" can be established among the other reactions with the free energy of hydrolysis of ATP expressed in the chemical species of L present. A complete analysis is not possible due to the large number of equations and the speculative nature of the chemical species. A very simple analysis suggests that at low phosphate potential the dominant forms of A (cytochrome) will be with the ligand L_1 while at high phosphate potentials the dominant forms of A will be with the ligand $L_2 - I$. If this is the case the behavior of the energy-transducing component in a "potential clamped" system may be described as a ligand exchange reaction in which the nature of the ligand is dependent on the phosphate potential. At low phosphate potentials the concentrations of $A^{2+}L_2 - I$ and $A^{3+}L_2 - I$ will be insignificant and the measured half-reduction potential will be that of Eq. (20), while at high phosphate potentials the opposite will be true and the measured half-reduction potential will approach that of Eq. (17). Although the complete dependence of the measured half-reduction potential on the phosphate potential cannot be derived, the transition between these two extreme values will have a slope of approximately 60 mV per 10-fold change in phosphate potential (one ATP is required to modify one ligand and the measured oxidation-reduction reactions have n values of 1.0) (see Clark, 1960).

In Fig. 3 the experimentally measured half-reduction potential of cytochrome b_T is plotted as a function of the phosphate potential (N. Sato, D. F. Wilson, and B. Chance, unpubl.). The half-reduction potential approaches -30 mV at phosphate potentials less than $1\ M^{-1}$ and then becomes more positive at approximately 60 mV per 10-fold

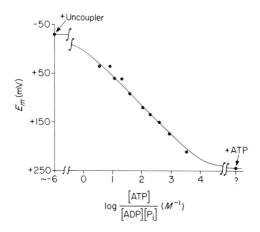

FIG. 3. The phosphate potential dependence of the measured half-reduction potential of cytochrome b_T. The half-reduction potential of the cytochrome b_T was measured as a function of the added concentrations of ATP, ADP, and orthophosphate in a "potential clamped" system. The experimental points represent approximately 20% of the measurements made using pigeon heart mitochondria. The omitted points all fall within ± 20 mV of the solid line. The solid line is a theoretical curve constructed as described in Appendix II.

increase in the phosphate potential. The value appears to limit at +245 mV with very high phosphate potentials. It is difficult to be certain that this is a genuine limiting value, although it would be expected that the addition of 6 mM ATP in the absence of added ADP or P_i would sustain a phosphate potential greater than $10^5 M^{-1}$ during the time required to make the measurements. If 245 mV is indeed the limiting value, then the most effective "high energy" intermediate in the thermodynamic sense (effective concentration ratio 5×10^4) is $A^{3+}L_2 - I$, offering the reasonable suggestion that Eq. (18) would not significantly contribute to the equilibrium of the "potential clamped" system.

The opposite is true for cytochrome a_3 for which the respective values are +385 mV and +150 mV (Wilson et al., 1972a; Lindsay and Wilson, 1972). In this case $A^{2+}L_2 - I$ is the most effective "high energy" intermediate by a ratio of approximately 5×10^3, and Eq. (16) would not be expected to contribute significantly to the equilibration of a "potential clamped" system.

One important result of the analysis is to show that the experimental requirements for a "potential clamped" system are not difficult to obtain in preparations which have little endogenous substrate. The mediators can be kinetically much slower than the maximal rates of the forward or reverse electron fluxes because the system will readily collapse to the "potential clamped" state. The exception is in the case of preparations in which the rate of endogenous respiration is high. The mediators must be able to transfer electrons much more rapidly than they can be donated by the endogenous donor because this electron flow directly contributes to the generation of a ΔE across the energy conservation sites.

D. THE REQUIREMENT FOR A CHANGE IN THE HALF-REDUCTION POTENTIAL OF THE ENERGY-TRANSDUCING COMPONENT

As has been noted, the energy-transducing component must have properties that allow its oxidation-reduction properties to be modified by the phosphate potential and conversely, the oxidation-reduction properties must be able to modify the phosphate potential. The minimum equations required (for this special analysis) for a two-electron carrier are:

$$B \text{ ox} + A \text{ red} \rightleftharpoons A^\circ \text{ ox} + B \text{ red} \tag{22}$$

$$A^\circ \text{ ox} + ADP + P_i \rightleftharpoons A \text{ ox} + ATP \tag{23}$$

$$A \text{ ox} + C \text{ red} \rightleftharpoons A \text{ red} + C \text{ ox} \tag{24}$$

where B and C are the high-potential acceptor and the low-potential donor, respectively, for the energy transducer A. As the system approaches equilibrium, the ΔG for each of the three reactions must be equal to zero. This can only be true if the E_h of the oxidation–reduction couple

$$A \text{ red} \rightleftharpoons A° \text{ ox} + 2\ e^- \tag{25}$$

is equal to that of the high-potential acceptor while the E_h of the couple

$$A \text{ red} \rightleftharpoons A \text{ ox} + 2\ e^- \tag{26}$$

is equal to that of the low potential donor. Thus it is necessary for the two couples to differ in E_h by at least 300 mV. In addition the ratio of $A°$ ox to A ox must be at least 10^{11} if the E_m values of the two couples [Eqs. (25) and (26)] are equal ($\Delta E_m = 0$). This has kinetic consequences in Eq. (24). The rate of electron transfer is equal to K_{24} [A ox] [C red] where A ox represents less than 10^{-11} of the total A. Assuming that A is equivalent in concentration to that of the cytochromes and that the cytochrome turnover number in state 4 is greater than 1 sec^{-1}, a rate constant of at least $10^{17}\ M^{-1}$ sec^{-1} is required to account for the rate of electron flow. This number is rather larger than that for diffusion limited second-order reactions. If, however, the two couples have half-reduction potentials which differ by 240 mV, a rate constant of $10^9\ M^{-1}$ sec^{-1} is adequate to explain the electron flux. If the half-reduction potentials are matched to those of the acceptor and donor, the required rate constant can approach $10^6\ M^{-1}$ sec^{-1}.

The justification for using an obviously oversimplified set of equations for this analysis lies in the fact that the diffusion limited, second-order, two-electron reaction is the fastest reaction possible and all other mechanisms which incorporate sequential single electron transfers or multiple reactions are inherently slower and require larger rate constants to attain the same turnover number. This oversimplified analysis is thus the correct one, and it is necessary to conclude that energy transduction can most effectively be carried out by a component that can be oxidized or reduced by two separate pathways. These two pathways represent oxidation-reduction couples which differ in half-reduction potential by at least 240 mV (Wilson and Dutton, 1970b).

VII. On the Nature of Respiratory Control

A. Localization of the Site of Respiratory Control.

When tightly coupled mitochondria are used to study mitochondrial respiration, the respiration is greatly stimulated when an "energy sink" is available. Thus if the mitochondria are suspended in a medium containing excess substrate and oxygen, a rate of oxygen consumption is measured which is much less (8–40 times less) than the rate measured when ADP and P_i (ATP synthesis), Ca^{2+}, valinomycin $+K^+$ (ion transport), uncouplers (heat production), etc., are present. In each case the latter additions introduce a mechanism whereby the available free energy can be rapidly removed from the respiratory chain and the respiratory chain responds by greatly increasing the rate of oxygen reduction. This phenomenon of respiratory control has been extensively studied (see, for example, Lardy and Wellman, 1952; Chance and Williams, 1956; Chance, 1961; Klingenberg, 1961; Klingenberg and Schollmeyer, 1961). Chance and coworkers used the crossover theorem in an attempt to identify the sites of interaction between the energy transfer pathway and the electron transfer pathway. The crossover theorem refers to kinetic control of a system strongly displaced from equilibrium. As such, it is reasonable to question its application to the mitochondrial respiratory chain and to ask if a treatment is available that can more completely explain the experimental observations.

If most of the respiratory chain is very close to equilibrium in state 4, then it follows that the control of respiration cannot originate within that portion of chain. This arises because a system at equilibrium is by definition uncontrolled; i.e., changes in the individual rate constants cannot change the state of the system. The respiratory control must then originate either in the supply of reducing substrate or the rate of reduction of oxygen. The most reasonable point for the control to be applied is in the oxygen reaction because this is the only reaction which has a large negative ΔG under conditions of high phosphate potential. Thus it is displaced from equilibrium and is subject to control. The rate of electron flow may be approximated by the equation

$$v = k[a_3^{+2}][O_2] \tag{27}$$

The control of respiration which is dependent on the phosphate potential derives from two separate effects on the respiratory chain. (1) Decreasing the phosphate potential decreases the ΔE required for each energy conservation site. Since the substrate potential remains constant, all components of the positive electron pools will tend to become more reduced (i.e., cytochrome a_3 becomes reduced). (2) Decreasing the phosphate potential makes the half-reduction potential of cytochrome a_3 become more positive (it becomes more reduced at the same E_h).

Increasing and decreasing the availability of substrate (effective substrate potential) leads to net reduction or oxidation of the cytochrome system and, as a direct consequence, a reduction or oxidation of cytochrome a_3. When the availability of ADP is chosen as the limiting reaction, a similar conclusion is reached.

The oxygen reaction obviously cannot be responsible for the respiratory control observed when, for example, ferricyanide is used as an electron acceptor. Exactly the same controlling mechanism is applicable, however, because the rate of ferricyanide reduction is dependent on the concentration of reduced cytochrome c. Changes in the phosphate potential are directly expressed as reduction of cytochrome c (increased flux) or oxidation of cytochrome c (decreased flux).

Wang (1967, 1970, 1973) has proposed a hybrid mechanism for respiratory control in which the energy transducing element at each phosphorylation site attains a half-reduction potential more negative or more positive than its electron donor or acceptor. This is then postulated to impose a kinetic control at each site (crossover theorem applies), and control would be achieved at the expense of energy conservation. The minimum loss (for a respiratory control of 15) from NADH to a_3 in state 4 would be 1.6 kcal. At present it is not possible to experimentally determine the free-energy relationships with an accuracy adequate to measure such an energy loss.

An apparent control at each energy transduction site appears when excess ADP and P_i are added (state 3) and the mitochondria are phosphorylating against a very low phosphate potential. This is postulated to arise because the phosphorylation reactions are kinetically limiting and the phosphate potential which the respiratory chain "senses" is much higher than the actual phosphate potential.

B. The Origin of the Experimentally Measured "Crossovers"

If there are no kinetic control sites in the respiratory chain except the cytochrome a_3–oxygen reaction and possibly substrate availability, why does the state 4 to 3 transition elicit an oxidation of cytochrome b and a reduction of cytochrome c (Chance and Williams, 1956). The answer is that this behavior is expected from the phosphate potential dependence of the half-reduction potential of cytochrome b_T and the decrease in the ΔE between the two isopotential groups when the ΔG required for ATP synthesis is made less positive. This "crossover" can be demonstrated even in a system without net electron flux [see Eqs. (8) and (9) for the cytochrome b_K to cytochrome c crossover].

It has been observed that when mitochondria are suspended in a medium containing substrate and allowed to exhaust the oxygen in the medium, the presence of the high phosphate potential greatly decreases the rate of reduction of cytochrome a_3 on anaerobiosis (Wilson, 1967; Bonner and Plesnicar, 1967). This behavior has been interpreted as a "crossover" between cytochromes a and a_3. A more satisfactory explanation, however, is that the half-reduction potential of the cytochrome a_3 is more negative than that of cytochrome a (+150 mV and +250 mV, respectively) and the cytochrome a is maintained partially oxidized by equilibration through the respiratory chain to the substrate (an "open" system with two sites to the NAD couple or one site to the succinate–fumarate couple). As such the cytochrome a_3 does not become reduced until the phosphate potential is lowered (uncoupler or ADP + P_i added) or the substrate attains very negative potentials.

The state 4 to 3 transition induced oxidation of cytochrome c and reduction of cytochrome a (Chance and Williams, 1956) is difficult to explain by any hypothesis. For thermodynamic reasons this reaction cannot be used to conserve energy ($\Delta E = 0$), and only recently has a possible reason for this crossover appeared (Lindsay and Wilson, 1972). Heme–heme interaction in cytochrome oxidase causes the half-reduction potential and spectral properties of cytochrome a to change when cytochrome a_3 undergoes chemical change, such as ligand binding (see Wilson et al., 1972d; Wilson and Leigh, 1972). ATP induces modification of cytochrome a_3, which then appears to modify the spectral properties and half-reduction potential of cytochrome a (E_m from 220 mV to 260 mV: Lindsay and Wilson, 1972). Under special conditions for cytochrome a_3, such as when it is reduced in the presence of CO, the ATP can induce a negative shift in the half-reduction potential of cytochrome a (+255 mV to +220 mV: Lindsay, 1972). Thus, depending on the experimental conditions, it is possible to observe a "reversed crossover," a "forward crossover," or no crossover between cytochromes c and a. None of these provide significant information on the site of energy conservation.

VIII. Evidence for a Direct Involvement of the Oxidation-Reduction Components in Energy Transduction

The observation that the half-reduction potentials of cytochromes b_T and a_3 of mitochondria are dependent on the mitochondrial energy state has provided direct evidence for a role of these cytochromes in the energy conservation reactions. One of the predictions arising from theoretical considerations related to the energy dependence of the half-reduction potentials is that the energy transducing components have more than one oxidized or reduced species (or both), the interconversion of which is energy dependent [see Eqs. (16) and (18)]. It is expected that such conversions would give rise to measurable changes in the absorption spectra of the cytochrome, but the size and nature of these spectral changes cannot be predicted. We have undertaken a systematic search for these predicted spectral changes. Evidence has been obtained for phosphate potential-dependent spectral change in an oxidized cytochrome of cytochrome oxidase (Wilson *et al.*, 1972b; Erecińska *et al.*, 1972c), and in reduced cytochrome a_3 (Wikström and Saris, 1967; Linday and Wilson, 1972).

The addition of ATP to a suspension of pigeon heart mitochondria in which the cytochromes are highly oxidized induces a spectral change in cytochrome oxidase (Wilson *et al.*, 1972b; Erecińska *et al.*, 1972c). The difference spectrum characteristic of the ATP induced change has minima near 416 nm, 480 nm, and 655 nm and maxima near 436 nm and 580 nm. This difference spectrum is characteristic of that for the change of a ferric hemoprotein from high spin to low spin. The ATP-induced change is energy dependent as evidenced by the observation that it is prevented by uncouplers and the energy-transfer inhibitor oligomycin. In addition the transformation has been titrated as a function of the phosphate potential and has been found to conform to the relationship:

$$A + ATP \rightleftharpoons A^{\circ} + ADP + P_i \tag{28}$$

where A and A° represent the more high spin and more low spin components, respectively (Erecińska *et al.*, 1972c). The apparent equilibrium constant for the reaction is approximately 10^{-3} M (for comparison see Eq. 16).

The ATP-induced spectral change identified as arising from either cytochrome a or a_3 on the basis that the change is insensitive to antimycin A in the presence of substrate and oxygen (a condition under which the b cytochromes are reduced). In addition when the mitochondria are treated with cyanide, the cyanide induces a similar spectral change (by forming the ferricytochrome a_3–cyanide compound). Cyanide pretreatment prevents the ATP-induced change and, conversely, addition of ATP inhibits the cyanide reaction (Wilson *et al.*, 1972b; Erecińska *et al.*, 1972c).

The phosphate potential-dependent interconversion of two reduced forms of cytochrome a_3 may be readily identified from the observed spectra. Wikström and Saris (1967) reported an ATP-dependent spectral change in the alpha band of cytochrome oxidase.

This change has been conclusively demonstrated to be a spectral shift in cytochrome a_3 and not an oxidation–reduction reaction (Lindsay and Wilson, 1972). The interconversion of two reduced forms of the cytochrome oxidase is dependent on the phosphate potential, and is prevented by uncouplers and oligomycin etc., but the quantitative dependence on the phosphate potential has not as yet been measured.

No spectral evidence has been found for additional species of either oxidized or reduced cytochrome b_T: in regard to this, the energy-dependent "red shift" reported by Slater and co-workers (Slater et al., 1970b; Wegdam et al., 1970) has been reported to arise from a combination of the intrinsic spectral differences and oxidation and reduction potentials of cytochromes b_K and b_T (Wilson and Dutton, 1970b; Sato et al., 1971a,b; Wikström, 1971; Dutton et al., 1972).

IX. Is an Intact Membrane Required for Energy Conservation?

The "energy-dependent" half-reduction potential changes of cytochromes b_T and a_3 are useful for the study of the role of the mitochondrial membrane in the energy conservation reactions. It has been postulated (Mitchell, 1968; Hinkle and Mitchell, 1970) that the measured half-reduction potentials of the cytochromes should, under special measuring conditions, be dependent on the existence and sign of the electrical potential (or the pH gradient or both) across the mitochondrial membrane.

It is supposed that an ATP-induced electrical potential will cause an apparent change in the half-reduction potential of any cytochrome not in direct electrical contact with the outer aqueous phase. An ATP-induced pH gradient will give a similar result if a pH-dependent oxidation-reduction component is exposed only to the pH of the matrix aqueous phase, not to the outer aqueous phase.

Hinkle and Mitchell (1970) used the ferri-ferrocyanide couple and obtained evidence that cytochrome a_3 (and to a lesser extent cytochrome a) of rat liver mitochondria assume more negative half-reduction potentials on addition of ATP. This is consistent with the energy-dependent generation of a net negative charge or a more alkaline pH inside the mitochondrial vesicle. When the "potential clamped" system is used, however, the ATP induces a more negative half-reduction potential for cytochrome a_3 (+385 mV to +155 mV) (Wilson et al., 1971; Lindsay and Wilson, 1972) and a slight *positive* shift in cytochrome a (+220 mV to +250 mV) (Lindsay and Wilson, 1972). In addition, the cytochrome b_T shifts from -30 mV to $+245$ mV, a change opposite in direction to that postulated by Mitchell (1968). When similar measurements are made using phosphorylation sub-mitochondrial particles, approximately one-half of the cytochrome b_T shifts from -30 mV to $+245$ mV (Dutton et al., 1971; Lindsay et al., 1972), and approximately one-half of the cytochrome a_3 shifts from $+375$ mV to $+155$ mV. Thus although the submitochondrial vesicles have been postulated to be "inside out" and therefore to have a re-versed polarity and pH gradient relative to intact mitochondria, the phosphate potential-dependent properties of the cytochromes remain unchanged. The half-reduction potentials of cytochromes b_T and a_3 in the "low energy" state are pH dependent, both becoming 60 mV more negative with each pH unit that the suspending medium is made more alkaline than pH 7 (Wilson et al., 1972b,c). In this respect the cytochrome b_T is similar to the cytochrome b_K. That both b cyto-chromes have nearly the same pH dependence explains the agree-ment with previous reports (Straub and Colpa-Boonstra, 1962; Urban and Klingenberg, 1969) which assumed a single b cytochrome.

Thus the different direction of the ATP-induced shift (negative for a_3 and positive for b_T) cannot result from different pH dependencies. Moreover, the 60 mV/pH indicates that for the oxidation of each of these cytochromes is coupled to the dissociation of a proton. If this is true, the oxidation-reduction process is electrically neutral for the cytochrome and it should not respond to an electrical potential per se, only to the "proton pressure."

Evidence for energy conservation in the absence of an intact mem-brane or complete respiratory chain has been obtained (Rieske, 1971; Wilson et al., 1971, 1972c). When a preparation of purified succinate–cytochrome c reductase (free of cytochrome oxidase) is suspended in an anaerobic medium containing a succinate–fumarate ratio of 1:10 ($E_h = +65$ mV) the cytochromes c_1 and b_K are reduced but cytochrome b_T is oxidized. After treatment with antimycin A the addition of a specific oxidant for cytochrome c_1 (ferricyanide, cytochrome c + cyto-chrome oxidase + O_2, etc.) causes an oxidation of cytochrome c_1 followed by a reduction of cytochrome b_T. When the oxidant is ex-hausted, reduction of cytochrome c_1 precedes the reoxidation of cytochrome b_T. This reduction of cytochrome b_T ($E_m = 30$ mV) with electrons from a $+65$ mV source requires energy.

In the experiment described, the behavior of the cytochrome b_T is consistent with its half-reduction potential becoming more than 155 mV more positive when electron transport through site II is activated. This electron transport-dependent shift in the half-reduction potential of cytochrome b_T is also observed in coupled mitochondria and submitochondrial particles in the absence of antimycin A (Erecińska *et al.*, 1972b). It is largely uncoupler sensitive but in uncoupled preparations or in the purified succinate–cytochrome *c* reductase, lowering the temperature to 4° or below "recouples" the preparation (Erecińska *et al.*, 1972b; Wilson *et al.*, 1972c). The available data are consistent with the schematic diagram in Fig. 4. The shift in the half-reduction potential of cytochrome b_T can also be driven by the phosphate potential in a reaction sequence which is inhibited by oligomycin, by uncouplers, and by antimycin A (Wilson *et al.*, 1972c).

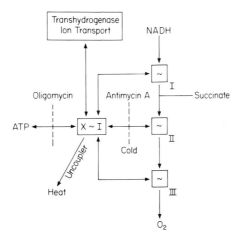

FIG. 4. The energy transfer pathways in mitochondria. Antimycin A and lowering the sample temperature are represented as inhibiting energy transfer between the primary "high energy" intermediate at site II and the uncoupler-sensitive site (Wilson *et al.*, 1971; Erecińska *et al.*, this volume).

When it is driven by electron transfer through site II, the initial change is very rapid and complete, but the steady-state change, and thus the steady-state "energy level," is decreased by adding uncouplers. Subsequent addition of antimycin A or lowering the temperature inhibits the energy drain through the uncoupler site and increases the "energy level" of the cytochrome b_T. Thus all the available kinetic and thermodynamic data indicate that the "high potential" cytochrome b_T is the primary "high energy" intermediate at site II (for a complete kinetic analysis, see Erecińska *et al.*, this volume). Its generation in preparations such as the succinate–cytochrome *c* reductase and the b–c_1 complex indicates that the primary "high energy" intermediate is chemical in nature and does not require an organized membrane structure.

X. Summary

Thermodynamic analysis has been used to suggest experimental methods for identifying and characterizing the oxidation–reduction components responsible for energy transduction in oxidative phosphorylation. Application of one of these methods (the "potential clamped" system) to the mitochondrial respiratory chain has demonstrated that cytochromes b_T and a_3 have phosphate potential dependent half-reduction potentials. This strongly implicates them in energy transduction at sites II and III, respectively. The phosphate potential dependent interconversion of two oxidized and two reduced forms of cytochrome a_3 provides additional evidence for its role in site III. The half-reduction potential change in cytochrome b_T (and presumably that of cytochrome a_3) has been shown to be caused by either activation of electron transport or by the addition of ATP. The kinetic and thermodynamic properties of the cytochrome b_T are consistent with the forms having the more positive half-reduction potential being the primary "high energy" intermediate at site II. This "high energy" intermediate is readily formed in fragments of the respiratory chain prepared by detergents. Therefore its formation does not require an intact respiratory chain or highly organized membrane structure.

Appendix I

The "potential clamped" system is artificial in the sense that it can be obtained only by special experimental techniques. In principle it is obtained by adding oxidation-reduction mediators which have multiple interaction sites on the respiratory chain. These mediators then bypass the normal electron flow pathways and, under appropriate conditions, provide an electron transport system in which all the oxidation-reduction components have the same potential. The added mediators should have the following properties:

1. The mediators must be able to accept or donate electrons to components more negative and more positive than the component under investigation.

2. The mediators must be able to exchange electrons directly (without mediation of the respiratory chain).

3. The mediators must have half-reduction potentials which allow them to span the required potential range (to a first approximation an active mediator is effective from 90% oxidation to 90% reduction,

equivalent to ± 60 mV ($n = 1.0$) or ± 30 mV ($n = 2.0$) on either side of the half-reduction potential. Experimentally, however, this range depends on the nature of the mediator and the concentration used.

4. The mediators should not interact with the components so as to modify them chemically.

5. The mediators should not interfere with the measurements of the component of interest.

The experimental requirements for a "potential clamped" system are essentially those used to test for the existence of equilibrium coupled with the tests for chemical reaction between the mediators and the components of the respiratory chain:

1. The measured values must be independent of the time allowed for measurement (except in the case where the concentration of a reactant is time dependent).

2. The same results must be attained by both oxidative and reductive titrations.

3. The results must be independent of the concentration of mediator over a considerable concentration range (4-fold may be regarded as a minimum).

4. Where possible the same data must be obtained using a completely different set of mediators.

Appendix II

The equations given in the text for a "potential clamped" system are more complex than are necessary to demonstrate the essential features of the "phosphate potential" dependent half-reduction potential. The final analysis is perhaps better understood by examining an abbreviated model

$$\text{A ox} + 2e^- \rightleftharpoons \text{A red} \tag{1}$$

$$\text{A ox} + \text{I} \rightleftharpoons \text{A ox I} \tag{2}$$

$$\text{A ox I} + 2e^- \rightleftharpoons \text{A red I} \tag{3}$$

$$\text{A red} + \text{I} \rightleftharpoons \text{A red I} \tag{4}$$

$$\text{I} + \text{ATP} \rightleftharpoons \text{ADP I} + \text{P}_i \tag{5}$$

This model is not capable of net ATP synthesis associated with electron transfer but is suitable for analysis. The respective equilibrium constants are:

$$K_1 = \frac{[\text{A red}]}{\text{A ox}(e^-)^2} \qquad K_2 = \frac{[\text{A ox I}]}{[\text{A ox}][\text{I}]}$$

$$K_3 = \frac{[\text{A red I}]}{[\text{A ox I}](e^-)^2} \qquad K_4 = \frac{[\text{A red I}]}{[\text{A red}][\text{I}]}$$

$$K_5 = \frac{[\text{ADP I}][\text{P}_i]}{[\text{I}][\text{ATP}]}$$

at equilibrium Eqs. (1) and (3) are at the same oxidation–reduction potential (e^-)

$$\frac{K_1}{K_3} = \frac{[\text{A red}][\text{A ox I}]}{[\text{A ox}][\text{A red I}]} \tag{6}$$

This equation indicates that the two oxidation-reduction reactions will have the same E_h if the term on the right is equal to the appropriate constant. The experimentally measurable half-reduction potential $(E_m{}^*)$ is derived by setting the oxidized forms of A equal to the reduced forms

$$[\text{A red}] + [\text{A red I}] = [\text{A ox}] + [\text{A ox I}] \tag{7}$$

substituting from Eqs. (2) and (4)

$$[\text{A red}] + [\text{A red}][\text{I}] \, K_4 = \text{A ox} + [\text{A ox}][\text{I}] \, K_2 \tag{8}$$

solving

$$\text{A red} \{1 + K_4 \,[\text{I}]\} = \text{A ox} \{1 + K_2 \,[\text{I}]\} \tag{9}$$

or

$$\log \frac{[\text{A ox}]}{[\text{A red}]} = \log \left\{ \frac{1 + K_4 \,[\text{I}]}{1 + K_2 \,[\text{I}]} \right\} \tag{10}$$

and

$$\frac{E_m{}^* - E_{ml}}{0.030} = \log \frac{\{1 + K_4 \,[\text{I}]\}}{\{1 + K_2 \,[\text{I}]\}} \tag{11}$$

substituting from Eq. (5)

$$\frac{E_m{}^* - E_{ml}}{0.030} = \log \frac{\left\{ K_5 + K_4 \dfrac{[\text{ADP I}][\text{P}_i]}{\text{ATP}} \right\}}{\left\{ K_5 + K_2 \dfrac{[\text{ADP I}][\text{P}_i]}{\text{ATP}} \right\}} \qquad (12)$$

In general a phosphate potential dependent half-reduction potential will be observed when there is a phosphate potential dependence in the activity (concentration) of a component (I) which interacts directly with the oxidation–reduction component. In the model system the $E_m{}^*$ is equal to E_{ml} at high phosphate potentials while at low phosphate potentials the $(E_m{}^* - E_{ml})/0.030$ will equal $\log K_4/K_2$. The equations are written as $n = 2$ and the slope of transition between the two limiting values of the measured half-reduction has a slope of 30 mV per 10-fold change in the phosphate potential. A comparable set of equations written for $n = 1$ reactions for which one ATP modifies one ligand, changes the slope to 60 mV per 10-fold change in the phosphate potential.

The solid line in Fig. 3 is a theoretical curve calculated for the binding of a ligand to a hemoprotein (see Clark, 1960). The half-reduction potential of the hypothetical hemoprotein is assumed to be -30 mV in the absence of ligand and $+245$ mV in the presence of excess ligand. The dissociation constants for the ligand from the oxidized and reduced form were selected to allow a superposition of the theoretical curve on the experimental points assuming the abscissa is the logarithm of the concentration of ligand in arbitrary units.

References

Albracht, S. P. J., and Slater, E. C. (1970). *Biochim. Biophys. Acta* **223**, 457.

Berden, J. A., Opperdoes, F. R., and Slater, E. C. (1972). *Biochim. Biophys. Acta* **256**, 594.

Bonner, W. D., and Plesnicar, M. (1967). *Nature (London)* **214**, 616.

Boveris, A., Erecińska, M., and Wagner, M. (1972). *Biochim. Biophys. Acta* **256**, 223.

Boyer, P. D. (1968). *In* "Biological Oxidations" (T. P. Singer, ed.), p. 193. Wiley (Interscience), New York.

Bucher, T. (1947). *Biochim. Biophys. Acta* **1**, 292.

Caswell, A. H. (1968). *J. Biol. Chem.* **243**, 5827.

Caswell, A. H. (1971). *Arch. Biochem. Biophys.* **144**, 445.

Chance, B. (1961). *J. Biol. Chem.* **236**, 1544.

Chance, B., and Hollunger, G. (1961). *J. Biol. Chem.* **236**, 1577.

Chance, B., and Williams, G. R. (1956). *Advan. Enzymol.* **17**, 65.

Chance, B., Wilson, D. F., Dutton, P. L., and Erecińska, M. (1970). *Proc. Nat. Acad. Sci. U.S.* **66**, 1175.

Chance, B., Erecińska, M., and Chance, E. M. (1973). In "Oxidases and Related Redox Systems" (T. E. King, H. S. Mason, and M. Morrison, eds.), Vol. II. Univ. Park Press, Baltimore, Maryland (in press).

Clark, W. M. (1960). "Oxidation-Reduction Potentials of Organic Systems." Waverly Press, Baltimore, Maryland.

Cockrell, R. S., Harris, E. J., and Pressman, B. C. (1966). Biochemistry 5, 2326.

DeVault, D. (1971). Biochim. Biophys. Acta 225, 193.

Dutton, P. L. (1971). Biochim. Biophys. Acta 226, 63.

Dutton, P. L., Wilson, D. F., and Lee, C. P. (1970). Biochemistry 9, 5077.

Dutton, P. L., Wilson, D. F., and Lee, C. P. (1971). Biochem. Biophys. Res. Commun. 43, 1186.

Dutton, P. L., Erecińska, M., Mukai, Y., Sato, N., Pring, M., and Wilson, D. F. (1972). Biochim. Biophys. Acta 267, 15.

Erecińska, M., Chance, B., and Wilson, D. F. (1971). FEBS Lett. 16, 284.

Erecińska, M., Chance, B., Wilson, D. F., and Dutton, P. L. (1972a). Proc. Nat. Acad. Sci. U.S. 69, 50.

Erecińska, M., Chance, B., Wilson, D. F., and Dutton, P. L. (1972b). Fed. Proc. Fed. Amer. Soc. Exp. Biol. (in press).

Erecińska, M., Wilson, D. F., Sato, N., and Nicholls, P. (1972c). Arch. Biochem. Biophys. 151, 188.

Greville, G. D. (1969). Curr. Top. Bioenerg. 3, 1.

Hinkle, P., and Mitchell, P. (1970). Bioenergetics 1, 45.

Klingenberg, M. (1961). Biochem. Z. 335, 263.

Klingenberg, M. (1969). In "The Energy Level and Metabolic Control in Mitochondria" (S. Papa et al., eds.), p. 189, Adriatica Editrice, Bari.

Klingenberg, M., and Schollmeyer, P. (1961). Biochem. Z. 335, 243.

Klingenberg, M., and Schollmeyer, P. (1969). In "The Energy Level and Metabolic Control in Mitochondria" (S. Papa et al., eds.), p. 185. Adriatica Editrice, Bari.

Lardy, H. A., and Wellman, H. (1952). J. Biol. Chem. 195, 215.

Lindsay, J. G. (1972). Manuscript in preparation.

Lindsay, J. G., and Wilson, D. F. (1972). Biochemistry 11, 4613.

Lindsay, J. G., Dutton, P. L., and Wilson, D. F. (1972). Biochemistry 11, 1937.

McCray, J. A., and Anderson, N. (1972). Fed. Proc., Fed. Amer. Soc. Exp. Biol. 31, 886 (Abstr. No. 3808).

Mitchell, P. (1968). "Chemiosmotic Coupling and Energy Transduction." Glynn Res. Ltd., Bodmin.

Muraoka, S., and Slater, E. C. (1969). Biochim. Biophys. Acta 180, 221.

Ohnishi, T., Asakura, T., Wohlrab, H., Yonetani, T., and Chance, B. (1970). J. Biol. Chem. 245, 901.

Ohnishi, T., Asakura, T., Yonetani, T., and Chance, B. (1971). J. Biol. Chem. 246, 5960.

Ohnishi, T., Wilson, D. F., Asakura, T., and Chance, B. (1972). Biochem. Biophys. Res. Commun. 46, 1631.

Orme-Johnson, N. R., Orme-Johnson, W. H., Hansen, R. E., Beinert, H., and Hatefi, Y. (1971). Biochem. Biophys. Res. Commun. 44, 446.

Orme-Johnson, N. R., Orme-Johnson, W. H., Hansen, R. E., Beinert, H., and Hatefi, Y. (1973). In "Oxidases and Related Redox Systems" (T. E. King, H. S. Mason, and M. Morrison, eds.), Vol. II. Univ. Park Press, Baltimore, Maryland (in press).

Pumphrey, A. M. (1962). *J. Biol. Chem.* **237**, 238.

Rieske, J. S. (1971). *Arch. Biochem. Biophys.* **145**, 179.

Rieske, J. S., Hansen, R. E., and Zaugg, W. S. (1964a). *J. Biol. Chem.* **239**, 3017.

Rieske, J. S., Zaugg, W. S., and Hansen, R. E. (1964b). *J. Biol. Chem.* **239**, 3023.

Rosing, J., and Slater, E. C. (1972). *Biochim. Biophys. Acta* **267**, 275.

Sato, N., Wilson, D. F., and Chance, B. (1971a). *FEBS Lett.* **15**, 209.

Sato, N., Wilson, D. F., and Chance, B. (1971b). *Biochim. Biophys. Acta* **253**, 88.

Skulachev, V. P. (1971). *Curr. Top. Bioenerg.* **4**, 127.

Slater, E. C. (1970). *In* "Electron Transport and Energy Conservation" (J. M. Tager *et al.*, eds.), p. 363. Adriatica Editrice, Bari.

Slater, E. C. (1971). *Quart. Rev. Biophys.* **4**, 1.

Slater, E. C., Lee, C. P., Berden, J. A., and Wegdam, H. J. (1970a). *Nature (London)* **226**, 1248.

Slater, E. C., Lee, C. P., Berden, J. A., and Wegdam, H. J. (1970b). *Biochim. Biophys. Acta* **223**, 354.

Straub, J. P., and Colpa-Boonstra, J. P. (1962). *Biochim. Biophys. Acta* **60**, 650.

Tsudzuki, T., and Wilson, D. F. (1971). *Arch. Biochem. Biophys.* **145**, 149.

Urban, P. F., and Klingenberg, M. (1969). *Eur. J. Biochem.* **9**, 519.

Velick, S. F., and Furfine, C. (1963). *In* "The Enzymes" (P. D. Boyer, H. Lardy, and K. Myrbäck, eds.), 2nd rev. ed., Vol. 7, p. 243. Academic Press, New York.

Wang, J. H. (1967). *Proc. Nat. Acad. Sci. U.S.* **58**, 37.

Wang, J. H. (1970). *Science* **167**, 25.

Wang, J. H. (1973). *In* "Oxidases and Related Redox Systems" (T. E. King, H. S. Mason, and M. Morrison, eds.), Vol. II. Univ. Park Press, Baltimore, Maryland (in press).

Wegdam, A. J., Berden, J. A., and Slater, E. C. (1970). *Biochim. Biophys. Acta* **223**, 365.

Wikström, M. K. F. (1971). *Biochim. Biophys. Acta* **253**, 332.

Wikström, M. K. F., and Saris, N. E. L. (1967). *In* "Electron Transport and Energy Conservation" (E. Quagliariello *et al.*, eds.), p. 77. Adriatica Editrice, Bari.

Wilson, D. F. (1967). *Biochim. Biophys. Acta* **131**, 431.

Wilson, D. F., and Dutton, P. L. (1970a). *Arch. Biochem. Biophys.* **136**, 583.

Wilson, D. F., and Dutton, P. L. (1970b). *Biochem. Biophys. Res. Commun.* **39**, 59.

Wilson, D. F., and Dutton, P. L. (1971). *In* "Electron and Coupled Energy Transfer in Biological Systems" (T. E. King and M. Klingenberg, eds.), Vol. 1, p. 221. Dekker, New York.

Wilson, D. F., and Leigh, J. S., Jr. (1972). *Arch. Biochem. Biophys.* **150**, 154.

Wilson, D. F., Erecinska, M., Dutton, P. L., and Tsudzuki, T. (1970). *Biochem. Biophys. Res. Commun.* **41**, 1273.

Wilson, D. F., Koppelman, M., Erecińska, M., and Dutton, P. L. (1971). *Biochem. Biophys. Res. Commun.* **44**, 759.

Wilson, D. F., Dutton, P. L., Erecińska, M., Lindsay, J. G., and Sato, N. (1972a). *Accounts Chem. Res.* **5**, 234.

Wilson, D. F., Erecińska, M., and Nicholls, P. (1972b). *FEBS Lett.* **20**, 61.

Wilson, D. F., Erecińska, M., Leigh, J. S., Jr., and Koppelman, M. (1972c). *Arch. Biochem. Biophys.* **151**, 112.

Wilson, D. F., Lindsay, J. G., and Brocklehurst, E. S. (1972d). *Biochim. Biophys. Acta* **256**, 277.

Wohlrab, H. (1970). *Biochemistry* **9**, 474.

Kinetics of Cytochromes b

MARIA ERECIŃSKA, MICHAL WAGNER, and BRITTON CHANCE
Department of Biophysics and Physical Biochemistry,
Johnson Research Foundation,
University of Pennsylvania Medical School,
Philadelphia, Pennsylvania

I. Introduction

A. GENERAL ASPECTS

Experimental kinetics is one of the most widely used tools in the studies of biological systems. It is applied either independently of formal kinetics (i.e., kinetics which describes properties of the system without considering its identity) but in combination with other experimental methods to discover new, nonkinetic properties of the system or together with the formal reaction kinetics to elucidate the mechanism of the reaction. An application of both approaches is presented in this paper. The subject of the article is kinetics of cytochromes b, membrane-bound heme proteins with not completely understood chemical relations. The main body of the article is the experimental reaction kinetics, and the arrangement is done phenomenologically. Special emphasis has been put, however, on the evaluation of the available interpretations, and whenever possible the relations between the experimental and the formal kinetics have been clearly brought out.

B. HISTORICAL SURVEY

The peculiar behavior of cytochrome b under various experimental conditions has long attracted the attention of many investigators. Only recently, however, introduction of the potentiometric titration technique to the studies of the mitochondrial respiratory chain (Caswell, 1968; Dutton, 1971; Wilson and Dutton, 1970) and the burst of activity in determining the equilibrium properties of the carriers (Wilson et $al.$, 1972a; Wilson and Dutton, 1971) have firmly established the existence of two cytochromes b: b_{566} (b_T, $E_{m7.0} = -30$ mV) and b_{560} (b_K, $E_{m7.0} = +30$ mV) (Wilson and Dutton, 1970). The finding has been confirmed by steady-state measurements and spectral studies, and the properties of both cytochromes have been described in great detail (Slater et $al.$, 1970a; Chance et $al.$, 1970; Dutton et $al.$, 1970; Sato et $al.$, 1971a,b; Wikström, 1971; Davis et $al.$, 1972). It was further demonstrated that the midpoint potential of cytochrome b_{566} becomes 280 mV more positive by the addition of ATP (Wilson and Dutton, 1970) thus providing the first direct evidence for the participation of this cytochrome in the energy-coupling reactions (see Wilson et $al.$, this volume). Since the kinetics of the reactions are equally or even more important than the equilibrium studies in providing information on the structure–function relationships and on the mechanisms of the reactions, it is not surprising that the rapid development of the equilibrium studies invoked seemingly intense activity in the kinetic investigation.

Kinetic studies on cytochrome b have their long history. Already in 1952 Chance (1952a) noted that the kinetics of reduction of cytochrome b in the Keilin-Hartree preparation were slower than the electron transfer through the chain under steady-state conditions; this led him to question, on kinetic grounds, the participation of this carrier in the nonphosphorylating oxidase system. In contrast, in intact yeast cells and isolated rat liver and rat heart mitochondria (Chance, 1955; Chance and Williams, 1955; Chance and Baltscheffsky, 1958) the reduction kinetics of cytochrome b were rapid enough to justify its participation in the electron transfer. It was later found (Chance, 1958) that in the Keilin-Hartree preparation, in the presence of cytochrome $c + c_1$ reduced by ascorbate, only a part of cytochrome b was reduced by the addition of succinate. More of cytochrome b with an absorption maximum at 566 nm could be reduced under these conditions by the addition of antimycin A. The rate of reduction of cytochrome b in the absence of antimycin A was much slower than in the presence of the inhibitor, and the calculated second-order velocity constants were $2 \times 10^4 \, M^{-1} \, \sec^{-1}$ and $10^{-6} \, M^{-1} \, \sec^{-1}$ for both conditions, respectively. These results were confirmed and extended by many investigators (Slater and Colpa Boonstra, 1961; Pumphrey, 1962; Tyler $et\ al.$, 1965; Storey, 1967), and the differences in quantitative values were attributed to the type of preparation and particular experimental conditions used.

In 1965, Tyler $et\ al.$ noted that in tightly coupled mitochondria, almost all the cytochrome b could be reduced by the addition of ascorbate plus TMPD. In loosely coupled preparations or in submitochondrial particles, cytochrome b remained oxidized unless ATP was added. Even then only a part of cytochrome b was reduced; the rest was reduced by succinate. ADP + P_i and uncouplers caused oxidation of the previously reduced cytochrome b, while antimycin A inhibited the ascorbate plus TMPD induced absorbance change (Tyler $et\ al.$, 1966). These results led to the postulate of the existence of two forms of cytochromes b: one form energy linked, reducible by either succinate, or ascorbate plus TMPD; and a second form, non-energy linked, reducible only by succinate. Similar conclusions were reached recently by Wikström (1971), who reported the energy-linked reduction of cytochrome b_{566} driven either by respiration with ascorbate plus TMPD or succinate, or anaerobically by ATP. In rat liver mitochondria, complete reduction of all b species could be accomplished anaerobically with ATP and in the presence of uncoupler if substrate couples of low redox potential or dithionite were added.

In 1955, Chance and Williams attempted to evaluate the rate of oxidation of cytochrome b and compare it with the rates of oxidation of the other members of the respiratory chain. It was found that at 4°C in the presence of ADP plus P_i oxidation of the cytochrome b did not lag appreciably behind the oxidation of cytochrome c, and both carriers were oxidized much faster than the pyridine nucleotide. The differences in the oxidation rates of various respiratory chain carriers as well as studies using the respiratory chain inhibitors led Chance and Williams to outline the sequence of the components in the respiratory chain (Chance and Williams, 1956) similar to that previously proposed by Keilin and Hartree (1939).

This brief glimpse through the literature shows that cytochrome b behaves nonuniformly under various experimental conditions. The nonuniform behavior is partly due to the existence of different cytochrome b species, one of which has potential negative enough to become difficult to reduce by succinate in the nonphosphorylating preparations. This has led to the hypothesis that one of the b cytochromes, b_{566} performs a dual function of an electron carrier and "energy-conserving" enzyme. Since it was demonstrated that after the addition of ATP the half-reduction potential of this cytochrome becomes over 250 mV more positive (Wilson and Dutton, 1970), it is possible to explain its ready reducibility in the coupled preparations.

II. Kinetics of Oxidation of the Cytochromes b

A. General Features

The steady-state measurements are confined to the determination of the degree of reduction (or oxidation) of the respiratory chain component under given sets of experimental conditions. Additional information can be obtained by simultaneous measurements of steady-state values of respiration rate and oxidation level of respiratory pigments at low oxygen tensions (Degn and Wohlrab, 1971; Oshino *et. al.*, 1972). However the rapid rates of oxidation or reduction of the carriers (in the absence of respiratory chain inhibitors) can be only measured by the use of rapid kinetic techniques.

The principle of the stopped-flow method, the technique used for the studies of cytochromes b kinetics, can be summarized as follows: the two solutions containing the reagents after being forced at a high speed into a mixing chamber enter an observation tube located at a point close to the mixing chamber. The flow is then suddenly stopped and the changes which occur in the portion of fluid present in the observation tube are followed with a rapid detecting system. The type of stopped-flow apparatus used for the turbid suspension of the mitochondrial membranes has been described by Chance *et al.* (1967).

The experiments follow either of the two patterns: (1) The initially anaerobic mitochondrial suspension is rapidly mixed with oxygen-saturated buffer (oxygen pulse technique), the carriers are transferred from their reduced to the oxidized steady state and after the exhaustion of oxygen return to their original anaerobic state. The available information concerns "on" kinetics, steady-state, and "off" kinetics, (2) The initially aerobic mitochondria are rapidly mixed with a solution of a reductant (e.g., durohydroquinone, NADH–reductant pulse technique) the carriers are reduced to a steady-state level and when reductant is exhausted they return to the oxidized state. The available kinetic information is similar to that obtained by the oxygen pulse technique: "on" kinetics, steady-state, and "off" kinetics. The electron transfer rates to and from the region of the respiratory chain, which is the very object of the kinetic investigation, can be further varied by the application of inhibitors and depletion procedures: in the case of cytochromes b, addition of malonate (or rotenone) and depletion of ubiquinone vary the electron transfer rates on the substrate side, addition of carbon monoxide and removal of cytochrome c affects the rates on the oxygen side, and antimycin A acts on the cytochrome b–c_1 complex itself (Estabrook, 1962). It should be added that for the reactions which occur faster than 20–50 msec the rapid flow method in combination with flash photolysis can be conveniently employed (Norrish and Porter, 1949; Porter, 1950; Norrish et $al.$, 1953; Gibson and Greenwood, 1963). The application of flow flash method to the turbid suspensions has been described recently in a number of publications (Chance and Erecińska, 1971; Chance et $al.$, 1972), and reactions occurring in 50–100 μsec can be measured.

The cytochromes b_{560} and b_{566} react on their substrate side with ubiquinone and on their oxygen side with cytochrome $c_1 + c$ and are tightly bound to the mitochondrial membrane in contrast to the quinone or cytochrome c (Lester and Fleischer, 1961; Jacobs and Sanadi, 1960). Furthermore, cytochrome b_{566} and c_1 seem to form a complex (Rieske et $al.$, 1964; Davis et $al.$, 1972) in which the behavior of the individual cytochromes will be different from that if they were completely separate entities. Under such conditions the kinetic behavior of cytochromes b is determined by the interactions with the adjacent carriers: ubiquinone and cytochromes $c + c_1$.

The rates of oxidation and reduction of the cytochromes b under the majority of conditions described in this review represent the sum of all reactions in which these carriers are involved (including the reactions involving the synthesis of high energy intermediate or state). Since the velocity of a reaction is related to the concentration of all reactants, the amounts in which ubiquinone or cytochrome $c_1 (+ c)$ are present in the membrane affect the kinetic behavior of cytochrome b. The best example illustrating this relationship is slowing of the apparent rate of cytochromes b reduction by durohydroquinone with the addition of ubiquinone to ubiquinone-depleted mitochondria (Boveris et $al.$, 1972). The only experimentally observed velocities which are assignable to one, single reaction (in this region of the respiratory chain) and are not the result of many different reactions are probably the initial rates of cytochrome b reduction by durohydroquinone in the ubiquinone-depleted mitochondria (Boveris et $al.$, 1972) and the initial rate of cytochrome b_{566} reduction by ubiquinone in the antimycin A-inhibited membranes (Erecińska et

al., 1972). It consequently follows that the kinetics of any cytochrome is of limited value if considered isolated from the experimental information about the behavior of its neighbors, and, if any conclusion is to be drawn on the behavior of cytochrome *b*, its kinetic properties have to be closely correlated with those of ubiquinone and cytochrome c_1 and *c*.

This brief introduction is intended as a guideline through the detailed analysis of the available experimental data.

B. OXIDATION KINETICS OF CYTOCHROMES *b* IN THE COUPLED AND UNCOUPLED PIGEON HEART MITOCHONDRIA

The oxidation of cytochromes *b*, c_1, and ubiquinone obtained after the addition of a pulse of oxygen to an initially anaerobic mitochondrial mixture supplemented with oxidizable substrate exhibit essentially the same overall characteristics (Fig. 1). The carriers

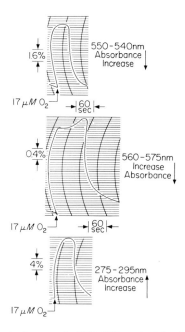

FIG. 1. Response of cytochromes *b* (560–575 nm) ubiquinone (275–295 nm) and cytochromes (*c* + c_1) (556–540 nm) to oxygen pulse. Pigeon heart mitochondria were suspended at 2.0 mg of protein per milliliter in 0.225 *M* mannitol, 0.050 *M* sucrose, 0.050 *M* morpholinopropane sulfonate, pH 6.9, and made anaerobic by the addition of 6.0 m*M* succinate + 3.0 m*M* glutamate. Then 4.5 m*M* malonate and 5.0 µ*M* rotenone were added; 17 µ*M* oxygen was injected where indicated, and oxidation of the carrier was followed by rapid kinetic technique (Chance *et al.*, 1970). Unpublished data of Erecińska and Chance.

abruptly change from their reduced to the oxidized state and remain in this state as long as oxygen is present. Exhaustion of oxygen is accompanied by a transition to the anaerobic state and the carriers assume the steady-state reduction level that existed prior to the oxygen pulse. However, in contrast to cytochrome c_1 or ubiquinone, the kinetic trace of the time course of cytochromes b oxidation is much more complex: the oxidation phase is preceded by an abrupt short downward deflection of the trace indicative of a transient reduction; the oxidation phase itself is biphasic and after the steady state is reached and oxygen is exhausted, cytochrome b is further oxidized. This particular characteristic termed the "late maximum" is not due to cytochrome c interference, and has been to us one of the most intriguing properties of cytochromes b. The extent of the "late maximum" is related to the absence or presence of the uncouplers and the flux through the system. The "late maximum" is followed by a slow reduction of cytochromes b much slower than that of cytochrome c_1 and ubiquinone. The reduction rate is further slowed down by the addition of malonate or uncouplers.

On an expanded time scale, which illustrates the initial part of the time course of oxidation (Fig. 2), the oxidation curve of cytochrome b exhibits a rather complicated character, explored recently in great detail (Erecińska and Chance, 1971; Erecińska $et\ al.$, 1973b). The

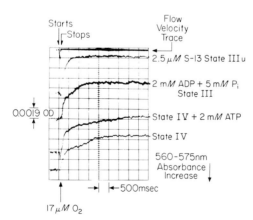

FIG. 2. Response of cytochrome b to oxygen pulse. Pigeon heart mitochondria were suspended at 2.8 mg of protein per milliliter in 0.225 M mannitol, 0.075 M sucrose, 0.0002 M EDTA, 0.020 M morpholinopropane sulfonate (MOPS), pH 7.4, and made anaerobic by the addition of 6.0 mM succinate, 3.0 mM glutamate. Then 3.0 mM malonate and 5.0 μM rotenone were added. The uncoupler used was S-13 (5-chloro-3-t-butyl-2'-chloro-4'-nitrosalicylanilide). Kinetic traces were obtained using rapid flow methods of Chance $et\ al.$ (1970).

oxidation phase is biphasic and is preceded by a rapid reduction of the carrier. This reduction phase, more pronounced in the presence of antimycin A or at +5°C, is discussed extensively in Sections IV and V.

The biphasic nature of the time course of oxidation of cytochromes is a function of measuring wavelength and depends on several factors: presence or absence of ADP + P_i, or ATP, uncouplers, type of preparation and degree of coupling; it becomes less pronounced in aged or loosely coupled preparations. At 560–575 nm about 50% of the absorbance change occurs in about 200 msec, the remaining 50% is completed in about 2 sec. At 566–575 nm only about 30% of the change is fast and the remaining 70% is slow. This suggests that the two different phases of oxidation do exhibit different spectral properties and may, in fact, belong to two different species. Plots of both phases against the measuring wavelength (Chance et al., 1970) show that the fast phase has an absorbance maximum at 560 nm and the slow phase at 566 nm characteristic of cytochromes b_{560} and b_{566}, respectively (Wilson and Dutton, 1970; Slater et al., 1970a; Chance et al., 1970; Sato et al., 1971a,b; Wikström, 1971; Dutton et al., 1972).

The spectral characteristics of both cytochromes $b–b_{566}$ and b_{560} — obtained on the basis of purely kinetic studies — agree with the spectral data obtained by Sato et al. (1971a,b), Slater and his collaborators (Slater et al., 1970a; Wegdam et al., 1970), and Wikström (1971). Identical spectral data were obtained by Dutton and co-workers (1972) (Fig. 3) in which a lucid separation of both cytochromes b could be accomplished owing to the fact that in the presence of ATP the difference in the midpoint potential of these cytochromes is close to 300 mV, thus cytochrome b_{566} is essentially 100% reduced when b_{560} is essentially 100% oxidized. Since the sum of the slow and fast absorbance changes in the spectral data of Chance et al. (1970) (as well as the sum of b_{566} and b_{560} in the data of Dutton et al., 1972) shows the total recorded in the presence of the uncoupler, it strongly suggests that ATP does not induce a spectral shift in cytochrome b_{566} (Slater et al., 1970a,b) from a shorter to a longer wavelength.

ATP, ADP, + P_i and the uncouplers exert a much more pronounced influence on the second slow phase of oxidation of cytochrome b, identified with cytochrome b_{566} (Erecińska and Chance, 1971). ATP slows it down by a factor of 4 while ADP + P_i stimulate the rate of cytochrome b_{566} oxidation. The most dramatic effect is exerted by uncoupler which increases the slow rate of absorbance change by an order of magnitude or more, and both b cytochromes are oxidized in a monotonic way, at rates indistinguishable from each other. In addition to ADP + P_i and the uncouplers, Ca^{2+} and K^+ plus valinomycin are

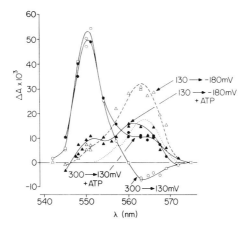

FIG. 3. Spectra of the cytochromes of pigeon heart mitochondria in the absence and presence of ATP under condition of equilibration titration. Experimental details are described by Dutton *et al.* (1972). In the absence of ATP: O, cytochrome $c + c_1$; Δ, b cytochromes. In the presence of 6 mM ATP; ●, cytochromes $(c + c_1) + b_{566}$; ▲, cytochrome b_{560}; $\cdots$ (O) values minus (●) values, thus high potential b_{566} (- - -) sum of b_{560} (▲) and the high potential b_{566} ($\cdots$). From Dutton *et al.* (1972).

capable of stimulating the rate of cytochrome b_{566} oxidation (Chance, 1965; Papa *et al.*, 1972; Erecińska *et al.*, 1973b).

The change in cytochrome b kinetics induced by the uncouplers or ATP is an overt sign that the carrier is under control of the energy-coupling reactions. Chance *et al.* (1970) suggested that the 200-msec initial phase represents the "energization time" of the mitochondrial membrane. The buildup of energy necessary to induce the change of cytochrome b_{566} from its low (-30 mV) to the high ($+245$ mV) potential form and consequent slowing down of the kinetics could occur through the operation of phosphorylation site III since by the time cytochrome b has undergone its first turnover seven electrons have already passed across phosphorylation site III. This, however, is difficult to reconcile with the studies on yeast mitochondria (Erecińska *et al.*, 1973a) in which oxidation of cytochrome c through cytochrome c peroxidase (Chance, 1951; Yonetani and Ray, 1966) yielded kinetics of cytochromes b indistinguishable from that when the oxidase was used to oxidize cytochrome c.

Slow rate of oxidation of cytochrome b_{566} and ubiquinone in the coupled mitochondria (and in the presence of ATP) suggests that ATP slows down the reaction(s) on the oxygen side of cytochrome b_{566}. If we assume in accord with previous suggestions of Klingenberg and

Schollmeyer (1961), Muraoka and Slater (1969), and Wilson et al. (this volume) that the oxidative phosphorylation reaction is near thermodynamic equilibrium in state 4 we may write an abbreviated scheme:

$$2c_{ox} + UQ_{red} + ADP + P_i \rightleftharpoons 2c_{red} + UQ_{ox} + ATP \qquad (1)$$

with equilibrium constant

$$K = \frac{[c_{ox}]^2 \cdot [UQ_{red}] \cdot [ADP] \cdot [P_i]}{[c_{red}]^2 \cdot [UQ_{ox}] \cdot [ATP]} \qquad (2)$$

This equilibrium constant will determine the redox levels of cytochrome c and ubiquinone in relation to the phosphate potential. It can be argued that the redox levels of cytochrome c (and a) are also determined by the activity of site III and that succinic dehydrogenase or the activity of site I (in the absence of rotenone) affect the redox level of ubiquinone. However, the kinetic behavior of the components of site II was shown to be unaffected either by the addition of rotenone or by eliminating the activity of site III (experiments on the yeast mitochondria, Erecińska et al., 1973a). In addition, it was demonstrated that the net flow of electrons in state 4 is at least three orders of magnitude slower than the forward and reverse rates between the carriers (Erecińska et al., 1972), which justifies our consideration of Eq. (2).

III. Kinetics of Reduction of the b Cytochromes

Studies on the reduction kinetics of the respiratory chain carriers have been handicapped by the lack of proper reductants, fast enough to be used in rapid kinetic measurements. The first successful attempt was made by Lee et al. (1969), who used pulses of NADH to study the kinetic behavior of the components of the respiratory chain in cyanide-inhibited beef heart submitochondrial particles. It was found that the initial rate of cytochrome b reduction was faster in the presence of oligomycin (4.1 μmoles per second per milligram of protein) than in the presence of FCCP (1.6 μmoles per second per milligram of protein). Conversely, the initial rate of cytochrome c reduction was slower in the presence of oligomycin (1.8 μmoles per second per milligram of protein) than of FCCP (3.5 μmoles per second per milligram of protein). Furthermore, in the presence of oligomycin the reduction of the cytochromes and especially that of cytochrome c revealed strikingly biphasic kinetics. The biphasic response of cytochromes c (and a) to an NADH pulse was interpreted as evidence for the occurrence of separate coupled and uncoupled respiratory assemblies in the oligo-mycin-supplemented system, with a slow cross-chain electron trans-port from the uncoupled to the coupled assemblies.

An alternative interpretation can be offered in terms of the existence of two different cytochrome b species. In the presence of oligomycin, i.e., in the tightly coupled submitochondrial particles, both cyto-chromes b_{560} and b_{566} are oxidized by NADH (Boveris $et\ al.$, 1972; Lee and Slater, 1972). In the presence of FCCP, cytochrome b_{566} is only slowly reduced by NADH and the amount of cytochromes b reduced under these conditions is smaller than in the absence of the uncoupler. Lee and Slater (1972), in order to account for the slow reducibility of cytochrome b_{566} by NADH, postulated the existence of an "accessi-bility barrier" that interferes with the redox equilibrium between NADH and cytochrome b_{566}. Alternately, faster flow of electrons through cytochromes b toward c_1 in the presence of uncoupler results in a low steady state reduction level of cytochrome b_{566} ($E_m - 30$ mV).

Since the mitochondrial membrane is not freely permeable to ex-ternally added NADH the same technique could not be reliably ap-plied to the studies on the intact mitochondria. In 1970 Ruzicka and Crane (1970a,b, 1971) introduced 2,3,5,6-tetramethylbenzhydroquinol (durohydroquinone) as a rapid reductant intercepting the respiratory chain at ubiquinone–cytochrome b level (Boveris $et\ al.$, 1971, 1972). It was found subsequently that durohydroquinone was able to react with the respiratory chain in a first-order reaction in the uncoupled state and in coupled mitochondria in the presence of high protein concentration (Boveris $et\ al.$, 1972) and in zero-order reaction in coupled mitochondria at low protein concentration and in an inhibited system (cytochrome c extracted mitochondria, antimycin A suppli-mented). The reduction of cytochrome b was remarkably fast ($t_{1/2}$ below 10 msec) in the ubiquinone extracted membranes and rein-corporation of ubiquinone resulted in a decrease of the cytochrome b reduction rate by at least 100-fold.

The reduction kinetics of cytochromes b was studied in cytochrome c depleted mitochondria (Boveris $et\ al.$, 1972) in which the rate de-termining step of the overall electron transfer is at the cytochrome c site without impairing the energy coupling reactions. (In contrast to the antimycin A inhibited system, extraction of cytochrome c does not affect the very immediate neighbor of cytochromes b and leaves it to react freely in the oxidation-reduction reactions.) In cytochrome c depleted mitochondria the residual flow of electrons from the endog-enous substrate decreases the oxidized steady state level of cyto-chrome c_1 as it is the last component before the rate determining step

(Fig. 4). Addition of durohydroquinone (in the absence of ATP or uncoupler) reduces the remaining portion of cytochrome c_1, both b cytochromes, and ubiquinone. Addition of ATP prior to a pulse of

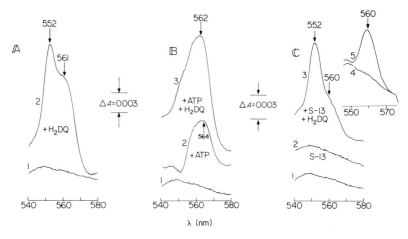

λ (nm)

FIG. 4. Cytochrome reduction by durohydroquinone in cytochrome c-extracted pigeon heart mitochondria (3.4 mg/ml 0.2 M mannitol, 0.050 M sucrose, 0.050 M morpholinopropane sulfonate pH 6.8). (A) Curve 1: baseline + 2 μM rotenone; curve 2: curve 1 + 100 μM (durohydroquinone) H_2DQ. (B) Curve 1: baseline + 2 μM rotenone; curve 2: curve 1 + 1.2 mM ATP; curve 3: curve 2 + 100 μM H_2DQ. (C) Curve 1: baseline + 2 μM rotenone; curve 2: curve 1 + 4 μM S-13(5-chloro-3-t-butyl-2′-chloro-4′-nitrosalicylanilide); curve 3: curve 2 + 100 μM H_2DQ; curve 4: new baseline with 5.1 mg pigeon heart mitochondria per milliliter; curve 5: curve 4 + 6 μM S-13 + 150μ M H_2DQ recorded versus a reference curvette supplemented with 4 mM ascorbate and 1 mM KCN. From Boveris et al. (1972).

durohydroquinone causes a disappearance of 552 nm peak of reduced cytochrome c_1 and the appearance of only the 564 nm peak of the reduced cytochrome b_{566}. The amount of cytochrome b_{566} reduced depends on the amount of endogenous substrate and pH of the medium and varies from 50 to 90% in different experiments. Subsequent addition of a pulse of durohydroquinone thus reduces mainly the other cytochrome b, cytochrome b_{560}.

Addition of the uncoupler (before durohydroquinone) causes oxidation of cytochrome c_1 previously reduced by the endogenous substrate. Durohydroquinone addition results in the appearance of 552 nm and 560 nm peaks indicative of reduction of cytochromes b_{560} and c_1 (but not 566 nm). The lack of 566 nm peak suggests that durohydroquinone, like succinate, is not able to reduce cytochrome b_{566} under these conditions.

Durohydroquinone-supplemented, cytochrome c-depleted mitochondria provide us with the opportunity of observing the steady-state
reduction levels of the components located around the second phosphorylation site: ubiquinone, cytochromes b and c_1 (Boveris *et al.*,
1972). In the presence of ATP (Fig. 5) the highest steady-state re-

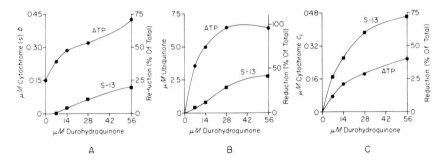

FIG. 5. Titration of cytochrome b, ubiquinone and cytochrome c in cytochrome c
extracted pigeon heart mitochondria. Cytochromes b (562–575 nm) and cytochrome c_1
(552–540 nm) titrations: 1 mM ATP or 2 μM S-13. Ubiquinone (285–305 nm), 5 mm light
path titration: 0.5 mM ATP or 2 μM S-13. In all cases 1.8 mg/ml c extracted pigeon
heart mitochondria and 3 μM rotenone in 0.2 M mannitol, 0.050 M sucrose, 0.050 M
morpholinopropane sulfonate pH 6.8. From Boveris *et al.* (1972).

duction level is attained by cytochrome b_{566} and ubiquinone. With 16
μM durohydroquinone, cytochrome b_{566} reduction is complete, ubiquinone is over 80% reduced and cytochromes b_{560} and c_1 are mostly
oxidized. This suggests that ATP substantially decreases the flow of
electrons toward oxygen across site II and that cytochrome c_1 is on the
oxygen side of the point of action of ATP. Since in the presence of
uncoupler cytochrome c_1 is more reduced than any other component
at site II, it can be supposed that the uncoupler eliminated the rate-
determining step existing in the presence of ATP. Direct measurements of the reduction rate of cytochrome c_1 by durohydroquinone in
a rapid flow apparatus (Boveris *et al.*, 1972) demonstrate that the reaction is faster in the presence of an uncoupler than in the presence
of ATP.

For the reasons discussed above both in the presence of ATP and
pentachlorophenol mainly one of the cytochromes b, cytochrome
b_{560}, is reduced by durohydroquinone. However, in the absence of
either ATP or PCP, at least a part of cytochrome b_{566} is present in the
oxidized form and can be reduced by the addition of the reductant.
The kinetic trace (Boveris *et al.*, 1972) recorded under such condi-

tions is biphasic: the initial phase (1.1 $\mu M/\text{sec}$) is attributed to the rapid reduction of cytochrome b_{566}, the second, slower one (0.04 $\mu M/\text{sec}$) to the reduction of cytochrome b_{560}. The biphasic reduction kinetics of cytochromes b in the presence of ATP is even more pronounced in the intact mitochondria due to the fact that all of cytochrome b_{566} is present initially in the oxidized form. The very fast rates of cytochrome b reduction with half-reduction times of 10–20 msec suggest that under such conditions cytochrome b_{566} preferentially accepts the electrons from durohydroquinone. The kinetic data of the reduction of cytochromes b by durohydroquinone in the depleted and intact membranes are summarized in Fig. 6.

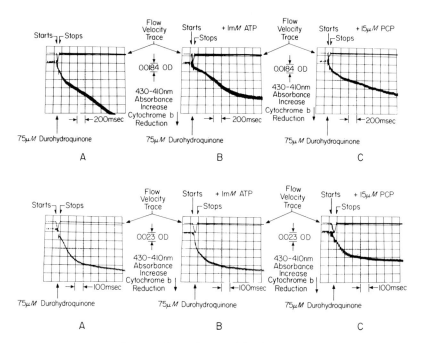

FIG. 6. Upper set: Reduction of cytochromes b by durohydroquinone in cytochrome c extracted pigeon heart mitochondria (2.4 mg of protein per milliliter in 0.2 M mannitol, 0.050 M sucrose, 0.050 M morpholinopropane sulfonate, pH 6.8). (A) 5 μM rotenone + 75 μM H_2DQ. (B) 5 μM rotenone and 1.2 mM ATP + 75 μM H_2DQ. (C) 5 μM rotenone and 15 μM PCP + 75 μM H_2DQ.

Lower set: Reduction of cytochromes b in intact pigeon heart mitochondria by durohydroquinone. Pigeon heart mitochondria, 2.3 mg/ml, in 0.2 M mannitol, 0.050 M sucrose, 0.050 M morpholinopropane sulfonate, pH 6.8. From Boveris $et\ al.$ (1972).

Studies with pulsed reductants on the intact (Boveris $et\ al.$, 1972) and fragmented (Lee $et\ al.$, 1969) membranes suggest that the slowest reaction in the electron transfer at site II is that between cytochrome

b_{566} and c_1, and that the rate of this reaction is affected by the energy state of the mitochondria. This is substantiated by the following lines of evidence: (1) faster rate of cytochrome c_1 reduction in the presence of an uncoupler (that in the presence of ATP); (2) faster rate of cytochrome b_{566} reduction in the presence of ATP (than in the presence of an uncoupler); (3) high steady-state reduction of cytochrome b_{566} and low steady-state reduction of c_1 in the coupled as compared with the uncoupled state (titration experiments, Fig. 5). It is worthwhile to note that the experimental observations of Boveris *et al.* (1972) furthermore indicate that the high potential oxidized form of cytochrome b_{566} formed by the addition of ATP to aerobic mitochondria is readily reducible by durohydroquinone without decreasing the ADP/O ratio, which implies that the energy transfer occurs predominantly in the reduced state of cytochrome b_{566}.

IV. Behavior of the b Cytochromes in the Antimycin A-Inhibited System

Antimycin A, owing to its specific binding at an inhibitory site in the respiratory chain between cytochromes b and c_1, is a widely used tool in the studies on phosphorylation site II (Chance, 1952a; Estabrook, 1962; Pumphrey, 1962; Rieske *et al.*, 1967; Bryla *et al.*, 1969; Berden and Slater, 1970; Dutton *et al.*, 1972). The titer is 1 molecule of antimycin A per 2 b-cytochrome hemes for ∼ 98% inhibition of the electron transfer. The effect of antimycin A on the spectral properties of cytochromes b and character of its titration curve is beyond the scope of the present contribution, and for detailed information the reader is referred to recent review articles and original papers (Berden and Slater, 1970; Bryla *et al.*, 1969; Brandon *et al.*, 1972; Wilson and Dutton, 1971; Dutton *et al.*, 1972).

It was noted already in 1952 (Chance, 1952b) that in anaerobic yeast cells treated with antimycin A, cytochrome b remains largely oxidized and becomes reduced upon introduction of oxygen. A similar aerobic reduction of cytochrome b was noted by Pumphrey (1962) in detergent-clarified beef heart mitochondria and by Kovàč *et al.* (1970) in yeast and heart muscle preparations in the presence of a high concentration of uncoupling agents. Baum and Rieske (1966) and Rieske (1969, 1971) observed that in the presence of antimycin A, the reducibility of cytochrome b in the purified cytochrome b–c_1 complex was enhanced by addition of ferricyanide. Wilson *et al.* (1971) reexamined this phenomenon in detergent-treated mitochondria and purified succinate–cytochrome c reductase and concluded that the aerobic reduction of cytochrome b_{566} occurred as the consequence of an energy-dependent change in the midpoint potential of this cytochrome which was induced through the activation of electron transfer at site II.

An extensive evaluation of the kinetic behavior of cytochromes b in the presence of antimycin A has appeared recently (Erecińska *et al.*, 1972). It was found that the phenomenon of the aerobic reduction of cytochrome b observed in the presence of the inhibitor relied on the fact that not all the cytochrome b_{566} was reduced under the "anaerobic conditions" of the experiment. Thus, when the system was mixed with oxygen, b_{566} was initially rapidly reduced and then slowly reoxidized (Fig. 7). The spectrum obtained by plotting the extent of the reduction phase against the measuring wavelength exhibited 566 nm absorbance maximum, thus confirming the suggestion that the cytochrome undergoing reduction was the long wavelength b.

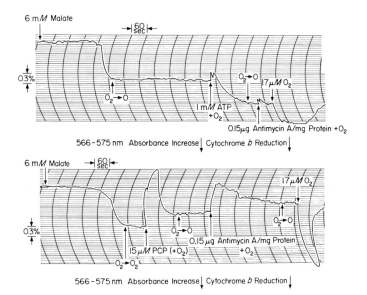

FIG. 7. Aerobic reduction of cytochrome b_{566} in antimycin A-blocked pigeon heart mitochondria. Medium: 0.225 M mannitol, 0.075 M sucrose, 0.050 M morpholinopropane sulfonate, pH 6.9, 2.4 mg of protein per milliliter. The addition of ATP, pentachlorophenol (PCP), and antimycin A included various amounts of oxygen, and the times to anaerobiosis ($O_2 \to O$) differed. Time proceeds from left to right. From Erecińska *et al.* (1972).

The phenomenon of the aerobic reduction of cytochrome b_{566} is not prevented by the presence of an uncoupler and requires: (1) that cytochrome c_1 could be rapidly oxidized; (2) that ubiquinone or another electron donor be able to donate electrons to cytochrome b_{566}.

The first is substantiated by the finding that when cytochrome c_1 is reduced by ascorbate plus TMPD (in the presence of cyanide) a pulse of durohydroquinone cannot reduce cytochrome b_{566} unless dithionite is added. Second, in cytochrome c-depleted mitochondria in which oxidation of cytochrome c_1 is slow as compared to that in intact membranes, aerobic reduction of b_{566} is seemingly slow and occurs at a rate parallel to that of c_1 oxidation. Reincorporation of cytochrome c not only stimulates the rate of oxidation of cytochrome c_1 but also equally enhances the rate of aerobic reduction of cytochrome b_{566}.

The experiments have raised the question of the most likely electron donor for the aerobic reduction of cytochrome b_{566}. Extraction of ubiquinone from the mitochondrial membranes (levels below 0.5 nmole of ubiquinone per milligram of protein, over 90% extraction) markedly decreases the rate of the reduction of cytochrome b_{566}, although cytochrome c_1 is rapidly oxidized by oxygen. The occurrence of the aerobic reduction of cytochrome b_{566} in the ubiquinone extracted mitochondria suggests that either the residual ubiquinone or other electron donors [flavoprotein, nonheme iron (Erecińska et $al.$, 1970; Wilson et $al.$, 1970; Ohnishi et $al.$, 1972)] might provide electrons for this reaction directly or indirectly through the small amount of residual coenzyme Q. The indication that ubiquinone is the most likely electron donor for the oxygen-induced reduction of cytochrome b_{566} is further confirmed by the kinetic studies on intact mitochondria in which a rapid phase of oxidation corresponding to the reduction of cytochrome b_{560} is observed. The amount of ubiquinone oxidized in the initial rapid phase is found to be greater (0.86 nmole per milligram of protein) than the amount of cytochrome b_{566} reduced under the same conditions (0.18 nmole per milligram of protein), thus indicating that more than enough electrons leave ubiquinone to account for the reduction of cytochrome b_{566}.

Since the midpoint potential of ubiquinone is more positive ($E_{m7.0} = +60$ mV) than that of cytochrome b_{566} ($E_{m7.0} = -30$ mV), rapid reduction of the latter by the former carrier can occur only when either the midpoint potential of the donor becomes more negative or that of the acceptor more positive. The data of Rieske (1971) and of Wilson et $al.$ (1971) indicate that the component which changes its midpoint potential from a more negative to a more positive value is cytochrome b_{566}. Two possibilities have been considered as the most likely reasons for the change in cytochrome b midpoint potential. The first one, put forward by Wilson et $al.$ (1971, 1972a,b), proposes that the activation of electron transfer at site II causes the change in cytochrome b_{566} midpoint potential from -30 mV to $+245$ mV. An alternative suggested by Chance (1972a,b) is based on the analogy with interactions occurring among the α and β chains in the hemoglobin molecule (Perutz, 1970; Huber *et al.*, 1970) and proposes that the midpoint potential shift may be evoked by a structural transition in a cytochrome $b_{566} - c_1$ complex. The model implies that the redox state of cytochrome c_1 controls the redox state of cytochrome b_{566} and electron flow through the antimycin A site is not necessary.

V. Behavior of the Cytochromes b at 0°C

Studies at low temperature have been extensively used to elucidate the electron transfer pathways in the bacterial systems (Chance *et al.*, 1966; DeVault and Chance, 1966) and to trap the intermediates in the case of purified enzymes (Strother and Ackerman, 1961; Douzou *et al.*, 1970; Douzou and Leterrier, 1970; Banerjee *et al.*, 1970). The same approach has been used recently to study the electron transfer in the intact microsomal membranes (P. Debey, unpubl., 1971) and in mitochondria to study the cytochrome oxidase oxygen reaction (Erecińska and Chance, 1972). Since it can be expected that various reactions in the respiratory chain occur with different temperature coefficients, this new approach can give us some insight into the mechanism of coupled electron flow. In connection with this, Kraayenhof *et al.* (1971) found that in chloroplasts at ~ 5°C the energy dissipation occurs at a much slower rate than at room temperature, thus the system appears to be much better coupled.

With decrease in temperature, oxidation rate of cytochromes b decreases. Furthermore oxidation phase is preceded by a reduction phase (already noticeable at 23°C — see Section II) similar to that observed in the presence of antimycin A (Erecińska *et al.*, 1973b) (Fig. 8). Spectral characteristics of the reduction phase indicate that the cytochrome which undergoes reduction upon addition of a pulse of oxygen is cytochrome b_{566} (Erecińska, 1972). Addition of the uncoupler to the coupled mitochondria does not affect the rate of the reduction phase but increases the rate of subsequent reoxidation. Comparison of the kinetic traces of the time course of oxidation of cytochromes b and c_1 indicates that at ~ 0° the oxidation of cytochrome c_1 precedes the reduction of cytochrome b (Fig. 9) in contrast to the data obtained at 23°C. This finding confirms the earlier suggestions (Wilson *et al.*, 1971; Erecińska *et al.*, 1972) that oxidation of cytochrome c_1 is a prerequisite for cytochrome b_{566} reduction.

The reduction of cytochrome b_{566} is accompanied by oxidation of ubiquinone, similar to that observed at room temperature. This indi-

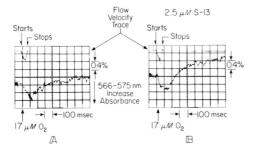

FIG. 8. Effect of uncoupler on the behavior of cytochromes b at 5°C under conditions of oxygen pulse experiment. Pigeon heart mitochondria were suspended in 0.2 M mannitol, 0.05 M sucrose, 0.030 M phosphate, pH 7.4, 5% ethylene glycol medium at 2.8 mg of protein per milliliter and made anaerobic by the addition of 6.0 mM succinate, 1.5 mM glutamate at 23°C. Then 5.0 μM rotenone was added and the temperature was lowered as described by Erecińska and Chance (1972). The uncoupler used was: 5-chloro-3-t-butyl-2′-chloro-4′-nitrosalicylanilide. Unpublished data of Erecińska.

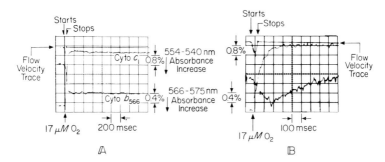

FIG. 9. Time relationship between oxidation of cytochrome $c + c_1$ and reduction of b_{566} at 23° (A) and at 0° (B) in pigeon heart mitochondria. Mitochondria were suspended at 2.5 mg of protein per milliliter in 0.2 M mannitol, 0.05 M sucrose, 0.03 M phosphate buffer, pH 7.0, 10% ethylene glycol and made anaerobic by the addition of 6.0 mM succinate and 1.5 mM glutamate. Then 5.0 μM rotenone and 3.0 mM malonate were added. In (B) the temperature was lowered to 0°C as described by Erecińska and Chance (1972). From Erecińska et al. (1972).

cates that the quinone pool is the most likely electron donor for the cytochromes b (Fig. 10).

The overall kinetic picture of the cytochromes b at temperatures below 23°C markedly resembles the changes invoked by the addition of antimycin A. The similarity between the two effects strongly suggests that they might affect a common group or the same reaction step. Since it has been known that the energy transfer reactions have higher

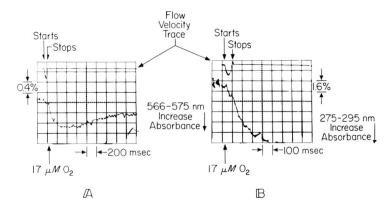

FIG. 10. Kinetic changes of cytochrome b_{566} and ubiquinone at 0°C in pigeon heart mitochondria upon addition of an oxygen pulse. Pigeon heart mitochondria were suspended in 0.2 M mannitol, 0.05 M sucrose, 0.030 M phosphate buffer, pH 7.0, 10% ethylene glycol, at 3.2 mg of protein per milliliter and made anaerobic by the addition of 6.0 mM succinate, 1.5 mM glutamate. Then 5.0 μM rotenone was added, and the temperature was lowered to 0°C. Unpublished data of Erecińska and Chance, 1971.

temperature coefficient than do the electron transfer reactions, it is possible that antimycin A affects the respiratory chain by impairing the energy-conserving mechanism with consequent inhibition of the electron flow (see also Dutton et al., 1972). This suggestion is consistent with the finding that antimycin A prevents the ATP, but not the electron-transport induced shift in the midpoint potential of cytochrome b_{566} (Dutton et al., 1972; Wilson et al., 1971; Erecińska et al., 1972).

VI. Kinetic Studies on Succinate–Cytochrome c_1 Reductase

Succinate–cytochrome c_1 reductase contains as its most integral part the components involved in the energy conservation at site II, namely, cytochromes b and c_1 (Davis et al., 1972; Sato et al., 1971a,b); Wilson and Dutton, 1970; Wikström, 1971; Okunuki and Yakushiji, 1941; Baum et al., 1967). Thus, it should be possible to demonstrate, under appropriate conditions, the occurrence of the energy-conserving reactions in this preparation. An additional advantage in using the succinate–cytochrome c reductase preparation lies in the fact that it is freely permeable to both succinate and fumarate, thus by proper adjustment of the ratios of both substrates the redox potential of the reducing couple is easy to calculate. Following this reasoning, Wilson et al. (1971) have adjusted the redox potential of the succinate/fumarate to +65 mV in the anaerobic preparation of antimycin A-supplemented succinate–cytochrome c reductase [the poise was monitored additionally using platinum and calomel electrodes and redox mediators as described by Dutton (1971)], and pulsed the system with an oxidant [at +65 mV cytochrome b_{566} ($E_{m7.0} = -30$ mV) is approximately 97% oxidized]. The observation that cytochrome b_{566} underwent almost quantitative reduction indicates that its midpoint potential must have changed by about 175 mV (95% reduction corresponds to $E_{m7.0}$ of 145 mV). Measurements at the wavelength pair where both cytochrome c_1 and b_{566} contribute to the absorbance changes demonstrate that the oxidation of cytochrome c_1 preceded the reduction of cytochrome b_{566}, and when ferricyanide was exhausted the re-reduction of c_1 preceded the reoxidation of cytochrome b_{566}. This suggested (Wilson *et al.*, 1972b) that during the energy conservation process the half-reduction potential of cytochrome b_{566} may become more positive by 10–20 mV than that of cytochrome c_1. The effect is not specifically induced by ferricyanide since the same result could be obtained using cytochrome c peroxidase, cytochrome c and H_2O_2, or cytochrome oxidase, cytochrome c, and oxygen as the oxidants of cytochrome c_1.

The time relationship between the oxidation of cytochrome c_1 and reduction of cytochrome b_{566} was studied using the rapid flow technique (Wilson *et al.*, 1972a) (Fig. 11). Addition of ferricyanide to an

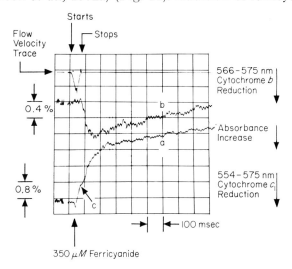

FIG. 11. The rate of reduction of cytochrome b_{566} and oxidation of c_1 upon addition of ferricyanide to the anaerobic preparation of succinate–cytochrome c reductase. Purified succinate–cytochrome c reductase (1 μM cytochrome c_1) in 0.02 M phosphate buffer, pH 7.0, was made anaerobic by adding 20 mg (wet weight/ml) of *Saccharomyces cerevisiae* yeast cells and 10 mM glucose. Succinate 1.5 mM, fumarate 15 mM, 0.1 μg antimycin A per milligram of reductase protein. C indicates jump in cytochrome c_1 oxidation preceding the reduction of b_{566}. From Wilson *et al.* (1972b).

anaerobic suspension of succinate–cytochrome c reductase in the presence of succinate:fumarate (1:10) and antimycin A, induced oxidation of cytochrome c_1 (half-time of 20 msec) and a reduction of cytochrome b_{566} (half-time of 80 msec) (Erecińska and Wilson, 1972).

VII.   Interpretation of the Reaction Kinetics of Cytochromes b

The wealth of the available experimental information on the kinetic behavior of cytochromes b has been interpreted in a number of different ways. Basically, all the interpretations can be classified in three groups: formal kinetic interpretation, qualitative kinetic interpretation, and nonkinetic interpretation. In the *formal kinetic interpretation* the model of the reaction is built on the basis of available information and the curves are calculated by integration and compared with the experimental results either qualitatively or also quantitatively by fitting procedures. An example of this type of approach can be seen in the studies of Chance *et al.* (1955), of Chance and Pring (1969), and of Wagner *et al.* (1971b; Wagner and Erecińska, 1971). The *qualitative kinetic* attitude uses reasoning with the same terminology as the formal kinetic approach, e.g., the terms of reactions and reaction rates, but does not involve a mathematical treatment of the data because of incomplete information on the system. The *nonkinetic approach,* probably most popular in the field of the kinetics of the respiratory chain, attempts to interpret the unexpected features of the experimental curves in terms of a new quality of the system. Successful application of this type of approach is the identification of the two cytochromes $b-b_{560}$ and b_{566}–on the basis of kinetic data (Chance *et al.,* 1970; Erecińska and Chance, 1971). The nonkinetic approach is well justified when the evidence for the existence of a new quality can be furnished independently by the other methods, e.g., by spectral or thermodynamic studies. When such an evidence is lacking, the danger arises that any deviation from the expected kinetic behavior is interpreted as being due to specific structural organization of the mitochondrial membrane, which per definition, cannot be tested by any independent method outside the methods of membrane biology.

The advantage of either the nonkinetic or the qualitative kinetic interpretation of the cytochrome system lies in the fact that they need not solve the problem of the mutual, structural relationships of the cytochromes. On the other hand, the formal kinetics approach which actually calculates the concentrations requires either assumptions or knowledge of certain fundamental facts on the structural arrangements of the cytochrome system in order to decide what type of a rate law should be used for the interpretation of the results. The initial simulation studies, carried out on an analog computer (Chance *et al.*, 1955, 1958), treated the cytochromes as molecules freely dissolved in solution. The most important achievement of these efforts was the crossover theorem (Chance *et al.*, 1958) which enabled the location of the coupling sites. This approximation considered neither the fact that the respiratory chain is located in the mitochondrial membrane nor the mutual binding or interactions of different cytochromes which could considerably influence the kind of rate law used for theoretical evaluation. Subsequently, Holmes (1960; for further discussion, see Pring, 1970) compared the models in which the cytochromes were treated as freely dissolved molecules with another extreme in which the cytochromes were physically bound to each other to form a rigid chain. Both models showed, in his hands, very little difference, though the experimental basis of these studies did not contain information obtained using depletion techniques (cytochrome c or ubiquinone) or respiratory chain inhibitors. Experimental evidence indicates that cytochrome c or ubiquinone can be treated as molecules freely dissolved in the membranes, and cytochromes a and a_3 or b and c_1 as structural complexes in which the redox state of one cytochrome can affect the redox state of the other. Furthermore, Wohlrab (1970) demonstrated that in mitochondria partially inhibited by carbon monoxide molecules of cytochrome a did not communicate rapidly with each other unless cytochrome c was present. Thus, the type of the rate laws used for cytochrome c does not necessarily apply to the treatment of cytochromes $a + a_3$ and b and c_1.

Definitive experimental evidence on the sequence of the respiratory carriers at site II, an important prerequisite for the formal kinetic studies on the system, is still lacking.

Slater (1971) and Ernster (see Nelson *et al.*, 1972) advocate the following schemes:

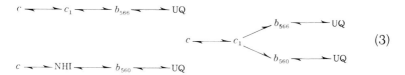

$$\text{(3)}$$

Our own kinetic data presented in Sections II and III seem to question the linear arrangement of the carriers; however, due to unavailability of the kinetic description of nonheme iron and the overlap of spectral properties of the cytochromes (b_{560}, b_{566}, c, and c_1), these kinetic studies do not provide at present firm experimental support for either of the alternative schemes.

The kinetic behavior of cytochromes b, ubiquinone, and cytochrome c in the oxygen pulse experiment was the subject of two fitting studies. The first one, that of Chance and Pring (1969) and Pring (1970), used the sequence

$$\longrightarrow c \longleftarrow c_1 \longleftarrow b \longleftarrow Fp \longrightarrow$$
$$\underset{UQ}{\uparrow} \qquad\qquad\qquad (4)$$

and demonstrated the impossibility of fitting the experimentally observed redox kinetics of the carriers in malonate-inhibited mitochondria to a single chain model. In order to fit the results, two sets of the rate constants were introduced, depending on the oxygen concentration. The second fitting study (Wagner *et al.*, 1971a) used the linear sequence of the carriers $c \rightleftharpoons c_1 \rightleftharpoons b \rightleftharpoons UQ$ and the experimental data of the initial (to the point where the steady state was reached) time courses of oxidation of cytochrome b, c, and ubiquinone in coupled and uncoupled mitochondria. The rate constants obtained this way demonstrated that the constants markedly affected by the coupled to uncoupled transition were those between cytochromes b and c_1. If we accept the ratio of the apparent rate constants as the equilibrium constant, the shift in the midpoint potential of one of the two cytochromes (b or c_1) which can be calculated from the kinetic data is within the range of values obtained for the ATP-induced midpoint potential shift of b_{566} determined by the equilibrium titration technique (Wilson and Dutton, 1970).

The same model, in which cytochrome b was considered as one chemical species and solely as an electron carrier, could not simulate the entire time course of oxidation of cytochromes b (and subsequent reduction) described in detail in Section II: the initial reduction preceding oxidation, the "late maximum" and the slow reduction rate following the exhaustion of oxygen. The failure to simulate these three details by a simple scheme further confirms that cytochrome b cannot be treated solely as an electron carrier.

VIII.   Kinetic Behavior of Cytochromes b and the Energy Coupling Reactions

Kinetic models and the forms of the rate laws discussed in the previous section were concerned with the chemistry of electron transport and with the function of cytochromes as simple carriers of electrons. Justification for this attitude comes from the studies with uncouplers which allow electron transfer to proceed without concomitant synthesis of ATP. The mode of action of a great variety of available uncoupling agents remains largely unknown though the phenomenon itself can arise from a number of possibilities: (1) the external "short circuiting" of the phosphorylation site, i.e., bypass of electrons over the site of performing the energy transduction; (2) internal "short circuiting," i.e., transfer of electrons along "normal" pathway but in such a way that the energy is not conserved. These two possibilities specifically locate the phenomenon of uncoupling within the respiratory chain itself; (3) loss of ability to maintain the pH gradient across the membrane (mechanism of uncoupling according to chemiosmotic hypothesis which is equivalent to the short-circuiting in the respiratory chain); (4) fast hydrolysis of the high energy intermediate (interpretation put forward by chemical hypotheses of the oxidative phosphorylation). The available experimental evidence seems to indicate that in the presence of the known uncoupling agents the respiratory chain carriers remain functional in their capacity to synthesize the high energy bond: (1) ATP synthesis can be demonstrated even in the presence of uncouplers if strong ATP-trapping system is employed (Margolis *et al.*, 1967); (2) ATP–P_i exchange which occurs in a preparation of soluble coupling factor (Fisher *et al.*, 1971) is uncoupler sensitive. (3) Aerobic reduction of cytochrome b_{566} interpreted as the primary energy conservation event (Wilson *et al.*, 1971; Erecińska *et al.*, 1972) is not prevented by the addition of uncoupler. Thus uncoupling by the thus far available uncoupling agents can be considered as a result of a shift of the rate-determining step from the energy conservation to the electron pathway.

The fact that cytochrome *b* is not exclusively an electron carrier was suggested years ago by Chance (Chance *et al.*, 1955; Chance and Williams, 1956) on the basis of crossover theorem and more recently by Slater (1971; Slater *et al.*, 1970a,b) on the basis of spectral studies on cytochromes *b* carried out in the presence of antimycin A and ATP. These elegant speculations derived either from the kinetic (Chance *et al.*, 1958) or spectroscopic (Slater, 1971) data did not succeed, however, in providing direct evidence for the role of cytochrome *b* in the energy coupling. The important piece of evidence comes from the experiments on the effect of phosphate potential dependence of cytochrome b_{566} midpoint potential which specifically predict that this carrier is intimately involved in the energy-conserving cycle (Wilson and Dutton, 1970; Wilson *et al.*, this volume). If cytochrome b_{566} does perform a dual function of an electron carrier and of an energy transducer, the question arises as to the mutual location of redox and energy-forming and transferring reactions. This consequently requires incorporation of the energy-coupling events into the reaction scheme, and such a reaction scheme, if considered as the working hypothesis, should be able to explain the available kinetic data and predict the behavior of the respiratory chain carriers.

The list of hypotheses of oxidative phosphorylation is impressive, but only very few cases contain clear suggestions for the experimental distinction between the hypothesis of interest and other schemes. Although they can be roughly divided into two groups: chemiosmotic and chemical experimentally testable, differences between the two have been wiped out with time. Probably the most essential difference between the available theories lies in the fact that some of them (Mitchell, 1966a,b; Green and Young, 1971; Green and Ji, 1972) ascribe to the mitochondrial membrane a primary role in the energy conservation. Mitchell's chemiosmotic theory (1966a,b) derives the primary driving force for the ATP synthesis from the hydrogen ion gradient or membrane potential generated during the transfer of electrons through the alternating sequence of hydrogen and electron carriers. Green's mechanical-chemical coupling hypothesis (Green and Ji, 1972) suggests that the redox energy of the electron transport is converted to a metastable conformational state of protein which leads to the generation of an asymmetric surface charge, a membrane potential and a redistribution of diffusible ions across the mitochondrial membrane and ATP synthesis. The vectorial character of these forces is affecting the electron transfer processes. Since ATP is considered as the product of electrochemical processes the kinetic measurement of the electron carriers cannot distinguish these hypotheses in regard to the mechanism of energy transfer.

The chemical hypotheses [including the sterical variant of Boyer (1965) which is indistinguishable from the former for the purpose of reaction kinetics] are easier to formulate in terms of reaction schemes and reaction rates. These models can be transferred to schemes which, by means of suitable computer programs, can be compared with the experiments. (This is not the case with theories which involve in one way or another the membrane structure, as yet impractical to express in mathematical terms.) A model can be compared with the experimental system in either of two ways: qualitatively by a simulation process and quantitatively in a fitting procedure where simulation is used usually as an introductory step to fitting. By the qualitative features of the experimental kinetics of the cytochrome system we consider: the minima and maxima on the kinetic curves, steady-state levels, and relative rates of reduction and oxidation of the carriers of interest. Since with cytochromes b, $c + c_1$, and ubiquinone the experimental kinetics is sufficiently "rich" in detail, many schemes can be readily excluded after a brief simulation treatment because of failure to reproduce the qualitative characteristics of the system. Though the failure of the model to reproduce the qualitative features of the system can be considered as a rather strong proof against its validity, the qualitative agreement between the model and the experimental results is only a necessary but not sufficient condition for the validity of the model. Nevertheless, availability of such a tool permits us to narrow the range of possibilities for valid mechanisms of oxidative phosphorylation.

Slater's hypothesis of coupled electron flow at site II (Slater et $al.$, 1970a,b; Slater, 1971) postulates as the active unit a dimer composed of two cytochromes $b - b$ and b_i (Fig. 12). Reduction of b^{3+} by a donor to site II results in the information of high energy form of b^{2+} $(b^{2+}\sim)$. Subsequent intracomplex energy transfer to b_i^{3+} accounts for its rapid reducibility and results in formation of $b^{2+} \sim b_i^{2+}$ (the high energy bond "returns" to b^{2+} after $b_i^{3+}\sim$ reduction). In the next reaction an electron is delivered from b_i^{2+} to an acceptor site II with conservation of energy in the product, $b_i^{3+}\sim$. In this formulation intramolecular electron transfer within the energized dimer, from a low-potential b to a high-potential b_i^{3+} is coupled to ATP synthesis. The mechanism can account for ready reducibility of cytochromes b in the presence of antimycin A and ATP. It postulates the involvement of two high energy intermediates, each of them providing equivalent of 300 mV for the synthesis of one molecule of ATP. Thus, both the thermodynamic requirements and the stoichiometry of ATP synthesis are satisfied. The model has many positive features as clear distinction between the intracomplex and extracomplex redox reactions and clear location of the reactions contributing to the "squiggle" formation. Although Slater (1971; Slater et $al.$, 1970a,b) presented no detailed scheme, which would permit calculation of the kinetic curves, we have made in accord with our best knowledge the necessary assumptions to complete the model: relative concentrations of cytochromes b were chosen to be $1:1$, ubiquinone and cytochrome c were treated as freely dissolved in the membrane and cytochrome b and b_i formed a complex. The sequence of reactions were taken as described by Slater (1971). Conversion of the scheme to a mathematically manageable form failed to simulate the experimental behavior of cytochrome b kinetics; specifically, the model could not account for the very slow reduction of the carrier following exhaustion of oxygen.

Wilson and Dutton's (Wilson et $al.$, this volume) formulation of oxidative phosphorylation treats the mitochondrial coupled electron flow as an equilibrium system. Since a number of equilibrium results have been incorporated into the interpretation of the kinetic data presented above, the relationship between the approaches deserves more detailed evaluation (cf. below).

A more concise model of oxidative phosphorylation has been presented by DeVault (1971). According to his formulation, the energy transduction process occurs in five steps: electron reception, electron donation, contact with I, release of I* and change from I* to I. The energy transfer reaction is located, in this formulation, between two electron transferring steps. The carrier which performs the energy transducing function is accepting electrons from one donor at redox potential E_1, giving them to an acceptor at potential E_2, and while taking the free energy available from the transfer of electrons and giving it to hypothetical entity I, it converts I to I*, a form able to do useful work (DeVault, 1971).

$$ne^- (E_1) + I \rightarrow ne^- (E_2) + I^*$$

Thus the standard redox potential of the energy transducer "oscillates" between that of E_1 and E_2, which corresponds to Wilson and Dutton's (1970) midpoint potential changes of a cytochrome performing the energy conservation function. Conversion of the model to the mathematically manageable form comparable with the experimental kinetic data required assumptions similar to those made in the case of Slater's (1971) hypothesis. With the complementary assumptions which we made, we failed to simulate experimentally observed kinetic behavior of cytochromes b. The model could not account for the initial reduction phase, the "late maximum" or the slow reduction following exhaustion of oxygen. Further, it failed to simulate the behavior of the system in the presence of antimycin A. A modification of this model which has not been tested mathematically is the recent presentation by Chance (1972b).

The two hypotheses of oxidative phosphorylation, Wang's (Tu and Wang, 1970; Wang, 1970) and Storey's (1970, 1971), are concerned with possible chemical models for the formation of the high energy compound rather than with the actual reaction pathway of the coupled electron flow. Wang on the basis of the studies with model compounds proposes that the high energy compound formed during redox reactions is the consequence of free radical (quinolyl or imidazolyl) formation. The sequence is considered to be: imidazolyl radical → phosphoimidazolyl → high energy phosphate compound. The high energy phosphate compound, is, according to this scheme, formed within the redox chain. In contrast, the primary high energy intermediate envisaged by Storey's hypothesis (1970, 1971) contains S-S or SH-SH groups and is converted to high energy phosphate intermediate by reacting with inorganic phosphate. Both theories are not contradictory but rather complementary to other chemical hypotheses of oxidative phosphorylation.

None of the hypotheses discussed thus far were built on the basis of the kinetic studies. Availability of the kinetic data prompted us to construct a scheme (Wagner and Erecińska, 1972) which tries to incorporate the available structural information on the mitochondrial respiratory chain and account for all the features of the kinetic behavior of cytochromes b, $c + c_1$, and ubiquinone. The model is based on the following assumptions: (1) cytochromes b_{566} and c_1 form a complex, which is treated as one chemical species capable of four redox states; cytochrome c and ubiquinone are independent chemical species; (2) cytochrome c reacts with the c_1 part of cytochrome b-c_1 complex, ubiquinone reacts with the b part of the complex; cytochrome c_1 and b can react with each other only within the complex ("intracomplex reaction"); (3) the sequence of redox reactions which leads to the formation of the high energy intermediate (this process occurs within the cytochrome b-c_1 complex) requires two electrons to pass sequentially through the cytochrome b-c_1 complex. Once formed, the high energy intermediate with 600 mV equivalent energy content

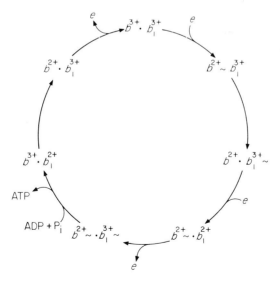

FIG. 12. Mechanism of oxidative phosphorylation at site II proposed by Slater *et al.* (1970a,b); Slater (1971).

TABLE I

LIST OF REACTIONS USED FOR SIMULATION

Reaction No.	Reactants	Products	Specific comments	Reaction group comments
1	$1/4\,O_2 + C^{red}$	$\rightarrow C^{ox} + 1/2[H_2O]$	Oxygen oxidizes cytochrome oxidase + Cyt c	These are three reactions, not directly related to Cyt b-c_1 complex; they represent 3 terminal exits to oxygen, substrate, ATP
2	$pool^{ox} + [SUB^{red}]$	$\rightarrow pool^{red} + [SUB^{ox}]$	Reduction of carriers on substrate side of Cyt b (pool)	
3	$AC(\sim) + [ADP, uncoupler]$	$\rightarrow AC^{LOW} + [ATP, HEAT]$	Dissipation of the high energy bond or ATP synthesis	
4	$C^{ox} + C_1{}^{red}B^{red}$	$\rightarrow C^{red} + C_1{}^{ox}B^{red}$	Cyt c oxidizes b-c_1 complex (1st oxidation)	The direct, irreversible redox reaction of b-c_1 complex, assumed by us to form one squiggle ($\sim$). Note, that to describe these reactions it was necessary to use (out of 12) 7 different redox and energy states of b-c_1 cyt
5	$C_1{}^{ox}B^{red}$	$\rightarrow C_1{}^{red}B^{ox}(1/2\sim)$	First intracomplex redox reaction (b gets oxidized, c_1 is reduced	
6	$C^{ox} + C_1{}^{red}B^{ox}(1/2\sim)$	$\rightarrow C^{red} + C_1{}^{ox}B^{ox}(1/2\sim)$	Cyt c oxidizes b-c_1 complex (2nd oxidation)	
7	$pool^{red} + C_1{}^{ox}B^{ox}(1/2\sim)$	$\rightarrow pool^{ox} + C_1{}^{ox}B^{red}(1/2\sim)$	Cyt b is reduced (1st reduction)	
8	$C_1{}^{ox}B^{red}(1/2\sim)$	$\rightarrow C_1{}^{red}B^{ox}(\sim)$	2nd intracomplex redox reaction (b oxidized, c reduced)	
9	$pool^{red} + C_1{}^{red}B^{ox}(\sim)$	$\rightarrow pool^{ox} + C_1{}^{red}B^{red}(\sim)$	Cyt b is reduced (2nd reduction)	
10	$C_1{}^{red}B^{red}(\sim) + AC^{LOW}$	$\rightarrow C_1{}^{red}B^{red} + AC(\sim)$	Energy transfer reaction, redox states remain unchanged, reactivity and midpoint potential change	

11	$C_1{}^{red}B^{red} + pool^{ox} \rightarrow C_1{}^{red}B^{ox} + pool^{red}$	Oxidation of b in substrate inhibited system	Reactions important in state III or in uncoupled system, inhibited with malonate, etc. Note that 2 new redox states of b-c_1 complex must be introduced (total 9)
12	$C_1{}^{red}B^{ox} + pool^{red} \rightarrow C_1{}^{red}B^{red} + pool^{ox}$	Reversible reaction to 11, important upon oxygen exhaustion	
13	$C_1{}^{red}B^{ox} + C^{ox} \rightarrow C_1{}^{ox}B^{ox} + C^{red}$	Oxidation of c_1 with b oxidized	
14	$C_1{}^{ox}B^{ox} + pool^{red} \rightarrow C_1{}^{ox}B^{red} + pool^{ox}$	Alternative to reaction 4 in substrate inhibited system	
15	$C_1{}^{red}B^{red}(\sim) + C^{ox} \rightarrow C_1{}^{ox}B^{red}(\sim) + C^{red}$	Reaction important if reaction 10 is slow	Expresses the fact that reversibility is observed in state IV.
16	$C_1{}^{ox}B^{red}(\sim) + C^{red} \rightarrow C_1{}^{red}B^{red}(\sim) + C^{ox}$	Experimentally evident reverse of electron flow	
17	$C_1{}^{ox}B^{red}(\sim) + AC^{LOW} \rightarrow C_1{}^{ox}B^{red} + AC(\sim)$	Important, if energy transfer is slower, that oxidation of c_1	Express reversibility and possible independence of the energy transfer reaction on the redox state of b-c_1 complex
18	$C_1{}^{ox}B^{red} + AC(\sim) \rightarrow C_1{}^{ox}B^{red}(\sim) + AC^{LOW}$	Probable in coupled mitochondria with no substrate inhibitors	
19	$C_1{}^{red}B^{red} + AC(\sim) \rightarrow C_1{}^{red}B^{red}(\sim) + AC^{LOW}$	Important if durohydroquinone is the substrate	
20	$C_1{}^{red}B^{ox} + AC(\sim) \rightarrow C_1{}^{red}B^{ox}(\sim) + AC^{LOW}$	Important in case of reversed electron flow	
21	$C_1{}^{red}B^{ox}(\sim) \rightarrow C_1{}^{ox}B^{red}(1/2\sim)$	Expresses reversibility of intracomplex transfer	Accumulated energy in b-c_1 complex
22	$C_1{}^{red}B^{ox}(1/2\sim) + pool^{red} \rightarrow C_1{}^{red}B^{red} + pool^{ox}$	Extremely slow reaction, dissipating accumulated energy	—

is transferred out of the complex by an enzymatic reaction; (4) additional reactions, considered in the model are the oxidation of cytochrome c with concomitant consumption of oxygen, reduction of ubiquinone by substrate and conversion of the energy accepting enzyme to the nonenergetic form (all three reactions are abbreviations of more complicated reaction pathways); (5) the first of the two electrons, contributing to the 600 mV equivalent cannot leave the complex before the second one enters.

The list of all reactions used for the simulation is presented in Table I, Fig. 13 gives a symbolic presentation of the reaction scheme analogous to the presentation of Slater's hypothesis (Fig. 12). From the comparison of the two (Table I and Fig. 13), one can easily see

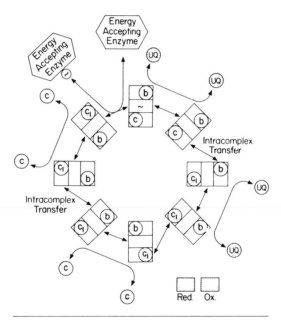

FIG. 13. Simplified mechanism of oxidative phosphorylation at site II used for the simulation studies of Wagner and Erecińska (1972) and corresponding to the reactions given in Table I.

differences in requirements for the verbal presentation of the model and the form of the scheme intended for computer simulation of the system comparable with the experimental data.

The agreement of the time-concentration dependencies of cytochromes b, $c + c_1$, and ubiquinone measured experimentally and the corresponding curves simulated by computer is good over the full range of conditions covered in this paper. The model can account for all the features of the system: for cytochrome b: fast initial reduction, subsequent oxidation leading to a steady state, "late maximum" after the exhaustion of oxygen and very slow subsequent reduction (Fig. 14); for cytochrome $c + c_1$ and ubiquinone: oxidation, steady state, reduction. Furthermore, the model can qualitatively simulate the experimentally observed behavior of the system following the perturbation by antimycin A, uncouplers, ATP and malonate.

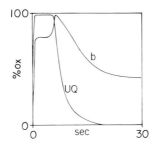

FIG. 14. Computer-simulated oxidation traces of cytochromes b and ubiquinone following the addition of 17 μM oxygen. Ordinate: concentrations of the oxidized form; abscissa: time in seconds. The model used for simulation is presented in Table I; experimental data obtained by rapid flow technique are given in Fig. 1.

The model identifies the cytochromes b with respect to energy content but does not attempt to distinguish between cytochromes b_{560} and b_{566}; the sum of the simulated b's was compared with the sum of the experimentally obtained value. In fact, in the kinetic experiments distinction between cytochromes b_{560} and b_{566} is never complete owing to the spectral overlap of the two carriers. A more complete resolution of the spectral data should permit formulation and testing of more elaborated models.

IX.   Summary

The equilibrium studies on the mitochondrial respiratory chain (for summary, cf. Wilson *et al.*, this volume) have established some basic phenomena involved in the process of the conservation of the negative free energy made available through the transfer of electrons from the substrates to oxygen. The question necessarily arises whether the respiratory chain can be treated as an equilibrium system. It has been generally assumed that state 4 (or state 4 plus ATP) represents a mean equilibrium state manifested by the fact that the direction of the net flow through the chain can be reversed, under suitable conditions, by added ATP (Chance and Hollunger, 1961; Klingenberg and Schollmeyer, 1961). Kinetic studies presented in this review concentrate on the phenomenological description of the behavior of the components performing the energy transduction at site II, cytochromes b and c_1, and their immediate neighbors — ubiquinone and cytochrome c. They demonstrate that the actual rates of electron transfer between the adjacent carriers at site II are as fast as at site III and thus in state 4 the net flow of electrons is at least three orders of magnitude slower than the forward and the reverse rates; the system can be treated as an essentially equilibrium system.

The complex behavior of cytochromes b under a variety of experimental conditions cannot be explained on the basis of the assumption that they are exclusively electron carriers. At least one of the b cytochromes, b_{566}, seems to be intimately involved in the energy conservation reaction. Kinetic data further indicate that the reaction pathway is more complicated than the sequential transfer of electrons through a linear arrangement of the carriers, and more complicated models involving parallel arrangement of two cytochromes b or a tetramer consisting of two cytochromes b, nonheme iron and cytochrome c_1 might be necessary to explain the behavior of the system. Models which involve such a scheme are briefly discussed in Section VIII. Results of the recent thermodynamic and kinetic measurements of the cytochrome system are closely connected with the application of the working hypothesis which considers the mitochondrial membrane as a two-dimensional solution to which the rules of chemistry derived for three-dimensional solution are, at least in first approximation, applicable. The possibility of verifying the ideas expressed within the chemical hypothesis of oxidative phosphorylation with the experimental data opens new perspectives for further progress.

REFERENCES

Banerjee, R., Douzou, P., and Lombard, A. (1968). *Nature (London)* **217**, 23.

Baum, H., and Rieske, J. S. (1966). *Biochem. Biophys. Res. Commun.* **24**, 1.

Baum, H., Rieske, J. S., Silman, H. I., and Lipton, S. H. (1967). *Proc. Nat. Acad. Sci. U.S.* **57**, 798.

Berden, J. A., and Slater, E. C. (1970). *Biochim. Biophys. Acta* **216**, 237.

Boveris, A., Oshino, R., Erecińska, M., and Chance, B. (1971). *Biochim. Biophys. Acta* **245**, 1.

Boveris, A., Erecińska, M., and Wagner, M. (1972). *Biochim. Biophys. Acta* **256**, 223.

Boyer, P. D. (1965). *In* "Oxidases and Related Redox Systems" (T. E. King *et al.*, eds.), Vol. 2, p. 994. Wiley, New York.

Brandon, J. R., Brocklehurst, J. R., and Lee, C. P. (1972). *Biochemistry* **11**, 1150.

Bryla, J., Kaniuga, Z., and Slater, E. C. (1969). *Biochim. Biophys. Acta* **189**, 317.

Caswell, A. H. (1968). *J. Biol. Chem.* **243**, 5827.

Chance, B. (1951). *In* "Enzymes and Enzyme Systems" (J. T. Edsall, ed.), p. 95. Harvard Univ. Press, Cambridge, Massachusetts.

Chance, B. (1952a). *Nature (London)* **169**, 215.

Chance, B. (1952b). *Abstr. Int. Congr. Biochem., 2nd, 1952* p. 32.

Chance, B. (1955). *Discuss. Faraday Soc.* **20**, 205.

Chance, B. (1958). *J. Biol. Chem.* **233**, 1223.

Chance, B. (1965). *J. Biol. Chem.* **240**, 2729.

Chance, B. (1972a). *In* "Molecular Basis for Electron Transport" (T. Schultz, ed.). Academic Press, New York, p. 65.

Chance, B. (1972b). *FEBS Lett.* **23**, 1.

Chance, B., and Baltscheffsky, M. (1958). *Biochem. J.* **68**, 283.

Chance, B., and Erecińska, M. (1971). *Arch. Biochem. Biophys.* **143**, 675.

Chance, B., and Hollunger, G. (1961). *J. Biol. Chem.* **236**, 1577.

Chance, B., and Pring, M. (1969). *Colloq. Ges. Biol. Chem.* **18**, 102.

Chance, B., and Williams, G. R. (1955). *J. Biol. Chem.* **217**, 429.

Chance, B., and Williams, G. R. (1956). *Advan. Enzymol.* **17**, 65.

Chance, B., Holmes, W. F., and Higgins, J. (1955). *J. Biol. Chem.* **217**, 439.

Chance, B., Holmes, W. F., Higgins, J., and Connelly, C. M. (1958). *Nature (London)* **182**, 1190.

Chance, B., DeVault, D., Hildreth, W. H., Parson, W., and Nishimura, M. (1966). *Brookhaven Symp. Biol.* **19**, 155.

Chance, B., DeVault, D., Legallais, V., Mela, L., and Yonetani, T. (1967). *Fast Reactions Primary Processes Chem. Kinet., Nobel Symp., 5th, 1967* p. 487.

Chance, B., Wilson, D. F., Dutton, P. L., and Erecińska, M. (1970). *Proc. Nat. Acad. Sci. U.S.* **66**, 1175.

Chance, B., Legallais, V., Sorge, J., and Graham, N. (1972). *Rev. Sci. Instrum.* **43**, 62.

Davis, K. A., Hatefi, Y., Poff, K. L., and Butler, W. L. (1972). *Biochem. Biophys. Res. Commun.* **46**, 1984.

Degn, H., and Wohlrab, H. (1971). *Biochim. Biophys. Acta* **245**, 347.

DeVault, D. (1971). *Biochim. Biophys. Acta* **225**, 193.

DeVault, D., and Chance, B. (1966). *Biophys. J.* **6**, 825.

Douzou, P., and Leterrier, F. (1970). *Biochim. Biophys. Acta* **220**, 338.

Douzou, P., Sireix, R., and Travers, F. (1970). *Proc. Nat. Acad. Sci. U.S.* **66**, 787.

Dutton, P. L. (1971). *Biochim. Biophys. Acta* **226**, 63.

Dutton, P. L., Wilson, D. F., and Lee, C. P. (1970). *Biochemistry* **9**, 5077.

Dutton, P. L., Erecińska, M., Mukai, Y., Sato, N., Pring, M., and Wilson, D. F. (1972). *Biochim. Biophys. Acta* **267**, 15.

Erecińska, M. (1972). *Fed. Proc., Fed. Amer. Soc. Exp. Biol.* **31**, 415 (abstr.).

Erecińska, M., and Chance, B. (1971). *In* "Energy Transduction in Respiration and Photosynthesis" (E. Quagliariello, S. Papa, and C. S. Rossi, eds.), p. 729. Adriatica Editrice, Bari.

Erecińska, M., and Chance, B. (1972). *Arch. Biochem. Biophys.* **151**, 304.

Erecińska, M., and Wilson, D. F. (1972). *FEBS Lett.* **24**, 269.

Erecińska, M., Wilson, D. F., Mukai, Y., and Chance, B. (1970). *Biochem. Biophys. Res. Commun.* **41**, 386.

Erecińska, M., Chance, B., Wilson, D. F., and Dutton, P. L. (1972). *Proc. Nat. Acad. Sci. U.S.* **69**, 50.

Erecińska, M., Oshino, N., Loh, P., and Brocklehurst, E. S. (1973a). *Biochim. Biophys. Acta* **292**, 1.

Erecińska, M., Chance, B., Wilson, D. F., and Dutton, P. L. (1973b). *Fed. Proc., Fed. Amer. Soc. Exp. Biol.* (in press).

302 MARIA ERECIŃSKA, MICHAL WAGNER, AND BRITTON CHANCE

Estabrook, R. W. (1962). *Biochim. Biophys. Acta* **60**, 236.
Fisher, R. J., Chen, J. C., Sani, B. P., Kaplay, S. S., and Sanadi, D. R. (1971). *Proc. Nat. Acad. Sci. U.S.* **68**, 2184.
Gibson, Q. H., and Greenwood, C. (1963). *Biochem. J.* **86**, 541.
Green, D. E., and Ji, S. (1972). *Proc. Nat. Acad. Sci. U.S.* **69**, 726.
Green, D. E., and Young, T. H. (1971). *Amer. Sci.* **59**, 92.
Holmes, W. F. (1960). Ph.D. Dissertation, University of Pennsylvania, Philadelphia, Pennsylvania.
Huber, R., Epp, O., and Formanek, H. (1970). *J. Mol. Biol.* **52**, 349.
Jacobs, E. E., and Sanadi, D. R. (1960). *J. Biol. Chem.* **235**, 531.
Keilin, D., and Hartree, E. F. (1939). *Proc. Roy. Soc. Ser. B* **127**, 167.
Klingenberg, M., and Schollmeyer, P. (1961). *Biochem. Z.* **335**, 243.
Kovàč, L., Šmigan, P., Hrušovska, E., and Hess, B. (1970). *Arch. Biochem. Biophys.* **139**, 370.
Kraayenhof, R., Katan, M. B., and Grunwald, T. (1971). *FEBS Lett.* **19**, 6.
Lee, C. P., Ernster, L., and Chance, B. (1969). *Eur. J. Biochem.* **8**, 153.
Lee, I.-Y., and Slater, E. C. (1972). *Biochim. Biophys. Acta* **256**, 587.
Lester, R., and Fleischer, S. (1961). *Biochim. Biophys. Acta* **47**, 358.
Margolis, S. A., Lenaz, G., and Baum, H. (1967). *Arch. Biochem. Biophys.* **118**, 224.
Mitchell, P. (1966a). *Biol. Rev.* **41**, 445.
Mitchell, P. (1966b). "Chemiosmotic Coupling in Oxidative and Photosynthetic Phosphorylation." Glynn Res., Bodmin, Cornwall.
Muraoka, S., and Slater, E. C. (1969). *Biochem. Biophys. Acta* **180**, 221.
Nelson, B. D., Norling, B., Nordenbrand, K., and Ernster, L. (1972). *Fed. Proc., Fed. Amer. Soc. Exp. Biol.* **31**, 416 (abstr.).
Norrish, R. G. W., and Porter, G. (1949). *Nature (London)* **164**, 658.
Norrish, R. G. W., Porter, G., and Thrush, B. A. (1953). *Proc. Roy. Soc., Ser. B* **216**, 165.
Ohnishi, T., Wilson, D. F., Asakura, T., and Chance, B. (1972). *Biochem. Biophys. Res. Commun.* **46**, 1631.
Okunuki, K., and Yakushiji, E. (1941). *Proc. Imp. Acad. (Tokyo)* **17**, 263.
Oshino, R., Oshino, N., Tamura, M., Kobilinsky, L., and Chance, B. (1972). *Biochim. Biophys. Acta* **273**, 5.
Papa, S., Scarpa, A., Lee, C. P., and Chance, B. (1972). *Biochemistry* **11**, 3091.
Perutz, M. (1970). *Nature (London)* **228**, 726.
Porter, G. (1950). *Proc. Roy. Soc., Ser. A* **200**, 284.
Pring, M. (1970). *In* "Concepts and Models in Biomathematics" (I. Heinmets, ed.), p. 75. Dekker, New York.
Pumphrey, A. M. (1962). *J. Biol. Chem.* **237**, 238.
Rieske, J. S. (1969). *Fed. Proc., Fed. Amer. Soc. Exp. Biol.* **28**, 471.
Rieske, J. S. (1971). *Arch. Biochem. Biophys.* **145**, 179.
Rieske, J. S., Zaugg, H. S., and Hansen, R. E. (1964). *J. Biol. Chem.* **239**, 3023.
Rieske, J. S., Lipton, S. H., Baum, H., and Silman, H. I. (1967). *J. Biol. Chem.* **242**, 4888.
Ruzicka, F. J., and Crane, F. L. (1970a). *Biochem. Biophys. Res. Commun.* **38**, 249.
Ruzicka, F. J., and Crane, F. L. (1970b). *Biochim. Biophys. Acta* **223**, 71.
Ruzicka, F. J., and Crane, F. L. (1971). *Biochim. Biophys. Acta* **226**, 221.
Sato, N., Wilson, D. F., and Chance, B. (1971a). *FEBS Lett.* **15**, 209.
Sato, N., Wilson, D. F., and Chance, B. (1971b). *Biochim. Biophys. Acta* **253**, 88.
Slater, E. C. (1971). *Quart. Rev. Biophys.* **4**, 35.
Slater, E. C., and Colpa-Boonstra, J. P. (1961). *In* "Haematin Enzymes" (J. E. Falk, R. Lemberg, and R. K. Morton, eds.), Vol. 2, p. 575. Pergamon, Oxford.

Slater, E. C., Lee, C. P., Berden, J. A., and Wegdam, H. J. (1970a). *Biochim. Biophys. Acta* **223**, 354.

Slater, E. C., Lee, C. P., Berden, J. A., and Wegdam, H. J. (1970b). *Nature (London)* **226**, 1248.

Storey, B. T. (1967). *Arch. Biochem. Biophys.* **121**, 271.

Storey, B. T. (1970). *J. Theor. Biol.* **28**, 233.

Storey, B. T. (1971). *J. Theor. Biol.* **31**, 533.

Strother, G. K., and Ackerman, E. (1961). *Biochim. Biophys. Acta* **47**, 317.

Tu, Inu-I, and Wang, J. H. (1970). *Biochemistry* **9**, 4505.

Tyler, D. D., Estabrook, R. W., and Sanadi, D. R. (1965). *Biochem. Biophys. Res. Commun.* **18**, 264.

Tyler, D. D., Estabrook, R. W., and Sanadi, D. R. (1966). *Arch. Biochem. Biophys.* **114**, 239.

Wagner, M., and Erecińska, M. (1971). *Arch. Biochem. Biophys.* **147**, 666.

Wagner, M., and Erecińska, M. (1972). *8th FEBS Meeting Amsterdam 1972, Abstr.* 776.

Wagner, M., Erecińska, M., and Chance, B. (1971a). *In* "Energy Transduction in Respiration and Photosynthesis" (E. Quagliariello, S. Papa, and C. S. Rossi, eds.), p. 17. Adriatica Editrice, Bari.

Wagner, M., Erecińska, M., and Pring, M. (1971b). *Arch. Biochem. Biophys.* **147**, 675.

Wang, J. H. (1970). *Science* **167**, 25.

Wegdam, H. J., Berden, J. A., and Slater, E. C. (1970). *Biochim. Biophys. Acta* **223**, 365.

Wikström, M. K. F. (1971). *Biochim. Biophys. Acta* **253**, 832.

Wilson, D. F., and Dutton, P. L. (1970). *Biochem. Biophys. Res. Commun.* **39**, 59.

Wilson, D. F., and Dutton, P. L. (1971). *In* "Electron and Coupled Energy Transfer in Biological Systems" (T. E. King, and M. Klingenberg, eds.), Vol. 1, Part A, p. 221. Dekker, New York.

Wilson, D. F., Erecińska, M., Dutton, P. L., and Tsudzuki, T. (1970). *Biochem. Biophys. Res. Commun.* **41**, 1273.

Wilson, D. F., Koppelman, M. C., Erecińska, M., and Dutton, P. L. (1971). *Biochem. Biophys. Res. Commun.* **44**, 759.

Wilson, D. F., Dutton, P. L., Erecińska, M., Lindsay, J. G., and Sato, N. (1972a). *Accounts Chem. Res.* **5**, 234.

Wilson, D. F., Erecińska, M., Leigh, J. S., and Koppelman, M. C. (1972b). *Arch. Biochem. Biophys.* **151**, 112.

Wohlrab, H. (1970). *Biochemistry* **9**, 474.

Yonetani, T., and Ray, G. S. (1966). *J. Biol. Chem.* **241**, 700.

Mitochondrial Coupling Factors

R. Brian Beechey
Shell Research Limited,
Woodstock Agricultural Research Centre,
Sittingbourne, Kent, and
Chelsea College, Manresa Road,
London, England
and Kenneth J. Cattell[1]
Shell Research Limited,
Woodstock Agricultural Research Centre,
Sittingbourne, Kent, England

[1]Present address: Department of Biological Sciences, The Polytechnic, Wolverhampton, England.

I. Introduction

One approach to the elucidation of the mechanism of a multienzyme process is to fractionate and study the component enzymes, and then use them in experiments designed to reconstitute the complete active system. This approach has been used successfully with many soluble multienzyme systems and with some degree of success with membrane-bound enzymatic systems, including the mitochondrial electron transfer chain. However, the intensive research efforts made along these lines during the past 15 years have not yet led to the positive identification of the components of the mitochondrial membrane which are involved in the synthesis of ATP. The purpose of this review is to summarize the progress made in the elucidation of the mechanism of oxidative phosphorylation using this approach, to critically discuss the rationale, the methods used, and the results obtained in the isolation and identification of coupling factors, and to suggest areas of future investigation. It is not within the scope of this review to describe in detail the properties of individual coupling factors, except where they are pertinent to the general discussion. If the impression gained by reading this review is one of pessimism and scepticism concerning the results obtained to date, it is more a reflection on the intractibility of the problem and the lack of a suitable technology rather than on the efforts of workers involved in this area of biochemistry.

For the purpose of this discussion, coupling factors are defined as being materials of mitochondrial origin which are essential for the process of energy conservation to function (Beechey and Cattell, 1972). Recent studies suggest (Skulachev, 1971; Racker, 1970a) that a substantially intact vesicular membrane is required for energy conservation reactions to proceed, thus it could be argued that all membrane components, i.e., proteins, lipids, proteolipids, glycoproteins, etc., are coupling factors. It is improbable that all these constituents are intermediates or catalyze the interaction of intermediates in ATP synthesis, therefore two types of coupling factors are postulated. (1) *Structural coupling factors* are required for maintaining the membrane in a conformation that permits those coupling factors directly involved in ATP synthesis to function. (2) *Functional coupling factors* are those components of the membrane that are directly involved in ATP synthesis in a true catalytic role.

In practice these roles are not mutually exclusive (Penefsky, 1964). Thus it is easy to envisage a functional coupling factor also having a critical structural role and until the mechanism of ATP synthesis is established, it is obviously going to be difficult to assess the precise role that a coupling factor plays in the process of ATP synthesis.

II. Problems Encountered in the Isolation, Identification, and Assay of Coupling Factors

Before discussing the problems that face investigators involved in the isolation, identification, and assay of coupling factors, it is worthwhile to summarize some of the characteristic features that one would expect an idealized coupling factor to possess.

1. The mitochondrial membrane loses its ability to synthesize ATP when the coupling factor is extracted from the membrane. This function can be restored when the coupling factor recombines with a membrane preparation specifically depleted of the coupling factor.

2. The ability of the mitochondrial membrane to catalyze those partial reactions of oxidative phosphorylation which do not require the coupling factor in either a structural or a functional role is not impaired by removal of the coupling factor.

3. The amount of coupling factor required, to be added or, more precisely, bound to the depleted membrane preparation in order to restore its ATP-synthesizing ability, should be similar to the concentration present in unextracted membranes.

Obviously these requirements are too stringent to be met by the use of present methods for the solubilization and purification of membrane constituents. Three of the major problems in this work arise through lack of intrinsic enzymatic activity, the heterogeneity of most individual coupling factor preparations and the lack of specifically depleted and characterized mitochondrial membrane preparations.

A. LACK OF KNOWN INTRINSIC ENZYMATIC ACTIVITY OF COUPLING FACTORS

Coupling factors are components of an uncharacterized multienzyme complex. The elucidation of the intermediate reactions in the process catalyzed by this complex is the main aim of the work under review. The lack of knowledge of these reactions makes the assay of coupling factor activity very difficult. This problem does not apply with factors A, F_1, $F_1.X$ and A.D (Andreoli et al., 1965; Warshaw et al., 1968; Pullman et al., 1958, 1960; Vallejos et al., 1968) since they all have apparent or latent ATPase activity. Factor A.D also catalyzes the ATP–P_i and ATP–ADP exchange reactions. These reactions can therefore be used to monitor the purification of the coupling factor. Whether or not the ATPase activity of these preparations is essential for their coupling factor activity will be discussed later.

Coupling factors with no known enzymatic activity are usually assayed by adding aliquots of solutions containing the coupling factor to suspensions of membranes deficient of an energy-linked function, e.g., a complete or decreased ability to catalyze one or more of the following partial reactions of oxidative phosphorylation, ATPase, ATP–P$_i$ exchange, ATP-dependent reduction of NAD by succinate and the energy-driven transhydrogenase reactions. Unfortunately the synthesis of ATP catalyzed by the membranes is not often used as a routine assay. The ability of the added coupling factor to stimulate or restore the chosen reaction catalyzed by the membranes is used as a measure of coupling factor activity. In many cases (see Tables I and III), the activity of the coupling factor under test is manifest or optimal

TABLE I   SUMMARY OF THE PREPARATION AND PROPERTIES OF COUPLING

Factor	Preparation	Homogeneity	Assay procedure
B	An acetone powder of lyophilized beef heart mitochondria is extracted with Tris buffer pH 7.5 containing dithiothreitol. A 30–55% ammonium sulfate cut of the extract is collected and redissolved in Tris buffer. After desalting on Sephadex G-25 the extract is applied to a DEAE-cellulose column. The sample is eluted with 270 mM Tris buffer and concentrated by precipitation with ammonium sulfate, redissolved in 2 mM Tris buffer, desalted on Sephadex, and applied to a CM-cellulose column. After the column is washed, factor B is eluted with 10 mM Tris buffer	Homogeneous by ultracentrifugation, density gradient centrifugation and polyacrylamide gel electrophoresis. A single precipitation band is observed on immuno-electrophoresis using semipurified antibody preparation	Stimulation of the ATP-dependent reduction of NAD by succinate catalyzed by AE-particles at 38°
B′	Essentially the method is the same as that for factor B. Factor B′ is present in the washings of the CM-cellulose column	No data available	As for factor B

only when additional coupling factor preparations are present in the incubation. In order to understand the precise role of the coupling factor in such a complex assay, it is essential that the variables be reduced to a minimum. Thus the depleted membrane preparation and the supplementary coupling factors should be purified and well characterized. Unfortunately, this is rarely the case and is a major reason for the confusion concerning the possible function of putative coupling factors.

FACTORS WHICH HAVE NO KNOWN ENZYMATIC ACTIVITY

Properties	Coupling factor activity	Relationships to other known coupling factors	References
Molecular weight 29,200. Contains two SH groups. Amino acid composition known	Addition of 2 nmoles of factor B mg^{-1} A particles protein gives maximal increase in P:O ratio, ATP–P$_i$ exchange, and ATP-dependent pyridine nucleotide transhydrogenase reactions. Slightly inhibits the ATPase activity of A-particles. The coupling factor activity of factor B is inhibited by treatment with sulfhydryl reagents or iodine	Probably identical with factor F_2	Lam *et al.* (1967, 1969), Lam (1968), Lam and Yang (1969), Racker *et al.* (1970)
Molecular weight approximately 45,000 s_{20w} = 3.47 S	Reacts with antibody prepared against factor B. Sensitive to sulfhydryl reagents	Factor B' is possibly factor B complexed with another membrane protein. The latter could be factor C	Lam *et al.* (1970)

(Continued)

TABLE I (*Continued*)

Factor	Preparation	Homogeneity	Assay procedure
F_2	There are two methods published for the preparation of factor F_2. (1) An acetone powder of heavy layer beef heart mitochondria is extracted under nitrogen with 0.1 M phosphate buffer pH 7.4 and then with 60 mM glycine pH 10.5. The supernatant is adjusted to pH 7.5 and 4 mM ATP added. Calcium phosphate gel is added and the gel is collected by centrifugation. It is washed 3 times with 0.3 M phosphate buffer pH 7.4 and ATP added to 4 mM. The desorbed material is further purified either by chromatography on a biogel P-100 column or by desalting on Sephadex G-50 and chromatography on CM-cellulose as for factor B (2)The supernatant solution of the 40% ammonium sulfate precipitation step of factor F_5 preparation is brought to 60% saturation. The precipitated material is adsorbed on calcium phosphate gel and eluted as in method 1	No data available	(1) the stimulation of P:O ratio in A particles supplemented with excess factors F_3 or F_4. (2) As for factor B
C	The final purification step in the preparation of factor B is chromatography on	No data available	As for factor B

Properties	Coupling factor activity	Relationships to other known coupling factors	References
	Direct evidence that phosphorylation at sites I and III is stimulated	Probably identical with factor B. There are few published data which show that the protein isolated by method 2 is identical to that prepared by method 1. Factor B is present in preparations of factor F_4	
	Stimulates the aerobic pyridine nucleotide transhydrogenase activity of AE particles	The ability to stimulate aerobic energy-linked transhydrogenase activity of AE	Fisher et al. (1971a), Lam et al. (1970)

(Continued)

TABLE I (*Continued*)

Factor	Preparation	Homogeneity	Assay procedure
C (*Continued*)	CM-cellulose. Factor C is present in the fraction which passes through the column in the washings		
OSCP, oligomycin sensitivity conferring protein (basic coupling factor, BCF)	The ATPase molecules are extracted from an oligomycin-sensitive ATPase preparation using 3.5 M NaBr. The residue is extracted twice with 1.2 N NH$_4$OH, and the extracts are adjusted to pH 8. After clarification by centrifugation ammonium sulfate is added to 40%. The precipitate is dissolved in Tris buffer, pH 8, and either chromatographed on CM-cellulose using a NaCl gradient or by gel filtration through Sephadex G-50. An OSCP can also be extracted from factor F_4 or F_c	Polyacrylamide gel electrophoresis in the presence of sodium dodecylsulfate or phenol–acetic acid reveals one major band and other minor bands. Polymerizes in solution, this is prevented by 0.5 M NaBr	No specific assay system
F_{c_1}	Bulos and Racker (1968a) named the preparation from factor F_4 factor F_c but later changed this to factor F_{c_1} (Knowles *et al.*, 1971)	Polyacrylamide gel electrophoresis shows F_{c_1} to be heterogeneous	Factor F_c is assayed by its ability to confer oligomycin sensitivity on factor F_1 in the presence of TUA particles
BCF	The OSCP preparation isolated from	None presented	As for factor B

Properties	Coupling factor activity	Relationships to other known coupling factors	References
		particles appears to differentiate this factor from factors A, A.D, B, OSCP, F_4, F_5, and F_6. The reviewers find it difficult to differentiate between factors C and B′ on the basis of the published data	
Molecular weight 18,000 by gel filtration and 17,000–40,000 by electron microscopy. Has typical protein UV spectrum and is inactivated by trypsin	Binds factor F_1 to depleted membranes with the reappearance of inner membrane spheres. This ATPase activity is oligomycin sensitive and cold stable. In the presence of factor F_1 OSCP stimulates the following reactions catalyzed by A particles; ATP-driven pyridine nucleotide transhydrogenase, ATP–P_i exchange, ATP synthesis, ATP-driven reduction of NAD by sucinate. OSCP decreases the permeability of ASU particles to protons (Hinkle and Horstmann, 1971)	Present in factors F_4, F_3, F_c, F_5, F_6, $F_1.X$. This protein is not the site of oligomycin action	MacLennan and Tzagoloff (1968), MacLennan and Asai (1968), Sanadi et al. (1971)
		Can replace factors F_3 and F_5 in certain assays	Fessenden-Raden et al. (1969), Senior (1971)
	This preparation has all of the properties of OSCP listed		Beechey et al. (1969a,b)

(Continued)

TABLE I (*Continued*)

Factor	Preparation	Homogeneity	Assay procedure
BCF (*Continued*)	factor F_3 by chromatography on CM-cellulose is designated basic coupling factor (BCF)		
F_{c_2}	TUA-particles are extracted with 2 M NaSCN, pH 8.0 for 10 min at 4°. The supernatant obtained after centrifugation is dialyzed and clarified by recentrifugation. Ammonium sulfate is added to 60–65% saturation. The precipitate is collected and resuspended in Tris buffer pH 7.5 and desalted on Sephadex G-25. The active material is chromatographed on a DEAE-Sephadex A-25 column, eluted with a NaCl gradient. The active fractions are pooled, dialyzed and the process repeated. A third DEAE-Sephadex A-25 chromatography step with gradient elution gives three poorly resolved bands, all of which have factor F_{c_2} activity	No data available. A 10-fold purification and a 1.5% yield is achieved in the preparation	Assayed as the amount of factor F_{c_2} protein which inhibits 0.1 units of factor F_1 activity in the presence of 20 μg of TUA-STA-particle protein, excess factor F_{c_1} (OSCP) and 5 nmoles of DCCD
D	Prepared from a crude sonic extract of mitochondria. The pre-	No data presented but described as "purified"	As for factor B

Properties	Coupling factor activity	Relationships to other known coupling factors	References
	above. It was also shown to stimulate the aerobic energy-linked pyridine nucleotide transhydrogenase		
Heat stable	Appears to promote the binding of factor F_1 to TUA-STA-particles but does not result in significant conferral of DCCD-sensitivity. Bovine plasma albumin must be added to the assay medium	Has many properties in common with factor F_6	Knowles *et al.* (1971)
MW 53,000 as determined by electrophoresis	No ATPase activity. The stimulation of the ATP-driven reduction of NAD	Does not react with antibodies prepared against factors F_1 or	Sani *et al.* (1970), Fisher *et al.* (1971b), Sanadi

(Continued)

TABLE I (*Continued*)

Factor	Preparation	Homogeneity	Assay procedure
D (*Continued*)	parative procedure is similar to that used for factor A except for the presence of 5 mM phosphate buffer, pH 7.5. Extracts are chromatographed on DEAE-cellulose and eluted with 10 mM, 50 mM, 80 mM, and 150 mM phosphate buffer, pH 7.5. The material eluted with 150 mM phosphate buffer, factor A.D is then incubated with 2 M urea at 0° for 1 hour. The urea is removed by dialysis and protamine sulfate added to 1%. The precipitate is removed by centrifugation. Factor D is in the supernatant		
F$_3$	There are three different methods published for the preparation of F$_3$. In the most commonly used method, beef heart mitochondria are sonicated at pH 9.0. After centrifugation the pH is adjusted to 8.0 and the supernatant is applied to a DEAE-cellulose column, which is washed with 20	No data presented. Purification protocol gives 8-fold increase in specific activity. Polyacrylamide gel electrophoresis at pH 2.3 and 8.5 reveals over 10 bands (C. R. Lindop, unpublished observations, 1970)	As for factor B or by the measurement of the stimulation of ATP synthesis catalyzed by A particles in the presence of factors F$_1$ and F$_2$

Properties	Coupling factor activity	Relationships to other known coupling factors	References
in polyacryla-mide gels con-taining sodium dodecylsulfate	by succinate is inhibited by pretreatment of factor D with mercurials	F_2. Does not have OSCP-like activity	*et al.* (1971), Sani and Sanadi (1971)
Has a tendency to polymerize	Confers oligomycin sensi-tivity on factor F_1 ATPase in the presence of either factor F_4 or TUA-particles. Increases the P:O ratio and stimulates the ATP-driven reduction of NAD by succi-nate and ATP–P_i exchange reactions catalyzed by A-particles	Contains a protein very similar to OSCP. Factor F_3 is present in factor F_4 prepara-tions. There are no published data that specifically demon-strate a relationship between the end products of the three different methods of preparation	Racker (1962), Fessenden and Racker (1967), Fessenden-Raden *et al.* (1969), Fes-senden *et al.* (1966), Beechey *et al.* (1969a,b), Senior (1971)

(*Continued*)

TABLE I (*Continued*)

Factor	Preparation	Homogeneity	Assay procedure
F_3 (*Continued*)	mM Tris sulfate, pH 8.0 and eluted with 0.1 M ammonium sulfate in 20 mM Tris sulfate. The active fractions are combined and the ammonium sulfate concentrations adjusted to 50% saturation. The precipitate is resuspended in 50 mM Tris sulfate pH 8.0 and reprecipitated with ammonium sulfate. The precipitate is redissolved and adsorbed on calcium phosphate gel. This is successively eluted with 0.1, 0.2, and 0.3 M phosphate buffer pH 8.0. The active fractions are precipitated with ammonium sulfate and resuspended in 50 mM phosphate buffer. The two other methods of preparation are from factor F_4 (Fessenden-Raden, 1972) and that described by Racker (1962), no subsequent reports of this work have appeared in the literature		
F_4	Beef heart mitochondria are extracted with an alkaline KCl solution. Ammonium sulfate is	Using polyacrylamide gel electrophoresis in the presence of phenol–acetic acid,	By the stimulation of the P:O ratio measured using P particles

Properties	Coupling factor activity	Relationships to other known coupling factors	References
Electron micros- copy shows factor F_4 prepara- tion to be amor-		Contains OSCP, factors F_2, F_3, and F_c and probably factor F_1 subunits	Conover and Zalkin (1967), Conover et al. (1963), Zalkin

(Continued)

TABLE I (*Continued*)

Factor	Preparation	Homogeneity	Assay procedure
F_1 (*Continued*)	added to the extract, and the precipitate is collected and redissolved in buffer solution. Ammonium sulfate is then added to 0.48 M. The precipitate is resuspended and assayed for factor F_4 activity. If ammonium sulfate (to 1.4 M) is added to the supernatant a second precipitate which also has factor F_4 activity is formed. This dissolves in a small volume of 0.02 M Tris pH 7.4 and can be dialyzed against 0.2 M KCl, but precipitates when the solution is diluted	at least 8 components are separated. Two major bands on the gel correspond to similar bands present in factor F_1 preparations	
F_5	Heavy layer beef heart mitochondria are suspended in 25 mM phosphate buffer pH 6.8 containing 10 mM EDTA and 2 M urea and sonicated. After centrifugation some protein impurities are precipitated by adjusting to pH 5.4. Yeast RNA is added to the supernatant, and the precipitated material is collected. This procedure is repeated twice with the subsequent supernatants. The activity is usually in the	A 400-fold increase in specific activity was obtained with 133% recovery. Electrophoresis on Sephaphose (no details given) showed a single major band both in factor F_5 and F_5–F_3 preparations. Analytical ultracentrifugation at pH 10–11.5 showed two components, 11.5 S and 3.7 S, which appeared to be related	The ability to stimulate the ATP-driven reduction of NAD by succinate in ASU particles supplemented with factors F_2 and F_3

Properties	Coupling factor activity	Relationships to other known coupling factors	References
phous. Addition of phospholipids gives rise to a vesicular preparation			and Racker (1965), Fessenden and Racker (1966), MacLennan and Tzagoloff (1968), Kagawa and Racker (1966c), Bulos and Racker (1968a)
Some evidence that the protein undergoes polymerization	Appears to stimulate ATP synthesis by ASU particles in the presence of factors F_1, F_2, and F_3 but the data are not specific; some essential controls are not reported. Addition of factor F_6 to TUA particles and factor F_1 confers some oligomycin sensitivity on the ATPase activity. Activity inhibited by iodine treatment	Some fractions of factor F_5 show considerable factor F_3 activity; these preparations also show some OSCP activity. Authors state that the relationships between factors F_5, F_3, and OSCP are ambiguous	Fessenden-Raden et al. (1969)

(Continued)

TABLE I (*Continued*)

Factor	Preparation	Homogeneity	Assay procedure
F_5 (*Continued*)	second precipitate. This precipitate is resuspended in 50 mM phosphate buffer pH 7.2 containing 10 mM EDTA. Protamine sulfate solution is added until no further material is precipitated. The supernatant is collected, and ammonium sulfate is added to 40% saturation. The precipitates are then taken up in 50 mM phosphate buffer pH 5.5. Calcium phosphate gel is added and eluted with phosphate buffer. The active fractions are adsorbed onto alumina C gel and eluted with phosphate buffer. The active material is concentrated by precipitation with ammonium sulfate and stored at $-70°$ in the presence of dithiothreitol		
F_6	Beef heart mitochondria are extracted with phosphate/borate buffer pH 7.5 for 16–18 hours, then with n-butanol at pH 9 for 20 hours. The extract is adjusted to pH 6.0	This material appears to be a complex of proteins, many of which show factor F_6 activity in the assay systems. These "isoproteins" have been separated using	No specific assay procedure

Properties	Coupling factor activity	Relationships to other known coupling factors	References
Heat stable, trypsin labile	Factor F_6 is required in addition to factors F_1, F_2, F_3, and F_5 to stimulate the ATP–P_i exchange, P:O ratio, aerobic and ATP-driven reduction of NAD by succinate and the aerobic and ATP-driven	—	Fessenden-Raden (1972)

(*Continued*)

TABLE I (*Continued*)

Factor	Preparation	Homogeneity	Assay procedure
F_6 (*Continued*)	before treatment with calcium phosphate gel. Factor F_6 is eluted from the gel with ammonium sulfate. The combined eluates are heated at 90° for 5 minutes. The soluble material is concentrated by lyophilization, redissolved, and dialyzed vs EDTA solutions and then water	preparative polyacrylamide gel electrophoresis and isoelectric focusing	

B. PREPARATION OF SPECIFICALLY DEPLETED MITOCHONDRIAL MEMBRANES

Ideally the membrane preparations used to assay isolated coupling factors should be specifically depleted of the coupling factor under test and should lack only the functions dependent upon the presence of this coupling factor. The most simple system would be one in which the depleted membrane was a by-product in the preparation of the coupling factor. Since this is technically impractical, most depleted membrane preparations are made by subjecting submitochondrial particles to procedures of varying harshness, such that they lose the ability to catalyze certain partial reactions of oxidative phosphorylation. The depleted membranes listed in Table II are made by procedures which include the treatment of submitochondrial particles with urea, detergents, sonication, trypsin, silicotungstic acid, etc. It would be naive to assume that these procedures give membranes depleted of specific components, and there is little published evidence that this is so. The depleted membranes are usually defined in terms of (i) the procedures used to prepare them; (ii) the lack of certain functions in the membranes when compared to submitochondrial particles; (iii) the coupling factors that must be added to restore these functions.

The rationale behind this approach is to prepare a fundamental, nonphosphorylating membranous framework containing an intact electron transfer chain into which the isolated and purified com-

Properties	Coupling factor activity	Relationships to other known coupling factors	References
	pyridine nucleotide transhydrogenase reactions catalyzed by STA particles		

ponents of the ATP-synthesizing mechanism can be built until oxidative phosphorylation is restored. If this is to be done successfully, we believe that the depleted membrane should be characterized with respect to the proteins and other components removed during its preparation.

The techniques available for separating and characterizing membrane proteins are not yet sufficiently advanced to give complete and unambiguous analyses. However, polyacrylamide gel electrophoresis goes some way toward this and has found application in studies on coupling factors. For example, Tzagoloff et al. (1968) have shown that washing an oligomycin-sensitive ATPase preparation with 3.5 M NaBr results in a loss of ATPase activity. Polyacrylamide gel electrophoresis in the presence of phenol–acetic acid–urea showed that the loss of ATPase activity could be related to the loss of specific proteins from the ATPase preparation and to their appearance in the washings. Beechey and Cattell (1972) have used polyacrylamide gel electrophoresis in the presence of sodium dodecyl sulfate to show the absence of bands corresponding to factor F_1 in SUU particles. These bands can be detected when preparations of submitochondrial particles or SUU particles reconstituted with factor F_1 are electrophoresed.

Electron microscopy using negative staining techniques has been employed by Racker et al. (1964, 1965) to correlate the loss of ATPase activity with the removal of inner-membrane spheres from T particles during urea treatment. However, this apparently clear-cut result should be treated with some caution, since Kagawa and Racker (1966c) stated that urea treatment leads to loss of ATPase activity at a rate faster than the apparent loss of inner-membrane spheres. In addition T particles which had been combined with [³H]acetyl F_1 lost their ATPase activity and inner-membrane spheres during a 5-hour treatment with urea, but 25% of the radioactivity remained bound to the membranes. These results indicate that either inactive ATPase mole-

TABLE II

SUMMARY OF THE PREPARATION AND PROPERTIES OF MITOCHONDRIAL

Name and abbreviation	Method of preparation	Some characteristic properties
Submitochondrial particles SMP, SP_{HL}, ETP	Sonication of beef heart mitochondria suspended in various media supplemented with ATP, succinate, Mn^{2+}, Mg^{2+}, etc. SMP are isolated by differential centrifugation	Catalyze (1) the synthesis of ATP coupled to the oxidation of either NADH, succinate or ascorbate-TMPD, (2) aerobic and ATP-driven pyridine nucleotide transhydrogenase, (3) energy-dependent reduction of NAD, (4) $H_2^{18}O–P_i$ exchange reaction, (5) $H_3P^{18}O_4–ATP$ exchange, etc.
Urea particles, U-particles SP_{HL}U-particles	SMP incubated under various conditions with urea solutions (1–4 M)	Low ATPase and ATP–P_i exchange activities. These activities can be restored by reconstituting urea particles with purified ATPase preparations
Ammonia particles A, AE, or EDTA particles	Beef heart mitochondria are suspended in 0.25 M sucrose solution containing 0.6–0.1 mM EDTA. The pH is adjusted to between 8.5 and 9.2 with NH_4OH. The suspension is sonicated, and the particles are isolated by differential centrifugation	Particles prepared at higher pH do not have succinate dehydrogenase activity. ATP synthesis, ATP-driven and aerobic transhydrogenase, and ATP-driven and aerobic transhydrogenase, and ATP-driven reduction of NAD by succinate activities are low, but can be increased by the additions of low concentrations of oligomycin (Lee and Ernster, 1965) or DCCD (Roberton et al., 1968)
AEU particles	AE-particles are treated with 3 M urea/0.125 M sucrose for 10 min at 0°. AEU particles are isolated by centrifugation	ATP-driven reduction of NAD by succinate activity is low, but can be increased by addition of factor B

cules or subunits (Penefsky and Warner, 1965) remain bound to the membrane despite urea treatment.

Immunological techniques have not been used extensively in the characterization of mitochondrial membrane constituents, but their successful use in experiments to prove the common identity of factors F_2 and B (Racker *et al.*, 1970) indicates that they could make valuable contributions to the characterization of coupling factors.

MEMBRANE PREPARATIONS USED IN THE ASSAY OF COUPLING FACTORS

Coupling factor requirements	Physical properties	References
None specifically	Membrane vesicles with inner membrane spheres on external surface	Andreoli *et al.* (1965), Racker (1962), Hansen and Smith (1964), Linnane and Ziegler (1958)
ATPase (factor A or factor F_1)	No inner membrane spheres. No characteristic bands of ATPase on polyacrylamide gels	Racker (1962), Andreoli *et al.* (1965), Beechey and Cattell (1972)
If prepared at pH 9.2 no specific coupling factor depletions. Addition of either ATPase or ATPase subunits together with factors OSCP, F_3, F_2, B, F_c, F_4, F_5, and F_1-X will stimulate energy-linked reactions. If prepared at pH 8.5–8.8 then addition of factor B alone will stimulate energy-linked reactions	Membrane vesicles	Lam *et al.* (1967), Fessenden and Racker (1966), Lee *et al.* (1964), Lam *et al.* (1969, 1970), McLennan and Paulson (1970)
Factors B, C, and A	—	Lam *et al.* (1970)

(*Continued*)

TABLE II (*Continued*)

Name and abbreviation	Method of preparation	Some characteristic properties
N particles	Beef heart mitochondria are suspended in 0.25 M-sucrose/2 mM EDTA pH 7.4 and shaken with glass beads at 4° in a Nossal shaker. N particles are isolated by centrifugation	Originally used to assay the coupling factor activity of factor F_1
P particles	Beef heart mitochondria are suspended in 0.25 M sucrose/0.5 mM EDTA pH 7.4 and 2% phosphatide suspension and sonicated for 2 min. The P particles are sedimented, washed in 0.25 M sucrose/0.5 mM EDTA pH 7.4 and 1% phosphatide solution and resuspended in 0.25 M sucrose	Used to assay the coupling factor activity of factor F_4. Has a low P:O ratio and low activity in catalyzing the ATP–P_i exchange and the ATP-driven reduction of NAD by succinate reactions
T particles	SMP treated with trypsin	Catalyzes the phosphorylation of ADP. High ATPase activity. Low ATP–P_i exchange. Oxidizes both succinate and NADH
TU particles	T particles are incubated in 2 M urea at 0° for 45 min and then collected by centrifugation	Low ATPase activity. Will recombine with factors F_1 or A to give an oligomycin-sensitive ATPase
TUU particles	TU particles retreated with urea as above	ATPase activity almost completely lost. Will recombine with factor F_1
TUT particles	TU particles treated with trypsin at 20° for 5 min at pH 7.4	Do not confer oligomycin sensitivity on added ATPase
TUA particles	TU particles in 0.25 M sucrose-ammonia solu-	In the presence of Mg^{2+} will bind F_1, the resultant ATPase

Coupling factor requirements	Physical properties	References
Not obvious, must be deficient in ATPase since the supernatant is used as a source of crude factor F_1 and factor F_1 stimulates ATP synthesis catalyzed by N particles. No data are available to indicate the extent of this depletion in factor F_1	—	Penefsky et al. (1960)
Factors F_1 and F_4 required for stimulation of the ATP-driven reduction of NAD by succinate. Factor F_3 also stimulates this reaction. The data regarding the deficiency in factor F_4 must be treated with caution (see text)	—	Conover et al. (1963)
—	Vesicles which have inner membrane spheres (Racker et al., 1965)	Racker (1962, 1963)
Factor F_1/A	Membrane vesicles with fewer inner membrane spheres than have SMP	Racker (1963), Racker et al. (1965), Kagawa and Racker (1966c)
Factor F_1/A	Vesicles, no inner membrane spheres	Kagawa and Racker (1966a)
Factors F_1/A, OSCP factor F_c	—	Kagawa and Racker (1966c)
Factors F_1/A, OSCP factor F_{c_i}	—	Bulos and Racker (1968a,b), Knowles et al.

(Continued)

TABLE II (*Continued*)

Name and abbreviation	Method of preparation	Some characteristic properties
TUA particles (*Continued*)	tion, pH 10.4, are sonicated. The particles are collected by centrifugation	activity is not oligomycin sensitive. However, in the presence of OSCP or factor F_c the bound ATPase is oligomycin sensitive. This complex is stable to trypsin treatment and heating at 55° for 12 min, but heat treatment of either TUA particles or factor F_c results in loss of oligomycin sensitivity
TUA–STA particles	TUA particles are incubated at 4° for 10 min in 0.15 M sucrose, pH 8, containing 1.5% silicotungstate. The suspension is diluted 10-fold and the particles are collected by centrifugation. They are resuspended and stored in 0.25 M sucrose–5 mM dithiothreitol	Require factor F_c or OSCP for conferral of oligomycin sensitivity on ATPase
STA particles	A suspension of A particles prepared at either pH 9.2 or 9.8 are added dropwise with stirring to a cold solution containing 0.15 M-sucrose and either 0.4% or 1% silicotungstate buffered to pH 5.5. The particles are collected by centrifugation	Oxidize NADH but not succinate. Low ATPase, ATP–P_i exchange ATP-driven reaction of NAD by succinate and ATP synthesis activities. Bovine serum albumin is essential for reconstitution of energy conservation reactions. The low level of aerobic energy-linked pyridine nucleotide transhydrogenase activity (TMPD and ascorbate as substrate) is increased by small amounts of oligomycin
ASU particles	A suspension of A particles are passed down a column of Sephadex G-50. The particles are collected by centrifugation at room temperature, resuspended	Low ATPase activity. Combines with factor F_1 to give an oligomycin-sensitive ATPase. Requires addition of factors F_1, F_2, and F_3 to give maximum rates of ATP synthesis. NADH in very small amounts is re-

Coupling factor requirements	Physical properties	References
Factors F_1, F_c, F_{c_2}, possibly factors B/F_2 and F_6	—	Knowles *et al.* (1971)
For particles prepared with 1% STA F_1, F_2, F_3, F_5, and F_6 (?). For particles prepared with 0.4% STA pH 9.8 factors A, OSCP, F_5, and F_6	Vesicles having no inner membrane spheres	Racker *et al.* (1969), Fisher *et al.* (1971a)
Factors F_1, F_2, F_3, and F_5 give enhanced rates of ATP synthesis, etc., but no evidence that the particles are greatly depleted of these factors. Factors F_1, F_3, and F_5 can act in structural role.	—	Racker and Horstmann (1967), Fessenden-Raden (1969), Fisher *et al.* (1971a)

(Continued)

TABLE II (*Continued*)

Name and abbreviation	Method of preparation	Some characteristic properties
ASU particles (*Continued*)	in 0.25 M-sucrose and cooled to 0°. This suspension is diluted 1:1 with a solution containing 4 M urea and the particles are isolated by centrifugation and resuspended in 0.25 M sucrose, 5 mM dithiothreitol	quired to give maximum rates for the ATP-driven reduction of NAD by succinate. Has a low aerobic energy-linked pyridine nucleotide trans-hydrogenase activity (TMPD + ascorbate as substrate) which is stimulated by small amounts of oligomycin
SU particles	Prepared in the same way as ASU particles except that SMP are used in place of A particles	Very high ATPase activity after passage through Sephadex G-50. Low ATP-driven reduction of NAD by succinate activity which is stimulated by the addition of factors F_1, F_2, F_3, and a crude, uncharacterized mitochondrial extract
F_0	TU particles are suspended in 0.25 M sucrose and sonicated for 4 min. The clear supernatant obtained after centrifugation is designated F_0	This preparation contains the entire respiratory chain. Confers oligomycin sensitivity on the ATPase activity of factor F_1
CF_0	TU particles are extracted with potassium cholate and ammonium sulfate. The supernatant after centrifugation is made 33% saturated with ammonium sulfate. CF_0 is collected by centrifugation	Inhibits the ATPase activity of factor F_1, but the addition of phospholipids restores the ATPase activity, which is oligomycin sensitive. Low NADH and succinate dehydrogenase activities
$CF_0 F_1$	As for CF_0 except that T particles are used in place of TU particles	Low succinate and NADH dehydrogenase and ATPase activities. The addition of phospholipids stimulates the ATPase activity which is sensitive to oligomycin and DCCD

Coupling factor requirements	Physical properties	References
A combination of OSCP, factors A and F_5 will give high activation of ATP-driven reduction of NAD by succinate		
—	Membrane vesicles having no inner membrane spheres	Racker and Horstmann (1967)
—	—	Racker (1963), Kagawa and Racker (1966a)
—	Electron microscopy shows that CF_0 is an amorphous membrane preparation. On recombination with factor F_1 some structures comparable to inner membrane spheres are visible	Kagawa and Racker (1966b,c)
—	An amorphous membrane preparation with structures comparable to inner membrane spheres	Kagawa and Racker (1966b,c), Holloway et al. (1966)

C. The Design of Assay Systems for Coupling Factors

The unavailability of membranes specifically depleted of single components and the lack of detailed knowledge concerning the composition of existing depleted membrane preparations make the assay of coupling factors extremely difficult. A membrane with several different lesions in the ATP-synthesizing system will presumably require as many coupling factors as there are lesions to completely restore its functional activity. Thus, in order to devise an adequate assay for a specific coupling factor, there are requirements for (i) a depleted membrane preparation, (ii) supplementary coupling factors, (iii) a purified preparation of the coupling factor to be assayed. It is essential that the coupling factor under test should be the rate-limiting factor in the assay system. A titration curve of the amounts of factor added against stimulation of the energy conservation process being measured should be determined. This is a very tedious process and is rarely done, but it is the only way by which a reliable estimate of the specific activity of the coupling factor can be made.

Further points that should be realized when determining the activity of a coupling factor are the possibilities that not all the coupling factor added to the assay incubation is bound to the membrane, and that the supplementary coupling factors, if not rigorously purified, may also contain the coupling factor under test. It should also be ensured that the coupling factor is acting catalytically and not by removing or inactivating a membrane bound inhibitor of the energy conservation reaction being used in the assay. For example, Kagawa and Racker (1966a) have shown that the oligomycin insensitivity of the ATPase activity of phospholipid-treated factor F_1-reconstituted TU particles could be reversed by factor F_4. This action of factor F_4 was simply due to its ability to bind phospholipids, which presumably were competing with the membranes for the oligomycin.

It is important that the assay conditions are optimized with respect to the amounts of depleted membranes, the supplementary coupling factors used in the incubation and the physical conditions of the incubation. Stekhoven et al. (1971) have made a valuable contribution to the study of the interaction of coupling factors with depleted membranes. These workers determined the temperature dependence of the stimulation by factors A or B of the ATP-dependent reduction of NAD by succinate catalyzed by A particles. They concluded that reconstitution experiments would best be done between 30° and 43°.

Racker (1970a) has indicated a further difficulty inherent in the reconstitution experiments used for the assay of coupling factors. This arises from the polarity of the inner membrane of mitochondria. There is a convincing amount of evidence which suggests that the components of the electron transfer chain are arranged vectorially within the mitochondrial membrane. This, together with the observation that factor F_1 is only seen on the matrix-facing surface of the inner membrane, strongly indicates that each mitochondrial membrane component has a discrete and unique place in the structure of the membrane. There is no reason to assume that coupling factors, apart from factor F_1 are located on the matrix-facing surface of the inner membrane rather than in or across the membrane or on its outer surface. All depleted membrane preparations used in the assay of coupling factors are derived from submitochondrial particles (membrane vesicles) which present the matrix-facing surface of the membrane to the medium. Therefore, unless the vesicles are rendered permeable to large molecules during procedures designed to deplete them, coupling factors originally located on the outer surface of the inner membrane would not be expected to reach and bind to their true location in the membrane.

The procedures used to prepare depleted membranes are so drastic that denaturation and inactivation of membrane components is inevitable. Therefore inactive forms of a coupling factor may be present in membrane preparations used in its assay and may reduce the efficacy of the added coupling factor by preventing its binding to the membrane.

III. Properties of Isolated Coupling Factors

A. COUPLING FACTORS WITH ATPase ACTIVITY

A brief summary of the preparation and properties of those mitochondrial ATPase preparations whose coupling factor activity has been investigated is presented in Table III. The relationships between factor F_1 and A have been discussed in detail elsewhere (Sanadi *et al.*, 1971). These two coupling factors have much in common, and heat treatment of factor A makes it even more similar to factor F_1. Despite some differences in the properties of these ATPase preparations, they have sufficient in common to suggest that they contain the same ATPase molecules which are complexed with different membrane components.

Factor A.D is claimed to be a highly purified fraction of the mitochondrial membrane with ATPase activity, and the ability to catalyze the ATP–P_i and the ATP–ADP exchange reactions, which makes it unique among the coupling factors that have been described previously. Its coupling factor activity has not yet been investigated in

TABLE III

SUMMARY OF THE PREPARATION AND PROPERTIES

Factor	Preparation	ATPase activity (μmoles min^{-1} mg^{-1} protein)
F_1	A crude extract is prepared from light layer beef heart mitochondria by either sonication or shaking with glass beads. ATPase molecules are purified by isoelectric, protamine sulfate, and ammonium sulfate precipitation steps. A final heat treatment gives an approximately 2-fold increase in specific activity and an overall increase in ATPase activity	Up to 100. Cold labile
	An ATPase has been isolated from rat liver which has a similar molecular weight (360,000) and a similar subunit structure to those of factor F_1	22
	A factor F_1 type molecule has been isolated from yeast mitochondria	60
A	The supernatant obtained from sonication of beef heart mitochondria is fractionated by isoelectric and ammonium sulfate precipitation steps and chromatography on DEAE-cellulose	Approximately 10, can be increased 5-fold by heating at 45°–65°. This is reversible. ATPase activity is stable at 0–5°
$F_1.X$	A suspension of acetone-dried beef heart mitochondria is sonicated. The supernatant fluid is fractionated with ammonium sulfate	1–26, varies with the stage in the preparation
A.D (ATP synthetase)	This is a protein fraction eluted from the DEAE-cellulose column during chromatography of factor A. This fraction is subsequently chromatographed on Sepharose 4B	1–3, increased by heating. Has ATP–P_i and ADP–ATP exchange activities, which are sensitive to oligomycin, DCCD and uncoupling agents. $^{32}P_i$ can be incorporated into the protein

Physical properties	Subunit structure	References
$s_{20,w} = 12.9, 11.7$. Molecular weight estimates 284,000, 360,000. Binds ATP	Various models of subunit structure have been proposed, including 10 equivalent subunits, 6 different subunits and 5 different subunits. Molecular weights in the 5 subunit model are (A) 53,000, (B) 50,000, (C) 25,000, (D) 12,500, (E) 7500, with the proposed structure (A,B)$_6$ CDE. Some preparations contain the ATPase inhibitor (Pullman and Monroy (1963)	Penefsky (1967), Horstmann and Racker (1970), Penefsky and Warner (1965), Senior and Brooks (1970, 1971), Forrest and Edelstein (1970), Lambeth et al. (1971), Zalkin et al. (1965)
384,000 $s_{20,w} = 12.15$	Subunits of molecular weights 62,500, 57,000 and 36,000	Catterall and Pedersen (1971), Lambeth and Lardy (1971)
360,000	–	Schatz et al. (1967), Tzagoloff (1969)
$s_{20,w} = 13.5$. Binds ADP	4 Subunits shown by electrophoresis on polyacrylamide gels containing acetic acid and urea. Factor F$_1$ shows the same subunit structure in this system. Contains ATPase inhibitor	Andreoli et al. (1965), Warshaw et al. (1968), Sanadi et al. (1971)
None	An equimolar complex of factor F$_1$ and OSCP which also contains 30% free factor F$_1$. The ATPase inhibitor is present in small amounts	Van der Stadt et al. (1972), Vallejos et al. (1968), Groot and Meyer (1969)
Molecular weight 400,000 as estimated by gel filtration. Claimed to be a soluble, nonmembranous protein complex	At least seven bands are shown by polyacrylamide gel electrophoresis in the presence of sodium dodecyl sulfate	Sani et al. (1970), Fisher et al. (1971a), Stekhoven (1972), Sanadi et al. (1972)

detail, but factor A.D has been shown to enhance the ATP–P$_i$ exchange activity and reversed electron flow catalyzed by U particles (Fisher *et al.*, 1971b; Sani *et al.*, 1970).

The inherent enzymatic activities of factor A.D, although low, are sensitive to oligomycin, DCCD, and uncoupling agents. These properties are characteristic of an intact phosphorylating mitochondrial membrane and have never before been demonstrated in a soluble preparation. Therefore the results obtained by Sanadi's group are of great potential significance. The significance of this work rests upon the absence of membrane fragments in the factor A.D preparations. The solubility and nonmembranous nature of the preparation is indicated by its low content of cytochromes and phospholipids, its appearance under the electron microscope, its behavior during centrifugation and gel filtration (Sanadi *et al.*, 1972), and its insensitivity to phospholipase treatments (personal communication). Pentachlorophenol, an uncoupler, stimulates the low ATPase activity of factor A.D severalfold (personal communication). However, many of these data have only appeared in preliminary form and have not yet been repeated in other laboratories. Therefore, a thorough critical assessment of the results cannot be made at this time.

B. Coupling Factors with No Known Enzymatic Function

The data given in Table I summarize the preparative procedures and some of the properties and interrelationships between coupling factors, which have no known enzymatic activity. Some of the preparations described in the early literature on coupling factors are not included because little subsequent work has been done on them and their properties are summarized in an earlier review (Lardy and Ferguson, 1969).

The detailed information regarding the isolation and purification of the coupling factors described in Table I is sometimes less than satisfactory. Often there is little information on the yields, the specific activities, the homogeneity of the products, and hence the degree of purification of the coupling factor preparations. Furthermore some of these preparative procedures are very complicated and lengthy. It is often difficult to determine the rationale behind the use of the different fractionation techniques.

A further problem arises from the use of different preparative procedures for the "same" coupling factor, e.g., different methods for the preparation of factor F$_3$ have been described by Racker (1962), and Fessenden and Racker (1967); Fessenden-Raden *et al.* (1969), and Bulos and Racker (1968a) described two methods for the preparation of factor F_c. Apart from experimental evidence to indicate that the coupling factors prepared by the different methods have similar functional effects, there is no evidence presented which shows that the products of the two procedures are identical. This, together with the observation that different coupling factors show the same functional activity (Bulos and Racker, 1968a), raises the valid question of whether these two products are indeed the same.

The presence of other components in a coupling factor preparation can profoundly influence its functional effects and physical properties. For example, Beechey et al. (1969a) showed that the fraction designated basic coupling factor (BCF) which is present in crude factor F_3 preparations, was eluted with 50 mM–KCl/20 mM Tris-sulfate, pH 8, during chromatography on a CM-cellulose column. However, after passing the crude factor F_3 extract through a DEAE-cellulose column, the basic coupling factor acquired the properties of a much more basic protein and was eluted from the CM-cellulose column with 200 mM–KCl/20 mM Tris-sulfate. The specific coupling factor activity of these fractions was two to four times greater than that of the material eluted with 50 mM–KCl/20 mM Tris·sulfate. These results were interpreted as indicating that in the crude factor F_3 extract, the basic coupling factor was associated with an acidic protein which modified its coupling factor activity and also its ability to adhere to CM-cellulose. This complex was dissociated during chromatography on DEAE-cellulose, resulting in an enhancement of coupling factor activity and an increase in the basicity of the molecule.

The isolation of complexes of mitochondrial proteins (e.g., factor A.D and factor F_1.X, see Table III) which have coupling factor activity have been reported by other workers. The ability of mitochondrial membrane components to adhere to each other and to remain complexed during isolation procedures is remarkable and is the greatest single problem in elucidating the mechanism of mitochondrial ATP synthesis. This ability of coupling factors to bind with other proteins could well be the major reason for the large numbers of coupling factors described in the literature. Many of these have functional properties that differ only in detail. Therefore it is imperative that before claims are made for the existence of a new coupling factor, the preparation should be rigorously purified, analyzed both functionally and physically and then compared in detail with other coupling factors which are isolated by similar methods.

A futher assumption which is implicit in most of the reports describing the properties of coupling factors is that the fractions prepared and designated as coupling factors are soluble or monodisperse proteins. The physical or mechanical methods used to "solubilize" the coupling factors from the membrane can lead to the preparation of very small membrane fragments. It has been our experience that it is difficult to differentiate between small membrane fragments and soluble coupling factors (Beechey and Cattell, 1972). Thus, the membrane fragments present in crude factor F_3 preparations can chromatograph on DEAE-cellulose columns in a manner typical of soluble proteins. The purification scheme for every coupling factor should include a stage which could separate monodisperse proteins from membrane fragments: for example, centrifugation in density gradients, prolonged centrifugation, gel permeation chromatography or membrane filtration, together with monitoring by electron microscopy.

IV. Evidence for the Functional Role of Coupling Factors

The literature on coupling factors is liberally scattered with statements similar to, "A more appropriate name [for coupling factors] would be 'energy transfer' factors since they seem to be acting in the steps subsequent to the coupling event" (Sanadi et al., 1968). Such statements generally imply that all coupling factors play a functional role in the synthesis of ATP. As will be shown, there is some evidence that the coupling factors with ATPase activity have such a role, but little evidence exists for the functional activity of the other coupling factors.

A. COUPLING FACTORS WITH ATPase ACTIVITY

The apparent or latent ATPase activities of factors A, A.D, F_1 and F_1.X and the ATP–P_i and ADP–ATP exchange activities of factor A.D (see Table III) are functions that can easily be rationalized as parts of the ATP-synthesizing system. Their postulated role in ATP synthesis is that of the final step of phosphorylating ADP. These molecules can combine with ADP (Zalkin et al., 1965; Warshaw et al., 1968; Sanadi et al., 1971), and it is postulated that they act by activating ADP and so facilitate its interaction with $X \sim P$ to form ATP. However, there is good evidence that the ATPase activity per se is not essential for coupling factor activity. Pullman and Monroy (1963) showed that the addition of 1.3 μmole of ATPase inhibitor mg^{-1} N-particle protein supplemented with factor F_1–ATPase gave 97% inhibition of the ATPase activity, but had no effect on the stimulation of ATP synthesis by factor F_1. In addition factor A, which has a low ATPase activity, is a very effective coupling factor (Andreoli et al., 1965).

A puzzling feature is the relationship between the ATPase activity and the phosphorylating capacity of the membranes. Assuming that given the correct substrates, i.e., ADP and $X \sim P$, the capacity of the membrane bound ATPase to synthesize ATP is equal to its capacity to hydrolyze ATP then the membrane should have the ability to synthesize 15–20 μmoles of ATP min^{-1} mg^{-1} membrane protein (Racker and Horstmann, 1967). If the P : O ratio $= 3$, then this rate of phosphorylation would require an oxygen consumption of 5–7 μatoms min^{-1} mg^{-1} protein. This is a value approximately 10-fold greater than that normally found. The discrepancy could be a further indication that the ATPase activity of mitochondrial coupling factors is artifactual.

The antibiotic aurovertin was shown by Lardy et al. (1964) to be a potent inhibitor of mitochondrial ATP synthesis and the ATP–P_i exchange reaction, but to be a less effective inhibitor of the uncoupler-stimulated ATPase reaction. These results have been extended and confirmed by Ernster et al. (1967), Lee and Ernster (1967), Roberton et al. (1967, 1968), and Mitchell and Moyle (1970). It would appear that aurovertin is a potent inhibitor of all reactions that involve the synthesis of ATP, but is less effective when ATP hydrolysis is involved. The similar sensitivities of the soluble and membrane-bound ATPase activities suggests that aurovertin is acting at the same site in both these systems. The addition of aurovertin to purified ATPase preparations from liver and heart mitochondria at the level of 1 mole of aurovertin to 280,000 gm of protein results in the formation of a fluorescent complex (unpublished data of Lardy et al., quoted in Lardy and Ferguson, 1969). (Other proteins do not bind aurovertin in this way.) Similarly, the addition of small amounts of aurovertin to intact mitochondria also results in the formation of a fluorescent complex. Thus it would appear that aurovertin has a high affinity for the mitochondrial ATPase molecule. Since it is improbable that there are two different high-affinity binding sites for aurovertin in mitochondria, and also the antibiotic is such a potent inhibitor of ATP synthesis, it is concluded that the site of action of aurovertin is the ATPase molecule. Thus it would appear that this molecule when bound to the membrane is functionally involved in ATP synthesis and utilization.

A further observation, which has been presented as indicating that the ATPase has a functional role, is the inhibitory effect of the specific antibody to factor F_1 on energy-linked reactions. Fessenden and Racker (1966) showed that the oligomycin-stimulated ATP synthesis in A particles was inhibited by an antibody prepared against beef heart factor F_1 ATPase preparations. Schatz et al. (1967) demonstrated that an antiserum prepared against yeast factor F_1 ATPase would inhibit: (a) the activity of purified yeast ATPase, and (b) the ATPase activity and the ability of yeast submitochondrial particles to synthesis ATP.

These workers also demonstrated that an antibody prepared against beef heart factor F_1 inhibited the ATPase activity of beef heart submitochondrial particles and also the ability of N particles supplemented with beef heart factor F_1 to synthesize ATP. In these experiments the factor F_1 was incubated with the N particles before the addition of factor F_1 antibody. Thus the *in situ* inhibition of the membrane bound ATPase is associated with an inhibition of ATP synthesis, supporting a functional role for this ATPase activity in mitochondrial ATP synthesis. It should be recognized, however, that the ATPase activity of factor F_1 is largely masked on binding to membrane particles (Kagawa and Racker, 1966b).

Racker (1967) quoted unpublished results of Fessenden which showed that "the antibody to beef heart ATPase inhibited all ATP dependent reactions." However, the data of Fessenden-Raden (1969), which apparently support the conclusions drawn from the work of Schatz *et al.* (1967), should be examined carefully. In these experiments ASU particles were supplemented with factors F_1, F_3, and F_5. This resulted in a stimulation of both the ATP-driven reduction of NAD by succinate and the ATP-driven pyridine nucleotide transhydrogenase. The addition of antibody to factor F_1 resulted in a diminution of these activities. However, factor F_1 was exposed to the antibody and the ASU particles simultaneously. Thus there is doubt whether the antibody reacted with factor F_1 before or after the latter complexed with the membrane. Therefore this evidence cannot be adduced in favor of factor F_1 acting in a functional role in beef heart submitochondrial particles.

B. COUPLING FACTORS WITH NO KNOWN ENZYMATIC ACTIVITY

From the data presented in Table I it is apparent that most of the nonenzymatically active coupling factor preparations have not been purified to homogeneity. Therefore a discussion of the possible functional role of these heterogeneous protein fractions would be pointless. Of the purified nonenzymatically active coupling factors, factor B, which is probably identical to factor F_2 (Racker *et al.*, 1970), is the only one for which substantial evidence for a functional role in ATP synthesis exists.

Lam and Yang (1969) have shown that the addition of the specific antiserum to factor B will give a partial inhibition of the ATP-dependent reduction of NAD by succinate catalyzed by AE particles or phosphorylating submitochondrial particles and the ATP–P_i exchange reaction catalyzed by phosphorylating submitochondrial particles. The ATPase activity of these particles was not affected by this antibody. Other experiments in which AE particles were supplemented with factor B and the antiserum to factor B resulted in a complete inhibition of the stimulation of energy-linked functions by factor B. These latter experiments are open to the criticism that the antibody could have reacted with factor B and prevented it from combining with the membrane. This also applies to similar experiments reported by Racker *et al.* (1970). Further circumstantial evidence for the functional role of factor B is its sensitivity to sulfhydryl reagents and the inhibitory effects of these reagents on energy-linked reactions (Sanadi *et al.*, 1968; Lam and Yang, 1969). But the latter authors concede that sulfhydryl groups on proteins other than those on factor B could be involved and indeed factors D and F_5 have subsequently been shown to contain sulfhydryl groups essential for their activity (see Table I). It is surprising that no attempts have been made to isolate factor B from particles treated with mercurial sulfhydryl reagents. The demonstration of modified sulfhydryl groups on factor B would show directly that this protein could be the site of action of sulfhydryl reagents which also gave inhibition of energy-linked reactions.

V. Structural Role of Coupling Factors

The possibility that individual coupling factors may play both structural and catalytic roles in mitochondrial ATP synthesis is suggested largely by the results of several investigations into the coupling factor activity of factor F_1. For example, Penefsky (1964, 1967) has shown that beef heart factor F_1 when treated with either iodine, DCCD, or dinitrofluorobenzene loses its ability to catalyze the hydrolysis of ATP, but retains the ability to stimulate ATP synthesis, the ATP–P_i exchange reaction and the ATP-dependent reduction of NAD by succinate catalyzed by submitochondrial particles partially depleted of factor F_1 (N particles). However, the chemically modified ATPase preparations will not stimulate ATP synthesis in submitochondrial particles which have been almost completely depleted of factor F_1 by urea treatments. This failure to stimulate ATP synthesis is unlikely to be due to the inability of the chemically modified factor F_1 preparations to bind to the membrane since [H^3]acetyl factor F_1 binds equally well to SU and N particles. These observations led Racker (1967) to propose that factor F_1 has both a catalytic and a structural function. In the latter role the coupling factor is suggested to either "block a leak" in the membrane or to "participate in the structure of the active site of oxidative phosphorylation."

Further support for the structural role of factor F_1 has been obtained by Fessenden (unpublished data, quoted in Racker, 1967; Fessenden-Raden, 1972) and by I. G. Knight and R. B. Beechey (unpubl., 1970), who showed that small amounts of beef heart factor F_1 stimulated the aerobic energy-linked pyridine nucleotide transhydrogenase activity of ASU or A particles. Since it is very unlikely that the mitochondrial ATPase is involved catalytically in this particular reaction and, in the case of A particles, the amounts of factor F_1 added had a much lower total ATPase activity than did the particles, it is unlikely that the factor F_1 acted in a functional role, and therefore a structural role must be ascribed to it.

In a series of interesting experiments Schatz *et al.* (1967) have shown that an antibody prepared against yeast factor F_1 inhibited the ATPase activity of yeast factor F_1, but not that of beef heart factor F_1. However, ATP synthesis catalyzed by beef heart N particles supplemented with yeast factor F_1 was not inhibited by the antibody to yeast factor F_1. This contrasts to the inhibition by this antibody of ATP synthesis catalyzed by yeast submitochondrial particles. Schatz *et al.* conclude that the yeast factor F_1 plays a functional role in ATP synthesis catalyzed by the yeast submitochondrial particles, and a structural role when stimulating the P:O ratios measured with beef heart N particles.

The results outlined above certainly support a structural coupling factor role for factor F_1. However, the work of MacLennan and Paulson (1970) suggests that the structural effects may be due solely to the presence of ATPase subunits present in factor F_1 preparations. Thus the demonstration that nonenzymatically active subunits of factor F_1 will stimulate ATP synthesis, the ATP–P_i exchange, and the ATP-dependent reduction of NAD by succinate reactions catalyzed by A particles led these workers to suggest that factor F_1 subunits repair undefined "ultrastructural lesions" in the A-particle membrane.

The experiments done to show that an isolated mitochondrial ATPase preparation can act as a structural coupling factor depended on the presence of a measurable enzymatic activity which can be inhibited and yet retain some coupling factor activity. Other coupling factors do not have enzymatic properties, and therefore it is difficult to establish whether they act in a structural or/and a functional role. However, the work with factor F_1 has shown that many of the results obtained in the assay of coupling factors could simply be due to structural effects. In addition it should be remembered that, at present, there is no direct evidence which shows that the mechanism of stimulation of the energy conserving reactions by putative structural coupling factors bears any relationship to the role of these membrane constituents in the intact membrane.

VI. Alternative Approaches to the Identification, Isolation, and Characterization of Coupling Factors

From the foregoing discussion, it is apparent that the identification of functional coupling factors using methods based on the disruption of mitochondrial membranes and the reconstitution of certain activities in depleted membrane preparations by addition of fractions from the "solubilized" components is a time-consuming and sometimes misleading process. Therefore it is pertinent to discuss here two alternative approaches to this problem. One approach which is currently being used by several groups of workers (Cattell *et al.*, 1971; Foucher and Gaudemer, 1971; Aldridge and Street, 1971) is to use specific inhibitors of oxidative phosphorylation to label the molecules at their sites of action. The other approach, which is in the early stages of development, involves genetic and/or metabolic manipulation of yeast cells to produce changes in the mechanism of mitochondrial oxidative phosphorylation which can be correlated with the alteration of specific membrane components involved in this process.

A. THE USE OF INHIBITORS OF ATP SYNTHESIS TO IDENTIFY COUPLING FACTORS

1. General Considerations

There are several groups of inhibitors of oxidative phosphorylation which react with certain chemical groups. These include carbodiimides (Beechey *et al.*, 1967), organotin compounds (Rose and Aldridge, 1972), maleimides (K. J. Cattell, unpubl., 1971), and organomercurials (Karup and Sanadi, 1968). It is possible that these inhibitors act by reacting with chemical groups on molecules directly involved in the mechanism of ATP synthesis. These molecules would be functional coupling factors. By using labeled inhibitor it should be possible to tag the molecule at its site of action so that procedures for its isolation could be developed. The isolated molecules could then be studied individually and used in reconstitution experiments.

Ideally the inhibitors used in such a study should have the following properties:

i. High specificity. The inhibitor should act at a single site and the optimum concentrations required for maximum inhibition should be equivalent or stoichiometric to the concentrations of the electron transfer chain components. In the case of ox heart mitochondria this would be of the order of 1 μmole of inhibitor gm^{-1} of mitochondrial protein. It should be noted that with certain inhibitors, e.g., DCCD, (Beechey *et al.*, 1967) and *N*-ethyl maleimide (K. J. Cattell, unpubl., 1971) the concentrations of inhibitor required can be drastically reduced by optimization of the experimental conditions.

ii. The location of the inhibitor site in the energy coupling mechanism should be known. Comprehensive experiments should be done to determine at which point in the energy transfer mechanism the inhibitor acts. It must be unequivocally demonstrated that inhibition is not due to other effects such as inhibition of substrate transport into the mitochondria, or structural modification of the mitochondrial membrane.

iii. The inhibitor should have a high affinity for, or preferably react covalently with, its site of action. An essentially irreversible binding is required so that the complex between the inhibitor and the molecule at its site of action can be isolated intact. In the case of inhibitors which react covalently with their site of action, the possibility of molecular rearrangements taking place during isolation procedures should be considered.

iv. The inhibitor should have a known structure and chemistry. This knowledge would help in designing experiments to elucidate its mode of action.

v. Chemical stability. The inhibitor and the adduct formed between the inhibitor and its site of action should be stable.

vi. The inhibitor should be available in a labeled form, either with a radioisotope or a fluorescent group.

None of the currently available inhibitors of oxidative phosphorylation meet all these stringent requirements. However, most of them are met by certain inhibitors. It should be noted that the characteristics of known inhibitors could be enhanced by structural modification. A structure–activity relationship study was done by I. G. Knight (unpubl. 1967), who demonstrated that the potency of a series of substituted carbodiimides as inhibitors of oxidative phosphorylation was related both to their lipophilicity and to the size of the substituent groups.

There are three main groups of compounds of known structure which inhibit oxidative phosphorylation and have been studied in detail. These are the carbodiimides, sulfhydryl group reagents, and organotins. The merits of these compounds as inhibitors which could be employed in the identification of functional coupling factors will be discussed in the following sections.

2. Carbodiimides

Although all of the lipophilic carbodiimides tested inhibit oxidative phosphorylation, most work has been done with N,N'-dicyclohexyl-carbodiimide (DCCD) because it is readily available and has a relatively low volatility which makes its handling safer. DCCD meets most of the criteria outlined above (Beechey et al., 1967). Concentrations of 1 μmole DCCD gm^{-1} of beef heart mitochondrial protein inhibits ADP-stimulated respiration in mitochondria, and all of the partial reactions catalyzed by submitochondrial particles which involve the synthesis or utilization of ATP. In contrast, equivalent concentrations of DCCD stimulate the aerobic energy-linked transhydrogenase reaction. The inhibitions caused by DCCD were shown to be dependent on time, temperature, and pH. These results were interpreted to mean that DCCD acts by reacting covalently with a group involved in the formation and utilization of a phosphorylated intermediate. Consequently, experiments were started using [^{14}C]-DCCD to label the molecule at its site of action so that isolation procedures could be developed for it. Preliminary experiments using salt, detergent, and solvent extractions to isolate the DCCD-labeled mitochondrial component were to varying degrees unsuccessful, but they did demonstrate that this component was tightly bound to the mitocondrial membrane (Cattell et al., 1971). I. G. Knight et al. (1968) then showed that 75% of the radioactivity could be extracted from [^{14}C]-DCCD mitochondria by chloroform–methanol (2 : 1, v/v) and appeared to be associated with a proteolipid. This work was extended by Cattell et al. (1971), who first showed by polyacrylamide gel electrophoresis that over 90% of the radioactivity in [^{14}C]-DCCD-treated submitochondrial particles was associated with a single protein. This protein was extractable with chloroform–methanol and purified up to 50-fold by solvent fractionation and chromatography on Sephadex LH20. The molecular weight of this protein is 13,500, as estimated by polyacrylamide gel electrophoresis and amino acid analysis. Stekhoven and his group have demonstrated the presence of this protein in rutamycin and DCCD-sensitive ATPase and factor A.D preparations from beef heart mitochondria (Stekhoven et al., 1972; Stekhoven, 1972).

Since it is likely that the protein functional group which reacts with DCCD may play an important role in ATP synthesis, it is of great interest to identify the nature of this group. Although DCCD shows a certain specificity for reacting with protein carboxyl groups (Kurzer and Douraghi-Zadeh, 1967; Carraway and Koshland, 1968; Carraway and Triplett, 1970) to form a stable N-acyl urea, it can also form stable adducts with hydroxyl, sulfhydryl, and amino groups. Because of this lack of specificity it is essential that the amino acid residue which reacts with DCCD be identified.

These studies with [^{14}C]-DCCD have led to the identification of its site of action as a markedly hydrophobic membrane protein and made amenable the characterization of a chemical group on this protein which may be involved in a phosphate-activating reaction, or in a regulatory role in ATP synthesis. The similarity of the modes of action of DCCD and oligomycin tempts speculation on the possibility that the proteolipid is the tightly bound membrane component which is involved in reconstituting oligomycin sensitivity to factor F_1, on its addition to membranes depleted of ATPase activity (Bulos and Racker, 1968a).

3. Sulfhydryl Group Reagents

The ability of reagents thought to be specific for sulfhydryl groups to inhibit oxidative phosphorylation and certain partial reactions catalyzed by submitochondrial particles has led to the conclusion that protein sulfhydryl groups may play a direct role in the reactions leading to ATP synthesis (Karup and Sanadi, 1968; Sabadie-Pialoux and Gautheron, 1971; Kielley, 1963). Since Gautheron (1970) has recently reviewed the possible role of sulfhydryl groups in oxidative phosphorylation, we will only briefly summarize the evidence and evaluate the possibility of using labeled sulfhydryl group reagents to identify their site of action.

Most of this work has been done using mercurial compounds (Karup and Sanadi, 1968; Sanadi et al., 1968; Kielley, 1963; Lee et al., 1971), but dithionitrobenzoic acid (Miyahara, 1969; Haugaard et al., 1969), ethacrynic acid (Foucher et al., 1969), and N-alkyl maleimides (Karup and Sanadi, 1968; K. J. Cattell, unpubl., 1971; Sabadie-Pialoux and Gautheron, 1971) have also been used. Results of inhibitory studies with whole mitochondria should be assessed in the light of the findings of Tyler (1969) and Fonyo and Bessman (1968), who showed that the transport of phosphate into mitochondria is inhibited by sulfhydryl group reagents. A further difficulty arises from the demonstration that under certain conditions respiratory chain enzymes also show sensitivity to mercurials (Tyler, 1969; Karup and Sanadi, 1968; Fonyo and Bessman, 1968). Therefore any studies on the inhibition of oxidative phosphorylation by sulfhydryl group reagents should include control experiments to minimize the possibility of inhibition of other reactions which would produce spurious results.

It is difficult to make detailed comparative assessments of the results from different groups of workers because the mitochondrial preparations, concentrations of inhibitors and experimental conditions used vary quite considerably. However, there are certain consistent findings in all the investigations. Mercurials inhibit the uncoupler-stimulated ATPase, ATP–P_i exchange, and ADP–ATP exchange activities of mitochondria and submitochondrial particles (Sanadi et al., 1968; Kielley, 1963; Boyer et al., 1966; Lee et al., 1971). These compounds also stimulate Mg-ATPase activity of both mitochondria and submitochondrial particles. Karup and Sanadi (1968) have investigated in detail the inhibition by mercuriphenyl sulfonate of both non-energy-linked and energy-linked pyridine nucleotide transhydrogenase reactions catalyzed by submitochondrial particles. They found that the energy-linked reaction was approximately four times more sensitive to the mercurial than was the non-energy-linked reaction. Similar results have been obtained by K. J. Cattell (unpubl., 1971) using N-ethyl maleimide. Lee et al. (1971) have shown that the inhibition by fluorescein mercury acetate of partial reactions catalyzed by beef heart mitochondrial and submitochondrial particles can be correlated with the titration of a set of high affinity binding sites. The concentration of these sites on the mitochondrial membrane, approximately 10 nmoles of sulfhydryl group mg^{-1} protein falls within the ranges quoted by other workers (Sabadie-Pialoux and Gautheron, 1971; Foucher and Gaudemer, 1971; V. A. Knight et al., 1968).

Ethacrynic acid, which has been used in studies on reactions catalyzed by whole mitochondria, has a similar mode of action to that of the mercurials. Dithionitrobenzoic acid and N-ethyl maleimide are significantly different to the mercurials and ethacrynic acid since they produce only slight inhibition of the ATP–P_i exchange reaction (Miyahara, 1969; K. J. Cattell, unpubl., 1971) whereas they inhibit the other reactions which are sensitive to mercurials. When all these results are considered in toto, they present a confusing and sometimes conflicting picture. However, it is likely that at least one set of sulfhydryl groups in the mitochondrial membrane is directly involved in the reactions leading to ATP synthesis.

Sanadi has suggested that this set of SH groups is involved in the formation of a nonphosphorylated intermediate, and much of the available evidence would support this view. The possibility that these sulfhydryl groups are identical to those which are essential for the coupling factor activity of factor B has been discussed by Lam and Yang (1969). As mentioned earlier, no attempt has yet been made to isolate factor B from mitochondrial membranes treated with a radio-labeled sulfhydryl group reagent.

In conclusion there is substantial evidence that sulfhydryl groups are involved in the reactions which involve the synthesis or utilization of ATP. It should, therefore, be possible to select a sulfhydryl group reagent which at low concentrations and under appropriate experimental conditions shows a selectivity for reacting with these groups. Since these compounds form stable covalent bonds, radio-labeled or fluorescently labeled sulfhydryl group reagent could be used to facilitate the isolation of the protein containing the reactive sulfhydryl group.

4. Organotin Compounds

Organotin compounds are potent inhibitors of oxidative phosphory-lation (Aldridge, 1958; Rose and Aldridge, 1972; Sone and Hagihara, 1964). Between 1 and 20 μmoles of trialkyl or triphenyl tin salts gm^{-1} mitochondrial protein inhibit phosphorylation linked to the oxi-dation of a variety of substrates, the ATP–P_i exchange reaction and uncoupler stimulated ATPase. Some inhibition of uncoupler stimu-lated respiration and stimulation of the Mg^{2+}–ATPase activity of mitochondria by organotins has been reported (Aldridge and Street, 1971). Byington (1971) has shown that 10 μmoles triphenyl tin salts gm^{-1} protein inhibits the Mg^{2+}-ATPase activity of beef heart sub-mitochondrial particles. Initially the inhibitory action of organotin salts was difficult to rationalize on the basis of a single site of action since certain mitochondrial functions were more sensitive to these compounds than were other reactions (Aldridge and Street, 1971; Rose and Aldridge, 1972). However, these anomalies have been ex-plained by more recent observations (Rose and Aldridge, 1972; Stockdale et al., 1970; Selwyn et al., 1970) which show that in the presence of permeant anions alkyl tin salts have two modes of action. One is an uncoupler effect caused by their ability to mediate an anion-hydroxide exchange across the mitochondrial membrane. The other, which is also observed in the absence of permeant anions, is an oligomycin-like inhibition of oxidative phosphorylation. However, it is suggested that more experimental evidence is required before the site of action of the organotins can be definitely related to that of oligomycin.

Aldridge and Street (1970) have shown that there are at least two sets of organotin binding sites on mitochondrial membranes. The higher affinity sites, which are present at a concentration of 0.8 μmoles gm^{-1} of rat liver mitochondrial protein appear to be the ones involved in the reactions of oxidative phosphorylation since there is a direct correlation between binding to these sites and the degree of inhibition of oxidative phosphorylation. The precise chemical nature of these sites is not known, but model studies with hemoglobin and a rat liver supernatant fraction suggest that each molecule of organotin salt may be chelated between two histidine residues (Rose, 1970; Rose and Lock, 1970). In contrast to this view, Byington suggests that the organotins may be reacting with sulfhydryl groups. It is obviously of great interest that the molecule containing the high-affinity organotin binding sites should be isolated and its possible role as a functional coupling factor evaluated. A preliminary study by Aldridge and Street (1970) has shown that all the high affinity sites are concentrated 7-fold in the insoluble residue obtained from Triton X-100 treated mitochondria.

5. Other Inhibitors of Oxidative Phosphorylation

Of the other inhibitors of oxidative phosphorylation which act at low concentrations and could be useful in identifying functional coupling factors, and isatogens and indolones (A. J. Sweetman, unpubl., 1972) and robenzidene [1,3-bis(p-chlorobenzylidene amino)-guanidine hydrochloride) (Wong et al., 1972) show promise. However, further experiments are required before their precise loci of action in ATP synthesis can be determined. It is possible that both or either of these compounds could be reacting with the same membrane nucleophilic groups that react with DCCD or with the sulfhydryl group reagents.

B. The Use of Yeast for Studies on Coupling Factors

1. Metabolic Studies

Because of the ease with which their growth conditions can be manipulated, studies on yeasts have yielded valuable information about mitochondrial biogenesis (Beattie, 1971). It is possible that the methods developed in this work can be adapted to investigate the nature of the membrane components involved in the mechanism of ATP synthesis.

The mitochondria of yeast repressed by growth in glucose-rich media are poorly developed and have low ATPase and respiratory activities, but they undergo a rapid phase of development to fully competent mitochondria on transfering the yeast to derepression media low in glucose. In a series of elegant experiments, Tzagoloff and Meagher have exploited this developmental phase and the differential sensitivities of cytoplasmic and intramitochondrial protein synthesis to cycloheximide and chloramphenicol, respectively, to elucidate the sites of synthesis of the protein components of a highly purified rutamycin sensitive-ATPase preparation (Tzagoloff, 1969, 1970, 1971; Tzagoloff and Meagher, 1971, 1972). These workers have shown that two components of the rutamycin-sensitive ATPase (factor F_1 and OSCP) are synthesized cytoplasmically and at least four other protein components are synthesized intramitochondrially. Some or all of these four proteins are involved along with OSCP in binding the ATPase to the mitochondrial membrane and conferring rutamycin sensitivity to it. One of these proteins has a molecular weight of approximately 10,000, is soluble in chloroform–methanol, and may therefore be analogous to the DCCD-binding proteolipid isolated by Cattell *et al.* (1971) from beef heart mitochondria. Although these studies have not yet led to the positive identification of a protein involved in ATP-synthesis, they have confirmed previous findings on the relationships between the ATPase and the mitochondrial membrane, and they have demonstrated the potential of studies using yeast for the identification of functional and structural coupling factors.

2. Genetic Studies on Yeast Mitochondrial Oxidative Phosphorylation

An alternative way in which yeast can be used to study oxidative phosphorylation is to induce mutations in the yeast which lead to changes in the ATP-synthesizing mechanism. Two main experimental approaches based on the use of mutants are being used.

One approach takes advantage of the facultative nature of yeast to develop mutant screening procedures that involve selecting mutants for their decreased ability to grow on nonfermentable substrates. Selected mutants that have a full complement of cytochromes and an unimpaired respiratory capacity are then used for further study (Parker and Matoon, 1969; Beck *et al.*, 1968; Kovac *et al.*, 1967). It is possible that the mutants which satisfy these criteria have lesions in the functional coupling factors of the ATP-synthesizing mechanism. Genetic and detailed biochemical analyses of the mutant mitochondria and comparisons with mitochondria from wild-type yeast could therefore lead to the identification of these components.

The approach being used by Griffiths and his co-workers (Avner and Griffiths, 1970) is to isolate yeast mutants that show an increased resistance to inhibitors of oxidative phosphorylation when compared to wild-type yeast. The increased resistance of these mutants is expected to be reflected in changes in the site of action of the inhibitors. A series of mutants showing a greatly decreased sensitivity to oligomycin has been isolated and shown to have cross resistance to

DCCD. A significant finding is that a quantitatively similar decrease in sensitivity to both oligomycin and DCCD is observed in preparations of a rutamycin-sensitive ATPase prepared from selected yeast mutants (J. M. Broughall, unpublished observation). Mutants of this type could be extremely useful in defining precisely the functional role of the DCCD-binding site on the mitochondrial membranes.

VII. Conclusions

1. On the basis of available evidence, only those coupling factors with ATPase activity (factors F_1 and A, A.D and F_1.X) can be rationalized as having a direct functional role in mitochondrial ATP synthesis.

2. Of the large number of coupling factors with no known intrinsic enzyme activity, only factor B (F_2) and the oligomycin sensitivity conferring protein (OSCP) have been purified to near-homogeneity. The precise role that these proteins play in ATP synthesis is not known although it is likely that a part of their function is to maintain the structural integrity of the mitochondrial membrane. The other non-purified coupling factors are too poorly characterized to discern any function.

3. Lack of progress in the isolation and characterization of coupling factors is mainly due to the absence of techniques for the solubilization of the mitochondrial membrane which do not denature its constituent enzymes. The present methods use harsh, disruptive procedures and result in (i) poorly characterized "soluble fractions" from which predominantly heterogeneous putative coupling factors have been isolated and (ii) membrane preparations that are poorly defined in terms of their constituents.

4. It is suggested that future work on coupling factors could profitably be concerned with: (i) the application of newer protein fractionation techniques for the purification of putative coupling factors; (ii) the characterization of the deficient membranes and auxiliary preparations used in the assay of coupling factors and further investigations into the use of model membrane systems in reconstitution experiments; (iii) the optimization of the physical conditions of the assay procedures used for coupling factors; (iv) the application of specific inhibitors of oxidative phosphorylation to isolate possible coupling factors; (v) the use of yeast mutants to identify coupling factors.

REFERENCES

Aldridge, W. N. (1958). *Biochem. J.* **69**, 367.
Aldridge, W. N., and Street, B. W. (1970). *Biochem. J.* **118**, 171.

Aldridge, W. N., and Street, B. W. (1971). *Biochem. J.* **124**, 221.

Andreoli, T. E., Lam, K-W., and Sanadi, D. R. (1965). *J. Biol. Chem.* **240**, 2644.

Avner, P. R., and Griffiths, D. E. (1970). *FEBS Lett.* **10**, 202.

Beattie, D. S. (1971). *Sub-Cell. Biochem.* **1**, 1.

Beck, J. C., Matoon, J. F., Hawthorne, D. C., and Herman, F. S. (1968). *Proc. Nat. Acad. Sci. U.S.* **60**, 186.

Beechey, R. B., and Cattell, K. J. (1972). *In* "Biochemistry and Biophysics of Mitochondrial Membranes" (G. F. Azzone *et al.*, eds.), p. 487. Academic Press, New York.

Beechey, R. B., Roberton, A. M., Holloway, C. L., and Knight, I. G. (1967). *Biochemistry* **6**, 3867.

Beechey, R. B., Knight, I. G., Lindop, C. R., and Cattell, K. J. (1969a). *In* "Electron Transport and Energy Conservation" (J. M. Tager *et al.*, eds.), p. 305. Adriatica Editrice, Bari.

Beechey, R. B., Knight, I. G., Lindop, C. R., and Cattell, K. J. (1969b). *Biochem. J.* **114**, 440.

Boyer, P. D., Bieber, L. L., Mitchell, R. A., and Szabolcsi, G. (1966). *J. Biol. Chem.* **241**, 5384.

Bulos, B., and Racker, E. (1968a). *J. Biol. Chem.* **243**, 3891.

Bulos, B., and Racker, E. (1968b). *J. Biol. Chem.* **243**, 3901.

Byington, K. H. (1971). *Biochem. Biophys. Res. Commun.* **42**, 16.

Carraway, K. L., and Koshland, D. E. (1968). *Biochim. Biophys. Acta* **160**, 272.

Carraway, K. L., and Triplett, R. B. (1970). *Biochim. Biophys. Acta* **200**, 564.

Cattell, K. J., Lindop, C. R., Knight, I. G., and Beechey, R. B. (1971). *Biochem. J.* **125**, 169.

Catterall, W. A., and Pedersen, P. L. (1971). *J. Biol. Chem.* **246**, 4987.

Conover, T. E., and Zalkin, H. (1967). *In* "Methods in Enzymology" (R. W. Estabrook and M. E. Pullman, eds.), Vol. 10, p. 532. Academic Press, New York.

Conover, T. E., Prairie, R. L., and Racker, E. (1963). *J. Biol. Chem.* **238**, 2831.

Criddle, R. S., Bock, R. M., Green, D. E., and Tisdale, H. (1962). *Biochemistry* **1**, 827.

Datta, A., and Penefsky, H. S. (1970). *J. Biol. Chem.* **245**, 1537.

Ernster, L., Lee, C-P., and Janda, S. (1967). *In* "Biochemistry of Mitochondria" (E. C. Slater *et al.*, eds.), p. 29. Academic Press, New York.

Fessenden, J. M., and Racker, E. (1966). *J. Biol. Chem.* **241**, 2483.

Fessenden, J. M., and Racker, E. (1967). *In* "Methods in Enzymology" (R. W. Estabrook and M. E. Pullman, eds.), Vol. 10, p. 530. Academic Press, New York.

Fessenden, J. M., Dannenberg, M. A., and Racker, E. (1966). *Biochem. Biophys. Res. Commun.* **25**, 54.

Fessenden, J. M., Dannenberg, M. A., and Racker, E. (1967). *In* "Methods in Enzymology" (R. W. Estabrook and M. E. Pullman, eds.), Vol. 10, p. 528. Academic Press, New York.

Fessenden-Raden, J. M. (1969). *J. Biol. Chem.* **244**, 6662.

Fessenden-Raden, J. M. (1972). *J. Biol. Chem.* **247**, 2351.

Fessenden-Raden, J. M., Lange, A. J., Dannenberg, M. A., and Racker, E. (1969). *J. Biol. Chem.* **244**, 6656.

Fisher, R. J., Sani, B. P., and Sanadi, D. R. (1971a). *Biochem. Biophys. Res. Commun.* **44**, 1394.

Fisher, R. J., Chen, J. C., Sani, B. P., Kaplay, S. S., and Sanadi, D. R. (1971b). *Proc. Nat. Acad. Sci. U.S.* **68**, 2181.

Fonyo, A., and Bessman, S. P. (1968). *Biochem. Med.* **2**, 145.

Forrest, G., and Edelstein, S. J. (1970). *J. Biol. Chem.* **245**, 6468.

Foucher, B., and Gaudemer, Y. (1971). *FEBS Lett.* **13**, 95.

Foucher, B., Geyssant, A., Goldschmidt, D., and Gaudemer, Y. (1969). *Eur. J. Biochem.* **9**, 63.

Gautheron, D. (1970). *Bull. Soc. Chim. Biol.* **52**, 449.

Groot, G. S. P., and Meyer, M. (1969). *Biochim. Biophys. Acta* **180**, 575.

Hansen, M., and Smith, A. L. (1964). *Biochim. Biophys. Acta* **81**, 214.

Haugaard, N., Lee, N. H., Kostrzew, A. R., Horn, R. S., and Haugaard, E. S. (1969). *Biochim. Biophys. Acta* **172**, 198.

Hinkle, P. C., and Horstmann, L. L. (1971). *J. Biol. Chem.* **246**, 6024.

Holloway, C. T., Roberton, A. M., Knight, I. G., and Beechey, R. B. (1966). *Biochem. J.* **100**, 79P.

Horstmann, L. L., and Racker, E. (1970). *J. Biol. Chem.* **245**, 1336.

Kagawa, Y., and Racker, E. (1966a). *J. Biol. Chem.* **241**, 2461.

Kagawa, Y., and Racker, E. (1966b). *J. Biol. Chem.* **241**, 2467.

Kagawa, Y., and Racker, E. (1966c). *J. Biol. Chem.* **241**, 2475.

Karup, K. R., and Sanadi, D. R. (1968). *Biochemistry* **7**, 4483.

Kielley, W. W. (1963). *Proc. Int. Congr. Biochem. 5th, 1961* Vol. 5, p. 379.

Knight, I. G., Holloway, C. T., Roberton, A. M., and Beechey, R. B. (1968). *Biochem. J.* **109**, 27.

Knight, V. A., Settlemire, C. T., and Brierley, G. P. (1968). *Biochem. Biophys. Res. Commun.* **33**, 287.

Knowles, A. F., Guillory, R. J., and Racker, E. (1971). *J. Biol. Chem.* **246**, 2672.

Kovac, L., Lachowicz, T. M., and Slonimski, P. P. (1967). *Science* **158**, 1564.

Kurzer, F., and Douraghi-Zadeh, K. (1967). *Chem. Rev.* **67**, 107.

Lam, K. W. (1968). *Arch. Biochem. Biophys.* **123**, 642.

Lam, K. W., and Yang, S. S. (1969). *Arch. Biochem. Biophys.* **133**, 366.

Lam, K. W., Warshaw, J. B., and Sanadi, D. R. (1967). *Arch. Biochem. Biophys.* **119**, 477.

Lam, K. W., Swann, D., and Elzinga, M. (1969). *Arch. Biochem. Biophys.* **130**, 175.

Lam, K. W., Karunakaran, M. E., and Sanadi, D. R. (1970). *Biochem. Biophys. Res. Commun.* **39**, 437.

Lambeth, D. O., and Lardy, H. A. (1971). *Eur. J. Biochem.* **22**, 355.

Lambeth, D. O., Lardy, H. A., Senior, A. E., and Brooks, J. C. (1971). *FEBS Lett.* **17**, 330.

Lardy, H. A., and Ferguson, S. M. (1969). *Annu. Rev. Biochem.* **38**, 991.

Lardy, H. A., and Wellman, H. (1953). *J. Biol. Chem.* **201**, 357.

Lardy, H. A., Connelly, J. L., and Johnson, D. (1964). *Biochemistry* **3**, 1961.

Lee, C-P., and Ernster, L. (1965). *Biochem. Biophys. Res. Commun.* **18**, 523.

Lee, C-P., and Ernster, L. (1967). *Eur. J. Biochem.* **3**, 391.

Lee, C-P., Azzone, G. F., and Ernster, L. (1964). *Nature (London)* **201**, 152.

Lee, M. J., Harris, R. A., Wakabayashi, T., and Green, D. E. (1971). *Bioenergetics* **2**, 13.

Linnane, A. W., and Ziegler, D. M. (1958). *Biochim. Biophys. Acta* **29**, 630.

MacLennan, D. H., and Asai, J. (1968). *Biochim. Biophys. Res. Commun.* **33**, 441.

MacLennan, D. H., and Paulson, C. W. (1970). *Canad. J. Biochem.* **48**, 1079.

MacLennan, D. H., and Tzagaloff, A. (1968). *Biochemistry* **7**, 1603.

Mitchell, P., and Moyle, J. (1970). *FEBS Lett.* **9**, 305.

Miyahara, M. (1969). *Arch. Biochem. Biophys.* **134**, 590.

Parker, J. H., and Matoon, J. F. (1969). *J. Bacteriol.* **100**, 647.

Penefsky, H. S. (1964). *Fed. Proc. Fed. Amer. Soc. Exp. Biol.* **23**, 533.

Penefsky, H. S. (1967). *J. Biol. Chem.* **242**, 5789.

Penefsky, H. S., and Warner, R. C. (1965). *J. Biol. Chem.* **240**, 4694.

Penefsky, H. S., Pullman, M. E., Datta, A., and Racker, E. (1960). *J. Biol. Chem.* **235,** 3330.

Pullman, M. E., and Monroy, G. C. (1963). *J. Biol. Chem.* **238,** 3762.

Pullman, M. E., Penefsky, H. S., and Racker, E. (1958). *Arch. Biochem. Biophys.* **76,** 227.

Pullman, M. E., Penefsky, H. S., Datta, A., and Racker, E. (1960). *J. Biol. Chem.* **235,** 3322.

Racker, E. (1962). *Proc. Nat. Acad. Sci. U.S.* **48,** 1659.

Racker, E. (1963). *Biochem. Biophys. Res. Commun.* **10,** 435.

Racker, E. (1967). *Fed. Proc., Fed. Amer. Soc. Exp. Biol.* **26,** 1335.

Racker, E. (1970a). *Essays Biochem.* **6,** 1.

Racker, E. (1970b). *In* "Membranes of Mitochondria and Chloroplasts" (E. Racker, ed.), p. 127. Van Nostrand-Reinhold, Princeton, New Jersey.

Racker, E., and Horstmann, L. L. (1967). *J. Biol. Chem.* **242,** 2547.

Racker, E., Chance, B., and Parsons, D. F. (1964). *Fed. Proc., Fed. Amer. Soc. Exp. Biol.* **23,** 431.

Racker, E., Tyler, D. D., Estabrook, R. W., Conover, T. E., Parsons, D. F., and Chance, B. (1965). *In* "Oxidases and Related Redox Systems" (T. E. King *et al.,* eds.), p. 1077. Wiley, New York.

Racker, E., Horstmann, L. L., Kling, D., and Fessenden-Raden, J. M. (1969). *J. Biol. Chem.* **244,** 6668.

Racker, E., Fessenden-Raden, J. M., Kandrach, M. A., Lam, K. W., and Sanadi, D. R. (1970). *Biochem. Biophys. Res. Commun.* **41,** 1474.

Roberton, A. M., Beechey, R. B., Holloway, C. T., and Knight, I. G. (1967). *Biochem. J.* **104,** 54C.

Roberton, A. M., Holloway, C. T., Knight, I. G., and Beechey, R. B. (1968). *Biochem. J.* **108,** 445.

Rose, M. S. (1970). *Biochem. J.* **120,** 151.

Rose, M. S., and Aldridge, W. N. (1972). *Biochem. J.* **127,** 51.

Rose, M. S., and Lock, E. A. (1970). *Biochem. J.* **120,** 151.

Sabadie-Pialoux, N., and Gautheron, D. (1971). *Biochim. Biophys. Acta* **234,** 9.

Sanadi, D. R., Lam, K. W., and Karup, C. K. K. (1968). *Proc. Nat. Acad. Sci. U.S.* **61,** 277.

Sanadi, D. R., Sani, B. P., Fisher, R. J., Li, O., and Taggart, W. V. (1970). *Proc. Int. Congr. Biochem. 8th, 1969* (in press).

Sanadi, D. R., Sani, B. P., Fisher, R. J., Li, O., and Taggart, W. V. (1971). *In* "Energy Transduction in Respiration and Photosynthesis" (E. Quagliariello *et al.,* eds.), p. 89. Adriatica Editrice, Bari.

Sanadi, D. R., Fisher, R. J., Panet, R., and Kaplay, S. S. (1972). *Fed. Proc., Fed. Amer. Soc. Exp. Biol.* (in press).

Sani, B. P. (1971). *Fed. Proc., Fed. Amer. Soc. Exp. Biol.* **30,** 809.

Sani, B. P., and Sanadi, D. R. (1971). *Arch. Biochem. Biophys.* **147,** 351.

Sani, B. P., Lam, K. W., and Sanadi, D. R. (1970). *Biochem. Biophys. Res. Commun.* **39,** 444.

Schatz, G., Penefsky, H. S., and Racker, E. (1967). *J. Biol. Chem.* **242,** 2552.

Selwyn, M. J. (1967). *Biochem. J.* **105,** 279.

Selwyn, M. J., Dawson, A. P., Stockdale, M., and Gains, N. (1970). *Eur. J. Biochem.* **14,** 120.

Senior, A. E. (1971). *Bioenergetics* **2,** 141.

Senior, A. E., and Brooks, J. C. (1970). *Arch. Biochem. Biophys.* **140,** 257.

Senior, A. E., and Brooks, J. C. (1971). *FEBS Lett.* **17,** 327.

Skulachev, V. P. (1971). *Curr. Top. Bioenerg.* **4,** 127.

Sone, N., and Hagihara, B. (1964). *Biochemistry (Tokyo)* **56,** 151.

Stekhoven, F. M. A. H. S. (1972). *Biochem. Biophys. Res. Commun.* **47,** 7.

Stekhoven, F. M. A. H. S., Sani, B. P., and Sanadi, D. R. (1971). *Biochim. Biophys. Acta* **226,** 20.

Stekhoven, F. M. A. H. S., Waitkus, R. F., and van Moerkerk, H. T. (1972). *Biochemistry* **11,** 1144.

Stockdale, M., Dawson, A. P., and Selwyn, M. J. (1970). *Eur. J. Biochem.* **15,** 342.

Sweetman, A. J., Green, A. P., and Hooper, M. (1971). *FEBS Lett.* **14,** 306.

Tyler, D. D. (1969). *Biochem. J.* **111,** 665.

Tzagoloff, A. (1969). *J. Biol. Chem.* **244,** 5027.

Tzagoloff, A. (1970). *J. Biol. Chem.* **245,** 1545.

Tzagoloff, A. (1971). *J. Biol. Chem.* **246,** 3050.

Tzagoloff, A., and Meagher, P. (1971). *J. Biol. Chem.* **246,** 7328.

Tzagoloff, A., and Meagher, P. (1972). *J. Biol. Chem.* **247,** 594.

Tzagoloff, A., MacLennan, D. H., and Byington, K. H. (1968). *Biochemistry* **7,** 1596.

Vallejos, R. H., Van den Bergh, S. G., and Slater   E. C. (1968). *Biochim. Biophys. Acta* **153,** 509.

Van der Stadt, R. J., Kraaipoel, R. J., and Van Dam, K. (1972). *Biochim. Biophys. Acta* **267,** 25.

Warshaw, J. B., Lam, K. W., Nagy, B., and Sanadi, D. R. (1968). *Arch. Biochem. Biophys.* **123,** 385.

Wong, D. T., Horng, J-S., and Wilkinson, J. R. (1972). *Biochem. Biophys. Res. Commun.* **46,** 621.

Zalkin, H., and Racker, E. (1965). *J. Biol. Chem.* **240,** 4017.

Zalkin, H., Pullman, M. E., and Racker, E. (1965). *J. Biol. Chem.* **240,** 4011.

Author Index

Numbers in italics refer to the pages on which the complete references are listed.

Subject Index